Sir Bernard Ingham
President
British Franchise Association (bfa)

It will be the ... iness that will bring the economy back to where it needs to be and franchising plays a great part in this.

Yet again the environment has been tough for many businesses over the past year. We have seen many companies across the UK suffer or cease trading and many people have been made redundant or have been faced with uncertainty for the future. The market is still not back to where it needs to be as the country tries to get its finances back in order, but at the same time we need to also take comfort from the great tenacity of British business.

It will be the success of business that will bring the economy back to where it needs to be and franchising plays a great part in this.

Time and again, whether in tough or prosperous times, franchising comes through as a robust and successful business model. Its powerful partnership between the franchisor – the owner of a proven business – and the franchise owner – who is there to bring his energies and ingenuities to the operation of an established system – creates great strength. In these straitened times we need more of these partnerships.

Franchising is not completely free from risk, as it is still a business that requires commitment and hard work, but it still consistently provides business growth, business ownership for many and employment for many more. Franchising is a reliable means of supporting the economy and giving people security for the future.

This is why the banks look favourably upon franchising and why more and more people are starting to consider franchising as their next step. In short, franchising has a lot going for it with a success rate consistently around 90 per cent, even in recessions.

The proof of the pudding is in what I have seen happen to British franchising during my 17-year stint so far as President of the British Franchise Association (bfa). In that time, covering booms and recessions, turnover has just about trebled and the number of brands and franchise owner outlets doubled. Last year the number of franchisors and franchise owners in the industry increased yet again and this is a trend that is showing no sign of changing.

In extolling the virtues of franchising I am always conscious that I may make it seem easy for would-be

entrants. If that is what they think, they should think again. Nothing in this life comes easy.

What franchising offers is greater certainty of a profitable future for those who embrace the model, provided they have researched their franchisor properly, understand what training support will be offered to them and what they need to commit themselves to and deliver.

It is not for the apathetic. It is not a licence to print money. But it does offer the individual a better future, provided the franchise owner is willing to put their back and common sense into following a proven system.

With that approach they will go places. Their partnership with their franchisor will prosper. And if we do our job at the bfa, the country will learn what an advantage franchising is in an economy that requires energy and success.

Sir Bernard Ingham

"It's an outstanding business opportunity...

...why wouldn't you want to be part of our modern, progressive brand that continues to perform successfully?"

- McDonald's continues to outperform the market
- Record sales growth in 2010
- McDonald's unwavering commitment has led to UK franchisees entering a second 20 year term

Recently McDonald's has seen record growth within the market place, contrary to the economic climate. This success is largely down to our unwavering commitment to our local franchisees. We continue to invest in them and this in turn gives our franchisees the confidence to make the changes to help them grow their business. Our confidence in our franchisee community pays dividends for both them and us and it has resulted in over two million more customers per month coming through our doors in the UK alone.

Our commitment to offering sustainable products and innovative menu options attracts customers of all ages from a wide range of market sectors. Our investment in the new modern look for our restaurants has significantly lifted sales. Furthermore, we've invested in technologies that enable our franchisees to offer free Wi-Fi and cashless payments, all of which helps to upgrade the overall customer experience. We are also opening more restaurants earlier and closing them later to meet the needs of our customers.

However, as a global company employing more than 80,000 employees in this country alone, our major investment is in our people. Some 80% of our restaurant management and one in five of our franchisees began as crew members and our long-term commitment to training and support gives them the opportunities to grow with the brand and share in its success.

In short, it's a confident picture of an ever-growing brand. Becoming a franchisee partner makes sound economic sense whichever way you look at it - ours is a modern, progressive and successful franchising brand.

SUMMARY:

Type of Franchise:
Restaurant
Industry Sector:
Food & Drink
Ideal Franchisee Profile:
Flexible, determined people with proven management skills and ambitions to operate more than one restaurant.
Year Established in UK:
1974
Franchising Since:
1986 in the UK
Number of Franchisees (UK):
159

Our successful candidates already have a proven track record in business. So why not come and meet us:

Open Days

14th May
The Aztec Hotel, 110 Aztec West
Almondsbury, Bristol BS32 4TS

18th June
Doubletree by Hilton, Milton Keynes
Stadiummk, Stadium Way West
Milton Keynes, Buckinghamshire
MK1 1ST

16th July
McDonald's Head Office, 11-59 High Road
East Finchley, London N2 8AW

17th September
Ramada Encore Barnsley, Whinby Road
Dodworth, Barnsley S75 3LF

15th October
Marriott Leicester, Smith Way
Grove Park, Enderby, Leicester LE19 1SW

Exhibitions

18th and 19th March
The British and International Franchise
Exhibition, Olympia, London

10th and 11th June
The British Franchise Exhibition
Convention Centre Petersfield, Manchester

30th September and 1st October
The National Franchise Exhibition
NEC Birmingham, Birmingham

To register and for further information:
www.mcdonalds.co.uk/franchising

McDonald's Restaurants Ltd,
11-59 High Road, East Finchley,
London N2 8AW

i'm lovin' it

Contents

Welcome to
The United Kingdom Franchise Directory
24th Edition

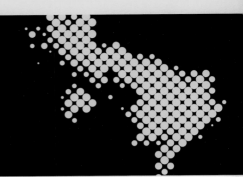

Richard Chatten
Editor

Lewis Dellar
Designer

Assistant Editors
Tiffany Brooking
Derin Ibrahim
Don Ricardo
Michelle Seaman

Fraser McKay
Production Editor

ISBN: 978-0-946861-24-8

© Copyright 1983-2011
Franchise Development Services Ltd,
The UK Franchise Directory, 24th Edition

Researched, compiled, designed, published
and distributed by:

Franchise Development Services Ltd,
Franchise House, 56 Surrey Street, Norwich,
NR1 3FD, United Kingdom.
Registered in London 1592312, October 1981.

Tel: 01603 620301   Fax: 01603 630174
Email: enquiries@fdsltd.com

24th Edition

Introduction

Professor Roy Seaman CFE
Managing Director
Franchise Development Services Ltd

Welcome to franchising in the second decade of the 21st Century!

When research was carried out to produce the first edition of *The UK Franchise Directory*, there were just 200 franchisors trading in this country.

Today there are over 1,500 franchisors and they have already established over 100,000 company and franchise owned locations. Brands from our first edition include Hertz, Avis, Wimpy, Tie Rack and today we have brands like Subway, which has over 1,500 locations in the UK and over 30,000 locations worldwide, and the goal to reach 100,000 locations before 2050! As we came towards the end of the 20th Century, brands like those mentioned above together with Hilton Hotels, Holiday Inn, Burger King and other household names have given franchising a very solid foundation upon which many other brands can now build, operate and develop to their full potential around the world.

Since establishing Franchise Development Services (FDS) in 1981, we have watched franchising grow and prosper. Today, just about every type of business with a product or service that has genuine growth potential and good profit margins is available as a franchise.

We have even 'franchised franchising' nationwide and world-wide. Our sister publication *The Franchise Magazine*, began as a quarterly printed publication, then grew to bi-monthly.

Today, eight print editions are published annually and the title is also available online at TheFranchiseMagazine.net, in digital format for more than 10,000 subscribers and as a mobile app.

Now we are in the 21st Century, we are witnessing two or more franchiser brands coming to the market every week. This is due to the fact that owners of successful businesses can see the many benefits that can be offered when they create a genuine Business Format Franchise.

However, the uninitiated may still believe every franchise has been very well thought out before being offered to the market. This is not so and one of the reasons for continuing to print *The UK Franchise Directory* is that those of you who are looking to obtain an overview of the market can turn these pages and discover for yourself some realities in relation to owning and operating a franchise.

While some of the long established brands like Dyno-Rod have long since achieved network

completion, this sector only represents around five per cent of the franchisors. Those franchisors that meet the requirement of being recognise as a Genuine Business Format Franchise represent just over 50 per cent.

This leaves around 40 to 50 per cent that need extreme caution before proceeding since some of the 21 essential elements may be missing from their Business Format Franchise. Those franchisors that are full members of the British Franchise Association (bfa) should meet all of these criteria and those that have involved bfa franchise consultants and lawyers should also qualify.

However, as a prospective franchise owner, always use our checklist (page 60) and check out the franchisor and their existing franchise owners in detail. This will be time and money wisely invested. If in any doubt – *never proceed*!

Franchising has responded to the ever changing consumer demands by offering opportunities

> **Today there are over 1,500 franchisors and they have already established over 100,000 company and franchise owned locations.**

that assist today's 'cash rich, time-poor' consumers. At one time, franchising's growth was from the fast food sector.

However, today it is from all sectors, from accountants, business services, children's education, cleaning, dry cleaning, estate agents, food and health, through to vending, water, yoghurt and for Z we have Z-Coil pain relief footwear.

Today, brand is king and it dominates not only this country, but some 200 other countries around the world where there are franchise locations operating. This directory will provide you with an insight to the broad range of franchise opportunities currently available.

The first aim of this publication is to educate you with what is being offered and help you to find the right franchise to suit your own skills, financial ability and aspirations for the future.

The common denominator in relation to the franchise opportunities on offer is that franchisors require you to make a financial commitment and, in return, they help you establish and

develop their particular brand, product and services. *The UK Franchise Directory* offers you a comprehensive overview and goes on to outline the steps necessary in order to help you make your decision work for you.

However, before you sign a Franchise Agreement, do check with established organisations such as FDS who will provide you with their professional opinion as to whether or not the franchise you are considering does, in fact, have a track record of success and meet the Genuine Business Format criteria.

There is little point in ringing anyone seeking advice and guidance after you have signed the Franchise Agreement and parted with your hard earned savings.

Remember that franchising is not for everyone. Having chosen the brand, you are required to work and to diligently follow all of their advice, guidance and methodologies that should have been carefully laid down in both initial and ongoing training programmes as well as in operating and training manuals.

For more information **visit:** www.theukfd.net

This directory is designed to present to you the basic facts to decide if owning a franchise is right for you. Once you have met with your prospective franchisor, we strongly recommend you talk to as many other franchise owners as possible before you reach a decision to invest in the brand under consideration.

These are the most valuable people who you can talk, meet, hear and learn from. Find out from them why they decided to buy that particular franchise and what goals they believe you should have in order to emulate the success they are achieving. Ask them to answer your important questions so you can have their professional opinion as an owner/operator rather than just from the franchisor who may be keen to bring you on board.

Some franchise opportunities are designed simply to sell the idea to a prospective franchise owner. Always ask for the total number of franchise opportunities sold to date and how many are trading profitably today. Try to find out exactly what they do each day in the running of the business and what the greatest challenges are, and what advice would they offer to you as a new member of the franchise network.

Never leave without asking the most important question of all, and that is: "How much money are you earning?" Some of the answers to these questions will be eye-opening and may well put you off the franchise. However, that is the reason for visiting existing franchise owners and obtaining such information face to face.

As you have bought a copy of *The UK Franchise Directory*, we can assume you are interested in exploring all of the opportunities on offer and educating yourself as to your own suitability to own, operate and develop a franchise to its full potential.

Since 1981, FDS has provided advice and guidance to over 10,000 people who today own and operate a franchise. Some of these have bought a McDonald's franchise and have committed themselves to a 20-year Franchise Agreement. These people will have a genuine opportunity and should be able to follow their footsteps and likewise exit with a substantial profit when they sell their franchise to either a new individual or back to McDonald's for a substantial profit. On the other hand, we have many individuals who have invested in less challenging franchises but these have suited their planned lifestyle and rewarded them adequately for their efforts. We then have individuals who have bought and sold many franchises and have enjoyed building up the equity.

Franchising in the 21st Century does offer some very genuine opportunities but there are also many franchises that we would strongly recommend that you walk away from.

No one can give you precise advice and guidance as to what is right for you. This has to be your decision, based upon careful research of what is on the market and recognising which franchise matches your skills, determination and genuine enthusiasm to work to your chosen franchisor's guidelines and succeed.

The ideal franchise will be one that will really excite you as you get up every morning. Remember, while you are on your own, you are never alone, since the franchisor and all other franchise owners in the network are there to help you succeed.

For more information **t:** 01603 620 301
e: enquiries@fdsltd.com **w:** www.theukfd.net

24th Edition

Get the best out of The UK Franchise Directory!

To get the best out of *The UK Franchise Directory* 24th edition, we recommend you follow these steps

Study the advice and guidance section

The Franchise Owner Advice section provides you with a general introduction to franchising, what it is, how it works and why franchise businesses are so successful.

It also looks at the key questions that should be asked when considering your future in franchising.

The Franchisor Advice section provides you with key information on why franchising is a successful method of business expansion and what it takes to franchise your own business. This section will present a comprehensive view of franchising in the UK today.

Review the franchise opportunities available

Franchising encompasses a broad range of industries and business types. With so much choice and information available it can be quite daunting to know where to start!

This section is organised into 12 different categories representing the major business sectors in the UK. Start by selecting a few industries that best suit your interests and investigate further.

Familiarise yourself with recommended suppliers

The Franchise Services showcase lists lawyers, consultants, banks, trademark lawyers and many other firms who specialise in franchising.

We encourage you to look closely at these companies as you may require their expertise when investing in a franchise opportunity or considering franchising your own business.

The UK Franchise Directory 24th edition is supported by the online version www.theukfd.net. This is by no means a replacement for the printed edition. The online version

provides further editorial, offering a background insight into the franchise and benefits from being continually updated.

All franchises listed in this directory will display a website link for example, theukfd.net/34192612. This link will lead directly to a further information page on www.theukfd.net. All this requires is typing the link into your web browser and the franchisor page will instantly appear.

With more than 1,500 franchise opportunities to consider, we advise you to thoroughly investigate before investing.

Don't forget to make use of the notes pages at the end of each category to draw up a shortlist for you to research further in your quest to discover the best franchise opportunity.

If you would like to leave me some feedback or want to include your franchise in the next edition,
t: 01603 620 301
e: richardc@fdsltd.com
w: www.TheUKFD.net

Richard Chatten
Editor
The UK Franchise Directory

Franchise Listings

What type of franchise
are you looking for?

SERVICES – Indoor/Outdoor Property Care

Franchises in this sector are either skilled or semi-skilled and frequently start as job franchises before moving on to managing a territory. Franchises range between gardening and landscaping to home improvements.

Pages 187-205

SERVICES – Indoor/Outdoor Property Care
188 GreenThumb
190 Granite Transformations

SERVICES – Leisure & Travel

From sports and leisure franchises to international travel agents, these are popular franchise opportunities in the UK.

Pages 207-213

SERVICES – Leisure & Travel
208 Global Cruising
209 Travel Center Worldwide

SERVICES – Print, Signs & Design

Sign franchises can involve creating, maintaining and installing signs as part of brand development for a number of businesses. This sector also includes a number of print and design franchises.

Pages 215-224

SERVICES – Print, Signs & Design
216 Agency Express
217 Freebies
218 Primesigns
219 Recognition Express

SERVICES – Real Estate & Lettings

There are a range of white collar franchise opportunities in both the estate agency and letting agency sectors. These include property management, letting agents and estate agents.

Pages 225-232

SERVICES – Real Estate & Lettings
226 Bairstow Eves
227 Platinum Property Partners

SERVICES – Sales, Delivery & Distribution

The most important background required in this category is sales and marketing. Opportunities are frequently home or van-based but can lead to premises as the business expands.

Pages 233-240

SERVICES – Sales Delivery & Distribution
234 Card Connection
235 Chemex International
236 Mac Tools Europe
237 Two Men And A Truck

SERVICES – Specialised

Children & Education – Child and educational franchise opportunities represent many low-cost investment levels required and are among the most popular.

Pet & Animal Services – Pet franchises are very enjoyable opportunities including dog training, at home pet care and pet sitting franchises.

Other Specialised Services – There are a wide variety of other specialist franchise opportunities which can cover niche business sectors.

Pages 241-266

SERVICES – Specialised
242 ComputerXplorers
255 Suit the City

Pages 267-279

The Irish Franchise Directory

Cash Converters is a franchise that offers multiple income streams. As well as the buying and selling of pre-owned goods it offers a range of financial services. A Cash Converters store that is well run can buy and sell pre-owned goods at margins far higher than new product retailers. At the same time Cash Converters aims to offer services that help customers get on with their lives.

Cash Converters started from a single store in Perth, Australia, in 1984. Now as the UK's number one retailer of pre-owned goods and a financial services provider, modern retailing practices, professional management techniques and high ethical standards are present in all Cash Converters franchised stores.

A Cash Converters franchisee needs to be able to demonstrate commitment, passion and a determination to succeed. The company actively encourages and facilitates store visits for potential franchisees where they have the opportunity to speak with existing franchisees. They are able to give valuable advice and tips to help in the decision making process. All have realised the great potential of the Cash Converters franchise concept, and in fact, many own more than one store.

One of the most comprehensive training programs in the industry is available to all Cash Converters franchisees. Investment levels start from £110,000 plus financing and franchisees receive ongoing support and advice, from choosing the perfect location to recruiting staff, marketing support and purchasing initial stock.

FORMER jewellery shop manager, Paul Saunders, took on his own Cash Converters franchise five years ago and has built it up to four stores.

Paul Saunders worked at the Woolwich, south London store as store manager before buying it from the existing franchisees in 2006. He opened his second store in Dartford in 2008 and a third in Orpington the same year. In December 2010 his fourth store in Sidcup, Kent, became the 600th Cash Converters outlet worldwide to open, and the 174th in Britain.

It was a logical step for Paul to take on his own Cash Converters franchise, with his retail background and having managed a store, but he also recognised the support available to new franchisees. "Cash Converters franchisees receive ongoing support and advice, from choosing the location, to recruiting staff, marketing support and purchasing initial stock. You are allocated a dedicated business development manager who works with you to help ensure a successful business," says Paul.

As a company, Cash Converters is constantly investing in its services and the brand to meet the needs of customers. "Our customer base is very loyal and in our stores we often know people on a first name basis. Increasingly though we are seeing people from all walks of life visit the store and being incredibly impressed with the extensive range of services on offer," adds Paul.

"I've had to be very proactive and take a hands-on approach to the business to make it work, but with four stores open already I plan to open two more this year and carry on growing until I have 10."

Richard Chatten
Editor
The UK Franchise Directory

The UK franchise industry facts & figures

Findings from the FDS UEA Survey Insight: An Industry Review Of Franchising In The UK 2010

With more than 250,000 people actively looking into owning their own franchise business and more than 1,500 franchise brands expanding nationwide, the franchise opportunities available in the UK are vast.

Norwich-based Franchise Development Services (FDS) has published the first comprehensive report reviewing all aspects of the UK franchise industry.

The report, *Insight: An Industry Review Of Franchising In The UK 2010*, was produced by MBA students from the Norwich Business School at the University of East Anglia (UEA).

It analyses historic, present and future trends in the UK franchise market incorporating the views of franchisors, franchise owners and banks with specialist franchise finance departments.

The survey findings themselves contribute to a stronger understanding of the inner workings of the franchise industry.

The report confirms the industry remains strong and is expected to flourish despite the current economic outlook. Results also emphasise that the success of the franchise industry is principally hinged on the mutually beneficial relationship between the franchisor and franchise owner.

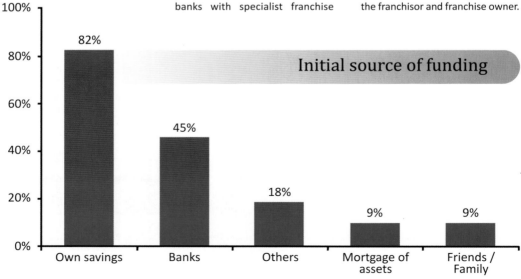

Initial source of funding

Own savings	Banks	Others	Mortgage of assets	Friends / Family
82%	45%	18%	9%	9%

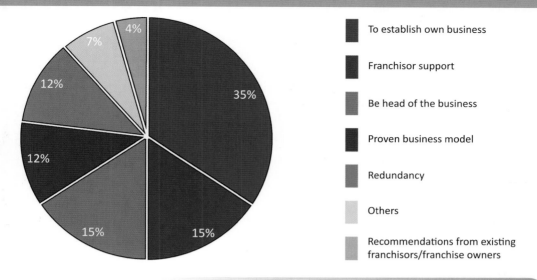

Legend:
- To establish own business
- Franchisor support
- Be head of the business
- Proven business model
- Redundancy
- Others
- Recommendations from existing franchisors/franchise owners

Pie chart values: 35%, 15%, 15%, 12%, 12%, 7%, 4%

Motivation for starting a franchise

A summary of some of the highlights and findings:

Franchisors

• 77 per cent of franchises in the UK are indigenous brands.

• Franchisors, on average, are receiving up to 40 monthly enquiries, of which one to two proceed to buy a franchise.

• In the future, more franchisors intend to expand their businesses via franchised outlets over company owned outlets.

• Despite the recession, franchisors achieved and exceeded their turnover targets.

• The most successful method of franchise owner recruitment is from franchise related websites and franchise magazines.

• 83 per cent of franchisors recover their initial investment within the first two years of business operations.

• 43 per cent of franchisors rate government tax incentives as the most helpful intervention in expanding their businesses.

Franchise Owners•

Initial investment costs are funded primarily through the franchise owner's own savings.

• Most people, who buy a franchise, do so because they want to start their own business and will select a franchise that relates to their previous work experience.

• 57 per cent of sampled franchise owners said that the franchise business they operate did not require any specialised skills in that industry.

• When deciding whether to take out a franchise-related loan or not, sampled franchise owners consider the amount of lending offered, the quality of support/service provided and applicable interest rates.

Within the report are key analytical models that provide discussion about external forces and key issues that impact on franchise systems.

As a result, this study underlines the importance to re-assess current industry performance and seek improvements to further attract investments into this sector.

Insight: An Industry Review of Franchising in the UK

2010 Report

MBA Student Group from Norwich Business School at University of East Anglia

UEA
University of East Anglia

Data was taken from *Insight: An Industry Review Of Franchising* conducted by *MBA Business Students from the University of East Anglia and Franchise Development Services.* To order a copy of this survey in digital format, £25 + VAT, or print, £45 + VAT:
t: 01603 620301
e: enquiries@fdsltd.com

Introduction to franchising

If you are new to franchising, this introduction will give you a basic understanding of the concept, the variety and the requirements of a format for rapidly replicating a proven successful business with the support and branding of a national organisation.

HOW FRANCHISING WORKS

Franchising is a 'business marriage' between an existing business (the franchisor) and an individual (the franchise owner).

The franchise owner buys licensed rights to clone the franchisor's business concept in a specific territory for a specified period, backed by full training and support from the franchisor. The franchisor provides a ready-made, established and tested business format including name, corporate power, know-how, training and ongoing support services.

Investing capital, time, effort and any relevant past experience to create their business, the franchise owner replicates the franchisor's business formula/system, gaining a safer, more structured, brand-led way of moving into independent business. The franchisor gains a new outlet in a new territory with minimum capital investment in setting it up.

BASIC TYPES OF FRANCHISING

Investment franchise: The franchise owner puts up substantial funds to capitalise on a high-cost franchise system and, although retaining overall strategic management, invariably hires others to manage the franchise outlet. Examples are hotel and restaurant franchises.

Management franchise: The franchise owner controls several territories or a region, or manages a team of operatives. Examples are van-based franchises run from regional HQs, depots or hubs.

Executive franchise: The franchise owner runs a one-man, white-collar business involved in areas including financial services, personnel, consultancy or project management. Premises are not vital because work tends to be taken to client premises. Examples are debt and cost control consultancy franchises.

Retail franchise: The franchise owner makes a significant investment in commercial property, costly equipment and staff to help operate a high-yield business system, which can often be sold at a profit should the franchise owner wish to retire and capitalise on the investment. Unlike the investment franchise, owner-operators are the norm here. Examples here are high street fashion and mobile phone chains.

Sales & distribution franchise: The franchise owner is on the road, selling and/or distributing products in the territory and where other driver-delivery personnel could be hired to cover areas as the customer base grows.

Mobile servicing (job) franchise: The franchise owner makes a lower level of financial investment to buy the right to operate, typically, a man-and-van home-based service, installation and/or repair business in areas like cleaning, motor services or maintenance.

Bear in mind that most franchisors now like to view their opportunities as more mature 'management franchises'. Even those that start as job-type franchises are generally accompanied by encouragement for franchise owners to aspire to developing a management franchise, whereby they employ operatives and focus more on managing and growing the business.

YOU WILL INVEST

Capital: Savings, rollover, redundancy pay, compensation, inheritance, loans to set up and operate the business in return for access to the franchisor's systems, know-how, training and ongoing support.

Time: Living and breathing the business to the exclusion of all else, certainly at first so that it builds on a stable foundation.

Effort: Committing to learning, building and sustaining the business, often with unsociable hours and going the extra mile.

Security: Giving up paid employment, unemployment benefit, company pensions and control over a possibly re-mortgaged home or savings in favour of borowing commitments, debt servicing and debt chasing.

Freedom: Unlike a self-start business, you will be limited by a contractual but constructive relationship with the franchisor, especially regarding work methodology, operating procedures, maintenance of quality standards, supervision, monitoring, foregoing the right to conduct a similar business of your own devising and being restricted in choice of buyers for your business when you want to sell it on to realise your investment or simply to move on to pursue something else.

YOU WILL NEED

Support from your family: Family members are often expected to assist in running the franchise.

Experience: Where relevant and applicable, for example management, accounting, technical or administrative skills can be transferable.

To be competitive: You may need to absorb the effects on your margins of tied supplies, mark-ups, royalties, marketing and other per cent levies.

Fraser McKay
Editor
The Franchise Magazine

The advantages of buying a franchise

Becoming a franchise owner is one of the safest methods of owning your own business and realising your dreams of becoming your own boss. Below are 10 reasons why you should seriously consider investing in a franchise.

1. A Proven Business Format

Franchising makes it possible to launch a new business following a proven business plan using methodologies, systems and a recognised trademark.

This will dramatically accelerate the process while cutting the risk involved, making for an easier entry into business.

2. Lower Failure Rate

Buying a Business Format Franchise offers the investor an established concept that has been successfully proven.

Statistics reveal that franchise owners stand a far better chance of success than people who start an independent business. The latter face an 80 per cent chance of failing in the first few critical years, while franchise owners stand a 90 per cent chance of surviving or better.

3. Higher Chance Of Obtaining Finance

Banks are more likely to finance the purchase of a franchise than the launch of a new business.

A well-established franchisor may even help its franchise owners secure the necessary finance and have close relationships with chosen banks.

4. Support From The Franchisor

Franchise owners benefit from comprehensive assistance in the form of training, mentoring and ongoing support, and help with statutory requirements and troubleshooting. Some franchisors also help with site selection, lease negotiation and more. Small business owners often have very little support or lack an experienced support team with business acumen.

5. Known Brand Name

Franchise owners typically operate under a brand name and image, which is already nationally or internationally recognised, promoted and respected. This speeds up the local market uptake and business development and reduces customer acquisition costs.

6. Lower Inventory Prices

The collective buying power of a franchise group can lower the cost of inventory and equipment, thereby saving franchise owners a great deal of money. Independent businesses usually have less bargaining power with suppliers.

7. Customer Confidence

Customers trust that the individual locations of a franchise network will offer reliability, good value and service.

8. A Peer Network

Franchise owners enjoy numerous opportunities to share their challenges and solutions, as well as seek advice from other like-minded entrepreneurs within their franchise system's network.

9. Easier Staff Recruiting

Finding good employees is a critical success factor for many independent small business owners. A franchise business with a recognised name will have greater recruiting power than an unknown business entity.

10. Exceptional Opportunities For Growth

Continuous research and development by the franchisor provides franchise owners with new business opportunities and increase the value of the business. The very development of the franchise business creates equity for the franchise owner by increasing the resale value of the business.

For further information
t: 01603 620301
e: enquiries@fdsltd.com
w: theukfd.net

Richard Chatten
Editor
The UK Franchise Directory

Are you suited to success with a franchise?

Be your own boss, build an asset for your retirement, correct your work/life balance. For whatever reason you've decided to look at franchise opportunities, your first step has to be a thorough self-analysis to measure your suitability to owning and operating a franchised business.

Franchisors that are committed to building a successful franchise network invest a lot of time and effort into qualifying franchise owners. The individuals they're looking for will have the ability to assimilate their knowledge and systems, and develop a successful business through a mixture of hard work and the proper implementation of their business concept.

So how do you know if you're truly suited to owning and operating your own business? It is a good idea to take a look at how franchisors assess franchise owner candidates and ask yourself some searching questions.

Do You Have The Motivation?

One of the principles of franchising that helps elevate the potential for success above company-owned expansion is the personal commitment of franchise owners.

Most franchisors are seeking franchise owners looking to run their businesses in a hands-on fashion, because they want to take advantage of the desire for business success inherent in a business owner. It's a desire that just can't be matched by a salaried manager, and it's also why franchised operations tend to offer greater quality of service and place more emphasis on customer satisfaction.

Franchisors are, therefore, seeking prospective franchise owners with a genuine enthusiasm for their industry, their service

or their product – and for building a successful business. This enthusiasm can actually be prized more highly than industry experience – because the franchisor's training and support should overcome any disparity in this area.

Can You Work Within The System?

When buying a franchise, you are investing in a proven business blueprint that has been finely tuned through a pilot operation and the experiences of the franchise network.

Franchisors are looking to award their franchises to people who fit a certain personality-type – a combination of entrepreneurial leadership with a willingness to work within the confines of established systems and procedures. This is partly because the franchisor has already gone through the trial and error stage of development – they've already learned how to avoid mistakes and performed the fine tuning in developing the business package.

But it's also because the franchisor is encouraging the standardisation of its products and services nationwide, ensuring no franchise owner produces products or services to a different standard than the rest of the network, which could then create a bad name for the brand.

Are You Prepared To Work Hard?

Whether prompted by a desire to escape employment, forced through redundancy or inspired by a drive to build a successful organisation, the decision to become self-employed involves a great deal of soul-searching.

However, if you're interested in becoming a business owner in order to cut down your hours, think again. With the future of your business in your own hands you won't be able to switch off at 5pm – in fact, you'll probably find yourself working well past this time six days a week, certainly in the initial stages. Franchisors do realise this, but they can't do the work for you – although they will offer you plenty of support and back-up to help you get your business off the ground successfully.

Naturally, you need to keep a balance between building the business and your personal life. With no boss to make sure you turn up on time or tell you to go home, you'll have to ensure your out-of-work commitments neither distract you from the business or neglect it. With the support of a franchisor, this is much easier than in a self start-up business, as you can rely on the experience of the franchisor to guide you.

Can You Afford It?

Franchises vary in prices and some are very affordable. You'll find a number of superb opportunities available for an initial investment of under £20,000.

While lending to business start-ups has suffered greatly over the last few years, there is a recognition among banks – especially those with franchise departments – that lending to franchise start-up businesses carries a much reduced risk.

However, the income you'll derive from owning your own business will prove much more irregular than that earned through employment. There'll be no pension or sick pay unless you set that up for yourself, and much of what the business earns may well be required for re-investment as you grow your operation. Will you be able to deal with this insecurity and will you be able to support yourself through it until your business finds its feet? Many franchisors will help you develop your business plan, but it will take genuine determination on your part to see it through.

Do You Have The Skills?

Franchised businesses employ just under 250,000 people in the UK according to research undertaken by Franchise Development Services (FDS). With many franchise concepts you'll either need to recruit and manage staff right away or after the business has grown beyond what you can realistically deliver on your own. Franchisors will cover management skills during your initial franchise owner training programme, but many elements will depend on your own personal abilities.

These skills are not only useful in dealing with staff – they will also play a vital role in dealing with clients.

As with any business start-up, a franchise owner will have to wear a variety of hats – that of manager, worker, salesperson, entrepreneur and administrator. An understanding of people and the ability to win confidence are vital to building a successful business.

Are You Ready To Take The Next Step?

If you think you are suited to operate a franchised business successfully, turn to page 60 for our Franchise Buyer's Checklist to help you start researching the opportunities available and visit our website to register your details for more information on specific brands of interest.

For further information
t: 01603 620301
e: enquiries@fdsltd.com
w: theukfd.net

Are you suitable for franchising?

Take the Test!

Are you considering investing in a franchise? Why not take this test and see if you have what it takes to make those first steps into becoming your own boss. Simply put your scores in the boxes and add up the total at the end.

SCALE **1:** Negative **10:** Positive

1 ————————————————— 10

1 Are your family and friends supportive about your plans to start your own business? ◯

2 Do you posses a flexible work mentality and can you focus on different jobs as may be required and multi-task effectively? ◯

3 Will you be able to cope with a drop in household income for perhaps more than a year? ◯

4 Are you open to receiving guidance and support, especially if it does not necessarily reflect your own views or opinions? ◯

5 Can you deal with high pressure and stressful situations effectively? ◯

6 Have you given much consideration to the financial impact starting a new business will involve? ◯

7 Do you usually have a positive mindset, as well as plenty of drive, determination and perseverance? ◯

8 Are you aware that self-employment, including franchising, often requires harder work and longer hours than employed positions? ◯

9 Do you have a decisive mindset and could you make the decision in the first place to step out of employment and into self-employment? ◯

10 Do you understand that a franchise does not bring a guarantee of success, but is more likely to be successful if you work hard and follow the proven business model that a franchisor provides? ◯

How did you score?

Maximum Score **100**

Above **75** points	You are **highly suitable** for franchising
50-75 points	You are **possibly suitable** for franchising following further research
Below **50** points	You are **not suitable** for franchising at this time but may be in the future

There has never been a better time to become a Pizza Hut franchise owner

Having celebrated a record year for franchise recruitment in 2010, Pizza Hut has a variety of initiatives in place to increase its delivery network across the UK. Fraser McKay reports

Pizza Hut consolidated its position as one of the best known pizza brands last year by almost quadrupling the number of franchise delivery units it opened in 2009.

The Business Director of Pizza Hut Delivery, Mark Fox, explained this success was the result of a number of developments made by Pizza Hut in 2010 to provide even more support to its growing franchise network.

"A dedicated delivery team was introduced in 2010 to give the franchise opportunity more focus while complementing the restaurant side of the business," says Mark. "This led to the opening of an impressive 29 new units in 2010 – the most in a single year since Pizza Hut introduced its home delivery franchise opportunity in 2001. By comparison, we opened eight units in 2009, which shows just how far we have come in an incredibly short space of time."

The franchise department provides its franchise owners with support for everything from business development to human resources, and each franchise owner is supported by one of Pizza Hut Delivery's dedicated Franchise Business Managers.

Another major development at Pizza Hut Delivery last year was its increased marketing activities, which resulted in exceptionally strong sales growth that, in turn, clearly helps to give investors confidence in building new units.

"Promotional products such as the Garlic Butter Stuffed Crust Pizza always prove very popular with our customers, while we are always looking for novel tie-ins to entice new customers and retain existing ones," says Mark.

Pizza Hut's highly integrated IT system has been helping make the brand's digital presence a market leader, resulting in online orders accounting for nearly 40 per cent of its franchise owners' trade.

"At present, Pizza Hut Delivery operates a network of 117 company-owned outlets and 187 franchised units, which are run by 48 franchise owners," adds Mark. "Our development goal for 2011 is to launch 40 to 50 new units and recruit 15 to 25 franchise owners.

"Our ideal franchise owner will be able to demonstrate success in their career or business life to date. We will consider candidates from a wide range of backgrounds but any experience in retail, hospitality, food or other customer-facing industries is valuable. What's important is they have the transferable leadership skills, drive, brand passion and aren't afraid to roll their sleeves up and get their hands dirty in the day-

to-day running of their business."

One of the biggest differences between Pizza Hut and other business opportunities is the training and development on offer.

"As well as the initial training, we hold a number of workshops concentrating on subjects like service, brand development and profit delivery," says Mark. "While some of these are compulsory, others are optional so our franchise owners can select a suite of training to supplement their existing skills and knowledge."

Such is the high regard in which they are held, Pizza Hut franchise owners have a direct say in the brand's strategy through various councils, boards and committees, which feature a number of elected representatives from the franchise community.

"As Pizza Hut is one of the best known brands in the world, it provides our franchise owners with huge confidence and our delivery business clearly has a significant runway for growth in the UK and Ireland," adds Mark.

"Our robust brand strategy coupled with the innovative promotions we have planned for the coming year mean there has never been a better time to become a Pizza Hut franchise owner."

For further information
t: 0208 732 9557
e: franchise.mail@pizzahut.co.uk
w: www.pizzahutfranchise.co.uk

Fraser McKay
Editor
The Franchise Magazine

Key questions to make a franchise a success

Once you have identified a franchise opportunity of interest and spoken to the brand's existing franchise owners, you should then quiz the franchisor.

Your meetings with the franchisor before signing up will be some of the most significant in your life. They give you the opportunity to put them in the 'hot seat', and dig deep into the realities of the franchise opportunity before you commit yourself to it.

Treat the franchisor like you would treat a date with a potential life partner – you don't want to make a bad impression but equally you do not want to end up tied to a franchise which doesn't tick all the right boxes for you.

The Franchise Buyer's Checklist (page 60) will give you some idea of what to ask but in order to take your questioning further, consider the following points, and write down a list of what you need to ask before you arrive.

Finances

There are a number of areas where you need to get the franchisor to explain in detail what will be expected of you and what will be provided to help you achieve it. Question every assumption, starting with the financial forecasts.

- How conservative are 'conservative estimates' – what assumptions are they based on?
- What growth have the current franchise owners been achieving?
- How long should it take the business to break even?
- How much working capital will you need?

Ideally you should request that your accountant or bank manager check these figures out, but a go-ahead from these people is no assurance of success. They are merely confirming the figures look OK on paper, not their precise knowledge of all the risk factors involved with your selected franchise opportunity.

You should also ask to see the franchisor's finances or obtain a bank reference. What are the company's main sources of income? If it appears to be the initial franchise investment fee, warning lights should be flashing. The franchisor's incentive should be to earn from the ongoing success of its franchise owners, not the initial sale of licences.

This is earned through the

management service fee – typically a percentage of your turnover or profits. However, examine closely how this affects the profits in the franchisor's financial forecasts. This levy pays for ongoing franchisor support, so compare it with the level of support you will be receiving and decide whether it represents a good deal.

If the franchisor is the sole supplier of the products, services or tools used by the franchise owner, find out how profitable this is and whether it is taken into account in the ongoing management service fee. Are the supplies priced above or below the market rate? The answer will significantly affect your competitiveness.

Your responsibilities

You should have a good idea of the role you will play in operating the franchise, specifically whether you will be required to be hands-on in delivering the service or taking a more managerial role.

You must question yourself on whether this corresponds with your own ambitions, and then question the franchisor on the potential for you to step back from this if you see yourself expanding the business further down the line.

Many franchisors recognise this desire and offer the opportunity to expand the franchise licence after you have established a successful operation. This could enable you to increase your territory or even become an area development franchise owner and grant sub-franchise licences – in effect becoming a franchisor in your own area.

Franchisor History

Most franchise brochures should provide you with some basic information about the franchisor, but make sure you fill in any gaps when you question them further.

- How long has the franchisor company been established and what is the background of the founder?
- How long has the franchisor company been posting profits?
- When did it begin franchising and how successful was the pilot?
- How many franchise owners are in operation?
- How fast is it growing and how many will complete the national network?

Territories

Is there an exclusive territory provided in the franchise contract? If so, how is it defined?

Many franchisors use postcodes to define a territory, but check out how many potential customers are in your territory. Your franchisor may require you to conduct your own market research into your own market; certainly you should at least be doing some research to check the franchisor's figures. Do this before any agreement is made.

Also, check the exclusivity of your territory. Some franchisors offer a territory exclusive of other franchise owners, but leave open the possibility of opening a company-owned operation. It is best to go into the agreement aware of whether the franchisor is

able to open a competing store in the same city at a future date.

Training

Your initial training is likely to be included in the initial investment fee, but does that include staff training? If you are starting as a sole trader, you may begin taking on staff as your business expands. If so, will the franchisor require all staff to be trained by the head office and, if so, how much of this cost will fall on your business?

Alternatively, the franchisor may require you to train your own staff. If so, is this covered in the initial franchise owner training and manuals?

Initial and Ongoing Support

The justification for the ongoing management service fee is the support of the franchisor, so check you are getting value for money. What support initiatives does the franchisor provide?

For instance, some franchisors operate a sales department in order to generate initial business for their franchise owners and provide business from day one.

Alternatively, the franchisor may take total control of the sales process, providing you with a constant flow of business and

leaving you to concentrate on providing the service.

- Does the franchisor operate field support managers?
- Who will make on-site visit to your business to help you cope with any problems?
- How regular will the visits be, particularly in the early stages of the business?

Also, consider how easily available this support is in a crisis. Some franchisors provide their personal mobile number to every franchise owner, while others operate helplines.

Your peers in the franchise owner network can also provide support. How does the franchisor encourage this? Such initiatives as a franchise owner intranet, or regional and national franchise owner conferences are excellent methods of forging closer links within a franchise owner network.

Marketing Support

Any business requires marketing and, as a franchise grows, it can begin national campaigns.

This is one of the responsibilities of the franchisor and when it begins to conduct such campaigns, the cost will need to be absorbed by the franchise owner network, which benefits.

If the franchisor is not already levying a national marketing fee, when does it plan to?

Alternatively, the franchisor may charge an administration fee on every national lead passed to you. Again you will need to take this into consideration in your own forward financial planning.

Around 16 per cent of franchise owners polled in the 2010 bfa/ NatWest Franchise Survey claimed their relationship with their franchisor is not satisfactory.

Of those 16 per cent, three quarters blamed the lack of direct support, while two in five stated the "franchisor not keeping initial promises" or "lack of communication with the franchisor".

A third claim that there is a lack of franchise brand marketing/promotion, while a quarter attribute unsatisfactory relationships to "personal reasons".

So remember make sure you have a clear understanding about the franchise you have chosen and about all the components which make it a success – that is why it is important to make your questions matter and help your journey on the road to franchise success a fulfilling one.

For further information
t: 01603 620301
e: enquiries@fdsltd.com
w: theukfd.net

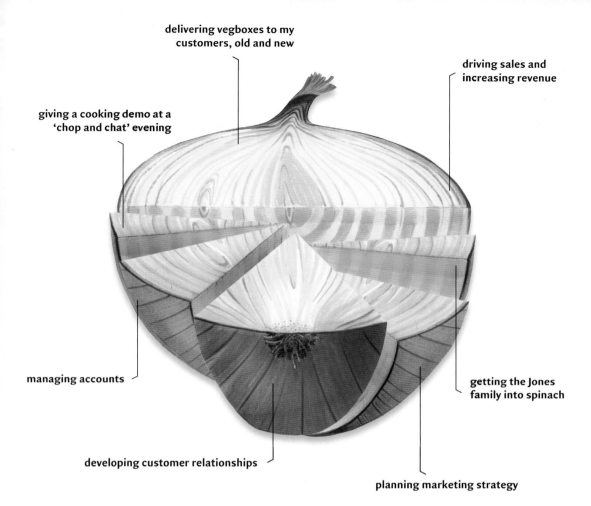

delivering vegboxes to my customers, old and new

driving sales and increasing revenue

giving a cooking demo at a 'chop and chat' evening

managing accounts

getting the Jones family into spinach

developing customer relationships

planning marketing strategy

franchise opportunities - uk wide
award winning vegbox home delivery company

Grab life by the onions! Spread the word about our delicious fresh organic grub! Become as essential to your customers' kitchens as salt and pepper! Yes, being a franchisee with the UK's leading and award winning organic vegbox home delivery company is about far more than just running a sound and ethical business. It's about building the kind of customer relationships that no other supplier can match, becoming a valued member of your community (as well as an expert on 1001 ways to use an onion) along the way. Like you we'll expect to see your business grow, so strong sales skills and a real determination to succeed are essential. Sure it can be backbreaking work and there'll be plenty of long hours too but you'll be building a business you can really call your own. So it might be tough, but it's as good for you as it is for your customers. Food for thought?

To find out more, email **franchise@riverford.co.uk** or visit **www.riverford.co.uk/franchise**

we grow the vegetables, you grow your business

www.riverford.co.uk/franchise

Riverford

Franchise Owner Advice

Professor Roy Seaman CFE
Managing Director
Franchise Development Services Ltd

How to become a successful franchise owner in 10 steps

Franchising offers a great way to become your own boss and own a business, while still retaining an association with a head office organisation.

1. Research

Start your research by reading printed franchise publications and their sister websites, e.g. *The Franchise Magazine* and *The UK Franchise Directory*.

By going through these publications, you will be able to create a shortlist of some of the most important and genuine business format franchises that appeal to you.

2. Register

Having made a shortlist of 10-20 opportunities, visit their websites and register your interest in owning and operating the franchise, as well as requesting copies of their prospectuses. This will often help you to identify the more serious players.

Alternatively, you can register on franchise publication websites to request further information on the opportunities of interest.

3. Re-visit

Ensure you cover everything by following check lists. *The UK Franchise Directory* publishes a Franchise Buyer's Checklist (page

60), which will assist you in due diligence with the franchisors.

There are four basic areas and these cover:
(a) What the franchise prospectus should contain
(b) What you need to find out from each franchisor you are considering pursuing further
(c) Warning signs and potential problem areas you should be looking out for
(d) The Franchise Agreement

4. Ask

What are you paying for? The franchise package should be broken down and all tangible elements identified, as should the licence fee. Are the amounts being charged for these fair and reasonable? If not, do not proceed.

Always ask to meet a number of existing franchise owners. Ideally, you need to find out from the franchisor how many franchise owners they have. If the answer is

50 but they only provide you with a shortlist of five, ask why. Ideally you should be given the full list.

If the existing franchise owners are negative, report this to the franchisor and if an acceptable explanation cannot be provided, do not proceed.

5. Advice

Ensure your bank will support your application to own and operate a franchise.

You should always seek advice and guidance, not just from your bank, your lawyer and accountant but also from experienced Franchise Consultants, since they are probably more alert than most professional advisors as to the status and standing of the brand you have under consideration.

6. Assess

It is important that you carry out a strengths and weaknesses assessment about yourself.

You should always ask the franchisor: "What are the essential skills that your successful franchise owners have?"

If your answer is 'no' this is obviously not a franchise you should consider any further.

7. Engage

Always engage a Franchise Lawyer to check your Franchise Agreement. Never go to a lawyer and ask them to provide you with advice and guidance and suggestions for any alterations.

A good Franchise Agreement is the same for each and every franchise owner that comes on board. The franchisor should provide you with an introduction letter for your lawyer.

8. Record

Keep notes about everything the franchisor says to you and any comments made by their franchise owners.

Before you make your final commitment to proceed, request that the franchisor helps you with your initial market research and business planning.

9. Satisfy

Ensure your bank will support your application to own and operate a franchise.

10. Decision making

When you are 100 per cent satisfied in relation to all areas, there is no reason why you should not proceed and realise your ambition of becoming a successful franchise owner and operator with your chosen brand.

CAUTION

Some franchise opportunities are offered for less than £10,000. You should be very careful with all low cost franchises, since they have the highest failure rate.

You should also be wary of those which cost more than £100,000 for the same reason.

Every element of the franchise package needs to be broken down and there will be up to 21 areas.

The franchisor then needs to justify the amount of money that they are charging for each of these elements.

For further information
t: 01603 620301
e: enquiries@fdsltd.com
w: theukfd.net

home care

nursing care

nurse recruitment

A year ago the thought of running my own business would have left me feeling panicked but you have all the necessary support and information at your fingertips with **Blue Ribbon** and I have never felt happier or more in control" Joanne Stocker - Blue Ribbon (Crawley & Mid Sussex)

Home Care
Nursing Care
Nurse Recruitment
Franchise

www.blueribboncare.org.uk

Tom Endean
Marketing Manager
British Franchise Association

The importance of bfa Membership

The British Franchise Association (bfa) is the not-for-profit voice of franchising in the UK. It operates to accredit and promote ethical franchising and therefore differentiate the good, from the bad and the ugly.

For a franchisor to be a member of the British Franchise Association, they must pass a strict accreditation process, which looks at all aspects of the franchise operation to make sure it proven, protected, ethical, sustainable and free of ambiguity and misleading statements.

So What Does This Mean?

Essentially, to see that a franchisor is a member of the bfa is to be given a huge boost in your confidence when moving forward with the company. Knowing that the company has been properly tested in every aspect of how their franchise works and has had references from existing franchise owners in the network tells you that this is a proper, ethical franchise business. However, it is a not a replacement for your own due diligence.

Buying a franchise could be one of the largest and most important investments that you make in your life. Not only will this investment be in terms of money, but also of your own time and commitment.

Franchising, allows many people to start entirely new lives, realising new lifestyles and ambitions, but only when done well. Therefore making the right choice at the very start, about which franchise to join, if any, is paramount. This includes making sure you have done all the possible research on opportunities available, what they involve and the market they operate in. This is something that you should never try to cut corners on. You not only need to be sure that the business can deliver what it says it can deliver, but you also need to be sure the day-to-day operations of the business are right for you – and just as importantly, you are right for it.

As you are looking at companies that are members of the bfa you will see that not all of them have the same type of membership.

Opposite you will find explanations about the differences between them.

What You Should Look For

bfa membership is just one of the elements to look out for, but there is also much more after that that you will want to investigate.

Even if the business is the best operated and most ethical company available, it doesn't necessarily make it ideal for your situation.

With hundreds of different brands, investment levels and business types, how can you know what you want?

For those looking into franchising, here are just a few simple considerations:

Investment Level

Levels of investment range from smaller amounts, that you may already have available, to larger amounts that you may need to take out a bank loan for. Lloyds Banking Group, RBS/NatWest and HSBC have specialist teams for franchising, so make sure you speak to them first.

Full Members

Full Members of the bfa are established franchised businesses with a proven trading and franchising record. They are prepared to have their reputation examined by the bfa, and have an established network of franchise owners.

Associate Members

Associate Members of the bfa have proven their ability to launch and support, at least one franchised outlet for 12 months and are now in the business of building their network. The franchisor will be investing in support and development. There will be few franchise owners whose experience you can research and a short period of time over which the business has been tested but the business will have evidence of its ability to establish a solid network.

Provisional Listing

Provisionally Listed Companies are at the beginning of their development in franchising although the franchise may be at pilot stage. There is a real business up and running where end products and services are being sold successfully to consumers. The Franchise Agreement is sound, and by joining the bfa the company has committed itself to develop the business in accordance with bfa industry standards.

Lifestyle

Franchising is not a hobby. You will need to make sure that you are happy with the commitments needed for this new business. You will also need to consider the support and understanding of those around you such as your family and friends.

Research

All franchise businesses are different, so do your homework. Speak to existing franchise owners, make sure you understand all the business operations and ensure that you fully understand the investment costs.

Professional Advice

There are a host of professional advisors accredited by the bfa that specialise in franchising, including consultants, accountants, solicitors, banks and even media. They are invaluable in making sure that you're taking the right steps and don't miss any vital information.

The robust business model of franchising, fuelled by dedicated individuals, encompassing many different skills and backgrounds, opens up countless opportunities for people looking for a new start. However, you need to put the work in upfront to ensure you are taking the right steps for you. This will give you the ability to commit to the business in the long run.

Visit the bfa's website at **www.thebfa.org** for objective advice and access to numerous educational and advisory resources.

Richard Chatten
Editor
The UK Franchise Directory

Considering buying a franchise as a going concern?

Buying an existing franchise for resale provides access to a ready made customer base. What should you take into account when considering investing in a going concern?

Opening the doors to your business on day one must certainly be a nerve-wracking experience. Now you've built it, will they come? Even with the setup and ongoing support of a franchisor, building a business is a gruelling effort with plenty of long days and short weekends. No wonder that many people look to take a shortcut by

purchasing an existing business as a going concern. With an established customer base, local brand awareness, existing staff and an established premises you can concentrate on taking the business on to its next level using real results and rewards as a starting point.

Many business owners build an exit strategy into their business plan from the start in order to

realise the capital value of their asset, possibly to fund retirement or even plough back into a new start-up.

Of course other businesses are put up for sale not because the owner planned to do so, but because they are struggling to make a go of it, finding the hours too much or have tired of the industry they're in. Or perhaps personal circumstances outside of the business have forced the sale, such as divorce or bereavement. Finding out the reason behind the sale is probably the most important research any prospective buyer will accomplish during the transaction, as this will have a huge bearing on the buying decision and sale price.

Existing franchise businesses can be made available for resale too. This is often encouraged by franchisors, who are keen to see franchise owners that have plateaued in their growth ambitions capitalise on the value of their enterprises and move their business into the hands of an individual eager and able to continue charting expansion.

Buying an established franchise can offer the best of both worlds –

an established customer base and existing financial performance along with the comprehensive training and support of the franchisor to smooth the transition of ownership.

If you have the capital ability to look at buying a going concern, how do you ensure you are buying the business of your dreams and not someone else's folly?

Get Professional Advice

Remember, a broker is acting on behalf of the seller so it is important to get your own advice from accountants and lawyers to check over the accounts, lease and sale agreement.

Bear in mind, however, that as you are paying for warnings, advisors are naturally going to point out everything that could possibly go wrong. You must balance their concerns against your own expectations of what could go right.

Check The Business' Third Party Agreements

For example, a business with a shortly expiring lease and no option to renew can quickly find itself homeless and losing its customer base. Similarly exclusivity agreements with suppliers need to be checked, although these are likely to fall under the remit and protection of your franchisor. If vehicles and equipment are leased, check the contracts and also the condition of the current stock.

Discuss How You Will Achieve Customer Retention

The least the owner should be prepared to do is arrange to formally introduce you to your customers. Some sellers may even consider linking the purchase price to a certain percentage of customer retention over a period of time.

Get A Realistic Estimation Of The Hours Required To Run The Business

Business ownership is rarely a 9-5 occupation, and especially if the business is struggling you may be required to put in nights and weekends. Don't leave yourself any nasty surprises.

Suggest Seller Financing

Loans on businesses are hard to come by at the best of times. If the seller is prepared to accept a down payment this demonstrates faith in the prospects of the business.

Agree A Hand-over Period

In most business transactions the seller will be required to stay on for a transitional period. The franchisor will be training you to operate the business, but nothing beats the intricacies of the local-specific knowledge of a franchise owner and the value of the seller's market knowledge is as much a part of the value of the business as everything else.

Check The Local Market

What's the level of competition? Are there any planned developments nearby that could bring competition to you? It's also a good idea to talk to other business owners in the area to get a feel of the market conditions and their opinions of your prospective business.

Calculate Your Own Valuation Of The Business And Get Ready To Haggle

Don't just accept the seller's or the broker's valuations. You will want to base yours on a multiple of the business' annual returns, but also take into account the seller's need to sell – how long has the business been on the market? It's rare for a business to have a number of buyers vying for them so you are likely to be in the driving seat.

For further information
t: 01603 620301
e: enquiries@fdsltd.com
w: theukfd.net

Betterclean Services

Founded in 1995, Betterclean Services is involved in the commercial cleaning of premises such as theatres, dental surgeries, office premises, holiday parks, doctors' surgeries and car showrooms – and holds contracts with organisations including the Dartmoor National Parks Authority.

The Betterclean Services franchise offering requires enthusiasm, drive and passion for exacting client service levels. In return, Betterclean Services' franchise owners will be rewarded with business growth which, in relation to other franchise opportunities, is relatively fast.

Betterclean Services Ltd provide everything the franchise owner requires to launch and develop the business.

Training

Betterclean Services' comprehensive training programme will focus on understanding the market, selling Betterclean Services, covering all sales and marketing and administrative systems, together with the essential quality assurance procedures, maintaining standards and how to undertake and service clients' needs.

Launch Programme

To help with an immediate and effective launch programme – with a view to creating brand awareness

and generating prospective client enquiries – Betterclean Services, as franchisor, will tailor an effective launch programme.

Personalised Stationery Package

For the provision of all the necessary stationery used within the Betterclean Services franchise and will consist of an initial supply.

Promotional Literature

To be used during the start-up period of the business, to ensure a successful launch.

Equipment and Products

This is for the initial supply of branded cleaning chemicals and equipment necessary to operate the business.

Corporate Dress

This is for the supply of the comprehensive corporate uniform for employees and will include the full complement of branded items to enhance brand recognition within the franchise owner's territory.

BLISS

Betterclean Services' bespoke software system that incorporates database software, the generation of quotes, management facilities and time-keeping records.

Website

Each franchise owner will be provided with their own page giving contact details, linked to the corporate website as part of the package deliverable. This will be used for second level marketing. In addition, a dedicated Betterclean Services email address will also be provided for the franchise owner to use and will enhance brand continuity.

Telephone Number & Email Address

Head office will set up each franchise owner's personal Betterclean 0845 telephone number.

Employment Law Support

Betterclean Services will also provide franchise owners with the initial support in relation to the complexities of employment law via its experienced employment law consultant.

Vehicle

The package provides for the initial down-payment rental and ongoing preferential terms with a major commercial supplier. Also included is full livery and suitable racking to carry the necessary equipment and products.

Operations Manual

A comprehensive operations manual will be supplied that details the A-Z of the business method.

Support Services

Betterclean Services provides comprehensive support services to all its franchise owners including:

- Ongoing development of the all-important BLISS software
- Special group purchases
- Field support
- Maintenance of a highly professional website
- Ongoing training courses
- Supply of quality branded cleaning products
- Membership of trade associations
- Betterclean Services forum
- Current health and safety legislation
- Exhibition support
- Maintenance of corporate image
- Effective communication systems
- Periodic meetings
- Regional support
- Public relations assistance
- Ongoing marketing strategy

Initial Investment Required: From £19,995 + VAT

For an informal discussion and further information, contact Dan van Kuyk telephone 08454 563536 or email franchise@bettercleanservices.co.uk

Professor Roy Seaman CFE
Managing Director
Franchise Development Services Ltd

How much does a franchise cost?

A guide through the many open and hidden costs, which should be taken into account when evaluating a move into franchising.

Before investing in a franchise opportunity, you should ensure that you set aside plenty of time to work out exactly what the final cost will be.

This latest edition of *The UK Franchise Directory* lists more than 1,500 companies and those that are actively recruiting do disclose the capital requirements. Some of the brands may also have established franchises for sale, but these will require a considerably higher investment.

Figures in relation to the investment required are usually clearly indicated in the franchisor's printed or online prospectus and should be confirmed in the Franchise Agreement.

Today, most Genuine Business Format Franchises cost £15,000 or more, since the initial training does need to be comprehensive, including a basic minimum recommendation of two weeks before the franchisor joins you in your territory to help get the business up and running.

Having identified the brands for your shortlist, you should request a complete prospectus with all of the financial information relating to both the initial investment and projected revenues in the first to third years.

Do Your Research

Before meeting the franchisor, you should talk to some of the brand's existing franchise owners to confirm exactly what the cost to own and operate their franchise has been.

When you meet the franchisor, you should again ask them the important questions in relation to total investment requirement.

Remember to include sufficient funds for working capital as well as unforeseen costs when creating your final business plan. For example, a budget of at least £2,500 should be put aside for any franchise up to £95,000 and thereafter 10 per cent of the total

investment requirement.

Some franchisors do not understand the tax benefits of breaking down the total investment requirement. If you see a franchise being offered where they talk about the total franchise package fee, they probably have not employed the services of a professional Franchise Consultant.

What Is Included In The Package?

A Genuine Business Format Franchise will have up to 21 elements that need to be carefully identified and either explained in detail or clearly illustrated in the franchise offering. These will cover the initial training, the ongoing training and every element of what the franchisor is delivering to you in order to achieve the goal of owning and operating a successful and profitable business.

Next, look at the length of time and content relating to the initial training.

The franchisor has the responsibility of training you in every area of not only running the business and understanding the products and services but has also helped you to thoroughly understand your responsibilities in every area. These will include time management, goal setting and creating a business plan that can be followed week by week.

While there are no franchise laws in the various legal jurisdictions of the UK, there are laws that relate to franchising. For example, should a franchisor not have registered and protected their trade or service marks, then they are not in a position to even offer you a franchise.

Working Capital

Working capital will vary from brand to brand with many different requirements ranging from acquiring a property or offices, equipment and fitting out the premises if appropriate.

Remember that in all cases you will be responsible for meeting all of the start-up costs other than those that the franchisor is agreeing to deliver in the franchise package.

If commercial premises and shopfitting are involved, this could be a major additional cost that you must take into account.

If you are seeking funding, you are encouraged to talk to all of the banks that have franchise departments. They will also be able to let you know whether they have previously supported the acquisition of your franchise for other franchise owners.

Always Borrow More Than You Need

Overdraft facilities will usually be required in a franchise business start-up situation so it is essential to arrange your finances so you have a reasonable financial safety net. Remember you should always try to borrow more than you need so that you do have that flexibility. It is also advisable when creating your cashflow projections to arrange an overdraft facility with your bank and let them look at your detailed business plan.

You will also need to cover your usual living expenses while you set up the business and are no longer receiving a salary. In other words your mortgage, utility bills, property maintenance, insurance etc. all need to be catered for. This is why you will need to ask the franchisor for a totally realistic assessment of working capital in addition to the franchise investment requirements.

Ongoing Fees

You should also check out what Management Service Fees you are liable to pay plus any additional costs, such as an advertising or marketing levy, when evaluating your financial requirements.

A Management Service Fee is the funding your franchisor needs in order to provide you with continual ongoing support, advice and guidance. It is normally a percentage of your total turnover and paid to the franchisor at regular predetermined intervals – usually monthly.

You may also be asked to make additional payments relating to services the franchisor will automatically offer you – again check out every detail.

When you have studied every element of the franchise package being offered then you can feel very comfortable to move forward.

Making Your Decision

Should you have any doubts about the true costs of buying into the franchise, ask the franchisor to provide a complete statement of all costs involved in buying, opening and operating the franchise outlet.

Work closely with your accountant when drawing up your business plan and ask them about the advantages of running a check on your intended franchisor to ascertain the true state of their financial health.

A wise franchise owner will also build into their calculations a budget to research not only the franchise but also any competition in the franchise and non-franchise sector.

You should also look at the different expenses you will need while choosing a franchise, including any travel and costs to attend franchise exhibitions

and anything else that you need so you truly understand the franchise market.

When you have examined all of the glossy brochures and spoken at length to the franchisor and to as many of their franchise owners as possible, it is time for you to sit back, review any advice and guidance you have received from experienced Franchise Consultants and your family. Only then should you decide whether or not you have, in fact, found your ideal franchise opportunity.

For further information
t: 01603 620301
e: enquiries@fdsltd.com
w: theukfd.net

Lloyds TSB can help you with your franchise plans.

Whether you're buying into a franchise or franchising your own business, it's important to have the right kind of support and guidance before you take the next step.

That's why we have a team of specially trained franchise managers who have a wealth of knowledge, and can offer you practical support and guidance.

To find out more call:

0800 681 6078

lloydstsb.com/franchising

Richard Holden
Head of Franchising
Lloyds Banking Group

Finance and business planning

Once you have chosen your franchise opportunity, creating and updating your business plan is crucial if you wish to obtain funding from the banks .

Franchising is generally regarded as a less risky way of setting up in business than if you were to start your own independent business. Although, as with any business opportunity, there are still risks. It is essential that anyone considering investing in a franchise thoroughly researches the market and takes appropriate professional advice. The banks' Franchise Departments are able to provide general guidance about franchise opportunities. They will also be able to assist you to carefully assess whether franchising will be the right option for you, what questions you should be asking a franchisor and help to get your business started.

Banks will require a business plan to set up a bank account and consider financial support for your business. Any lender will want you to demonstrate that you understand your chosen market and that you will be able to meet the financial commitment you are taking on. Banks will be able to provide a business plan template detailing what information should be included in the document. Some franchisors will support you in developing an effective business plan.

The business plan should be punchy and a common mistake is to make it too detailed. Ensure that it grabs the Bank Manager's interest. Presentation of the plan is important to create a positive impression and you should practice delivery of your plan beforehand so that you come across professionally. Let the Bank Manager have a copy of your business plan in advance so they can prepare for the meeting. Expect your plan to be challenged and you should be able to confidently answer questions about the operational and financial aspects of your plan.

It is often assumed that a business plan is needed just to secure funding. While this is an important benefit of producing a business plan it can also assist with the management of the business such as monitoring the ongoing performance against the original benchmarks and identifying areas for development. The plan is a working document and should be regularly reviewed and updated as the business develops.

A Business Plan Should Cover The Following Areas:

- Executive summary
- Personal details (contact details, age, martial status, dependants)
- Franchise owner's experience, skills and attributes
- Objectives/mission statement
- Overview of the franchise
- Local market (research, location, customers, competitors)
- Business operation (premises, IT, vehicles, equipment)
- Key personnel/ management team
- Marketing strategy

- Borrowing requirements
- Capital stake and security
- Personal assets, liabilities, income and expenditure statement
- Financial projections (cashflow and profit and loss forecasts)
- Financial assumptions
- Three years financial accounts (existing businesses only)
- SWOT analysis (Strengths, Weaknesses, Opportunities, Threats)
- Exit strategy

When looking to finance your franchise business, it is best to approach a franchise specialist bank. The banks' Franchise Departments regularly evaluate franchises and monitor the ongoing performance of franchise owners.

Preferential terms are often available from these banks, particularly for well-established and proven franchise opportunities. Banks without franchise units tend to treat franchises the same as a new independent start-up business.

The level of finance available from a franchise specialist bank will depend upon the strength of the franchise system as well as your business plan. Typically for well-established franchises the bank will lend up to 70 per cent of the total set up costs including working capital. For newer, less proven franchise systems, the amount of finance available may be reduced. The bank will probably require security for the loan, which commonly will be a legal charge over a residential property with sufficient equity.

Don't be put off if you haven't got any security to offer the bank. The Government backed Enterprise Finance Guarantee Scheme may be available for those who have a strong business proposal, but who

lack security that the banks usually require. Speak to the bank's Franchise Unit to discuss whether you qualify for finance under this scheme. Advice is also available on other financing options for your business such as Asset Finance, Leasing and Debtor Finance.

The bank manager may take a few days to review your plan and financial requirements. They may need to obtain sanction for the requested funds from the bank's Credit Department.

Once the lending has been sanctioned, the Bank Manager should set out in writing the terms of the agreed finance including the costs. If you wish to proceed, then confirm your acceptance of the bank's terms and the Bank Manager can prepare the documentation and security arrangements. You should be aware that it is likely to take several weeks to complete the security requirements.

Work closely with the Bank Manager to ensure that there are no delays in releasing the funds and for you to attend the franchisor's initial training course.

It is sensible to have sufficient capital to cover projected expenses for at least six months. Have a contingency reserve fund to fall back on in case the business takes

longer to get off the ground than you have anticipated.

Some banks like franchising as you are investing in a tried, tested and proven business model with initial training and ongoing support from the franchisor.

Finance is readily available at preferential terms for franchise investment from banks that have specialist Franchise Departments, such as the Lloyds Banking Group. Come and talk to our trained Franchise Managers at our business planning kiosk at the major franchise exhibitions.

Richard Holden heads up the Lloyds Banking Group Franchise Unit and is an expert speaker at exhibitions and seminars. He also regularly contributes to the national and trade press. The Lloyds Banking Group has Franchise Managers based throughout the UK to offer support to both franchisors and franchise owners. Lloyds TSB are affiliate members of the British Franchise Association.

For further information
t: 0800 681 6078
m: 07802 324018
e: richard.j.holden@ lloydstsb.co.uk
w: lloydstsb.com/franchising

ASSURED SECURITY SHREDDING LTD®

Assured Security Shredding is the only confidential document shredding franchise available in the UK with a reputation for excellent service, **Assured Security Shredding** has built its brand leading position in a lucrative service marketplace.

Operating from its head office in Surrey and its distinctively liveried, fully equipped vehicles, our national network of franchise owners can earn up to £1,500 a day per truck, providing professional, confidential shredding services to private and corporate customers.

With access to an impressive portfolio of Account customers, supplementing locally generated contracts, **Assured Security Shredding** franchise owners can enjoy a strong, resilient business base, geared for growth through the generation of regular, repeat and referred customers.

Assured Security Shredding, by contrast, has built its brand leading position in this sector by providing professional, business services by training its staff and franchise owners to have a can do attitude and fast response times, free on loan security containers and an on and off site shredding service all ISO 9001 and 14001 compliant.

For further information please call **0845 505 9999**

The Franchise Package

The **Assured Security Shredding** franchise is fantastic value. A starter pack includes uniforms, id badges, business cards, order pads, service agreements, letter heads, comp slips etc. NAID membership, software, full Google advertising, comprehensive training and full support package to help you in the early days.

Assured Security Shredding:

- Strong, well-recognised brand
- Large exclusive territories
- Comprehensive training
- Ongoing business development support
- Dedicated equipment
- Professional marketing materials
- Fully optimised national website
- Your own 'mini' website

Initial Investment Required: From £40,000 + VAT

or visit **www.assuredsecurityshredding.co.uk**

Liam Walker
Director
Anglia Finance

Raising finance to make your franchise dream a reality

When it comes to raising finance to buy a franchise, your first port of call should be an independent commercial finance broker.

Raising finance since 2008 has been a real struggle for both new and existing businesses. For those wanting to own a business it has been the real obstacle in making the decision to start and, for those already running a business, the Bank Manager is often a faceless person and there is a fear of approaching them for new lending as they will scrutinise your existing arrangements, which may well rock the boat.

For those people that are put off buying a franchise due to needing to raise finance it really is worth getting an independent opinion. Invariably the most difficult aspect of getting a loan agreed is dealing with the correct person in the bank. When you make an enquiry about a business loan you will normally be directed to the 'Local Business Manager'. While this may be the best solution if you are looking purely for a bank account, it certainly won't be the best person if some analysis of the business is required to make an informed lending decision.

Most lending decisions are now not made locally but go to a central credit department. These credit departments are seeing hundreds of lending applications a day and have to make a fast decision. They may well only have 10 minutes to fully analyse and decide whether they want to support what has been presented to them. It is therefore key that any lending proposition covers all the key areas, is to the point and leaves them looking for a reason to say 'no' rather than a reason to say 'yes'. Unfortunately, most Bank Managers you will be directed to when starting a business, will not have the experience to do this and that is why many potential business owners are put off at the first step when dealing with banks.

My advice would be not to be disheartened if your existing bank has declined your business loan. My second bit of advice would be don't be hasty and approach every bank, if you do this they may all do a credit search on you and knock your credit score and also may not look at the proposition again even if presented in a far clearer way. Also, if the bank that you know has declined you, a bit more work may

be needed in presenting the proposition to another bank else the chances are you will get a similar result.

For existing businesses there has been a fear to speak with your bank. We have all read the horror stories and have it in our head that the bank will automatically say no to any new lending request, they may even look at the proposition and decide they want you to rebank the whole relationship. In reality this happens in very few cases and I would always recommend staying as close as possible to your bank and forming a good relationship. I would also suggest reviewing what else is available in the market on a regular basis, your bank is a key partner to your business and while we all want loyalty to be rewarded, in the real world a long banking relationship can mean a complacent one.

To raise finance you will need to be putting in a minimum 30 per cent of the total investment yourself as a bank will want you to be taking a risk also. If you cannot raise all of this, involve your family who may be willing to help, alternatively there may be other options available through other forms of finance.

As well as traditional types of funding through loans and overdrafts, there are other options to raise finance for your business. These are usually easier to source and have a higher level of success rate of getting agreed than traditional finance. The main type of asset financed is vehicles. If you are buying a vehicle as part of your franchise package, or for your existing business, get in contact with a independent broker. They can run through the options with you in detail to find the best way to obtain the vehicle, which may include a loan secured against the vehicle through to you leasing the vehicle. Asset finance is also available on equipment you

purchase for your business, such as computer equipment and signage. As long as you are spending over £2,000 on these, we can look to raise finance secured against them.

Another source of finance is for those businesses that invoice other businesses. If you do this there may be an option to borrow typically 80 per cent against these outstanding invoices. This type of funding, called factoring, is far more flexible than using an overdraft and as your business grows, so does the amount of money you can borrow.

If you have had previous credit problems there are still 'invoice finance' companies that will be happy to lend to your business.

Anglia Finance has exclusive rates agreed with a selection of providers and we are confident in being the cheapest in the market.

Using an independent commercial finance broker when looking to raise finance will give you a better chance of success.

They should know who to deal with at a higher level in all institutions, they can put a lending pack together to go to the lender so less analysis needs undertaking by them and they will then negotiate the best price.

For any finance related questions please do not hesitate to contact Anglia Finance.

Liam Walker, Director of Anglia Finance, assists clients to secure commercial mortgages, business loans and works closely funding the franchise market.

For further information
t: 01603 620301
e: enquiries@fdsltd.com
w: fdsfranchise.com

Franchise Owner Advice

Fraser McKay
Editor
The Franchise Magazine

How to make the most of the exhibition experience

With the country having been hit by job losses across all sectors over the past few years, thousands upon thousands of people are now seeking to change their lives by finding the perfect franchise opportunity, and if you are reading The UK Franchise Directory, it is highly likely that are you one of them.

One of your research options will be a visit to an exhibition hall housing hundreds of franchisors, who have spent thousands of pounds to showcase their opportunity to potential franchise owners like you.

And with 21 per cent of franchise owners citing exhibition as their main source of information about brands, trade shows are as important as magazines and franchise recruitment websites in attracting strong leads, according to *Insight: An Industry Review Of Franchising In The UK*.

As well as the cost of booking stand space, exhibitors have invested money to create an eye-catching branded stand, devoted time, travel and hotel expenses to transport themselves and their staff to the event, and maybe even commissioned a promotional campaign in the newspapers and magazines to publicise their involvement.

So how can you avoid becoming a victim of over eager franchisor exhibitors? How do you avoid making a wrong decision in such a highly charged atmosphere? And how do you impress the franchisor you are interested in?

Attending a franchise exhibition should only be treated as a part of your franchise research and not all of it.

This pressured environment can be intimidating, so keep in mind your goals: to identify a number of promising opportunities, which deserve further investigation after the event and to meet and gain an impression of the management of those franchises, while retaining a level of detachment sufficient to avoid being swept up in the hype and enthusiasm.

Remember that every franchise is not right for you, even if it is affordable and the franchisor makes it sound right. They may be doing so because they are desperate to make a sale to warrant the exhibition investment. Wise visitors will set aside a whole day to visit as many stands and talk to as many franchisors as possible. By approaching the event with a strategy, perhaps sitting down with a copy of the exhibition catalogue when you arrive and identifying your 'must sees', you'll have a better chance of coming away from the event satisfied that you have gained an accurate picture of the range of opportunities you want to explore.

The Two-Way Interview

Meetings between franchisors and potential franchise owners are often described as two-way interviews, and this is the best way to approach franchise exhibitors. You are both assessing each other as potential partners in a franchise relationship and, as such, you must strive to maintain a balanced approach to the conversation.

On the one hand, you are attempting to discern the details of the franchise and the philosophy of the management team from your meeting, which may not be with a member of the management.

Arm yourself with a list of questions before the event to ensure you make the most of this opportunity – an excellent crib list of questions is *The UK Franchise Directory*'s Franchise Buyer's Checklist (page 60).

On the other, the person you are

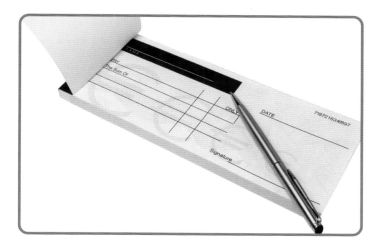

no franchisor should be seeking to sign franchise owners up on the exhibition floor and you should consider any attempt to get you to sign a franchise contract or signal of intent document as a highly dubious practise – one which could signal a franchisor keen to avoid too much investigation into its track record, or one desperate for the franchise fee to shore up a dodgy financial situation.

Assess Your Options

Approached properly, franchise exhibitions represent valuable and even fun opportunities to gain access to the people involved with the franchises available and secure the information you need to properly consider the opportunity being presented. By the end of the day you'll be returning home with a couple of bags full of brochures and promotional literature, which you can read through during your cooling off period. Combined with the research you have carried out on the internet and through reading our sister publication, *The Franchise Magazine*, you should now have enough information to begin identifying the opportunities that interest you most.

For further information
t: 01603 620301
e: enquiries@fdsltd.com
w: theukfd.net

talking to is charged with evaluating you. Their questions will tend to be open-ended, so that assessable feedback can be elicited as a guide to your potential and the more skilled stand personnel will be trying to identify you as a serious contender as early as possible.

Due to limited selling time, exhibitors try to ensure no time is wasted on an unqualified prospect. Their aim is to qualify you quickly with upfront questions and filter out those with vague answers about money.

Exhibitors will be asking themselves inward questions about you. Do you have the capital investment that you claim? Do you have what it takes to operate the franchised business and conform to the corporate values of the model? Are you capable of making the decision to invest or unlikely to commit?

It is possible they may misread your intentions and not class you as a genuine prospect, in which case they will then likely ask you to fill in a registration card for possible follow-up after the exhibition rather than devote their time explaining the opportunity being offered. If your interest in the opportunity is sincere, make it clear and ensure that you are provided with the attention you deserve.

Seminars

At most exhibitions you will find accompanying seminars designed to educate visitors about different aspects of franchising.

Subjects including 'An introduction to franchising', 'What to consider when choosing a franchise' and 'How to franchise your business' are covered, usually lasting the best part of an hour.

Keep Your Chequebook Closed

Most franchisors view the return on their investment as a significant amount of registered interest in their opportunity – a list of leads on which to follow up, with a percentage 'converting' by investing in the franchise. Certainly

- Exercise great caution and be suspicious if a franchisor remarks that no one takes professional advice before entering its franchise or that there is no point taking legal advice because they are not prepared to alter the franchise agreement.
- Taking professional advice is vital – it could very well identify certain areas to negotiate around, or indeed persuade you not to go ahead at all. Don't be too anxious to sign up for what you think is a golden opportunity – you could be wrong.
- If you are prepared to spend thousands of pounds on a franchise, is it not sensible to invest a few hundred pounds on advice from a solicitor, an accountant and a franchise consultant? Not only can they help you find your ideal franchisor – they could protect your nest egg.

Franchising terms *explained*

Area Development Franchise – A franchise which includes the rights to expand a region through appointed sub-franchise owners or multiple managed outlets.

British Franchise Association (bfa) – The bfa grants membership to those franchisors it considers meet its Code of Ethics and procedures.

Block Exemption – The European Union concessions to franchising which bypass the normal EU anti-restrictive trade practices legislation seeking to protect competition – which, for example, 'exclusive areas' can be deemed to contravene.

Business Format Franchise – The franchise owner buys into a total turnkey system of brand, know-how, training, methodology and support.

Buyback – Where the franchisor agrees to purchase a franchise back from a franchise owner if the latter no longer wishes to continue.

Disclosure – The practice of revealing detailed information about the franchisor's business track record and franchise package. This is a legal obligation in, for example, the USA, but voluntary in this country.

Exclusive Area – That territory licensed out to the franchise owner in which to conduct the business. The exclusivity is defined by the terms of the Franchise Agreement.

Franchise Agreement – Also known as the 'Franchise Agreement', it documents the legal relationship of obligations existing between the franchisor and a franchise owner.

Franchise Owner – The person who buys a licence to replicate a business system. Also known as 'franchisee'.

Franchising – Method of marketing goods and services via a business formula licensed for others to copy.

Franchisor – A company that offers the licence to replicate its system.

Franchise Package – The sum total of franchise system rights licensed to the franchise owner, including branding, know-how, systems, territory and training for which an initial Franchise Fee is charged by the franchisor.

Intellectual Property Rights – The franchisor's secrets of doing business and various trademarks, branding, manuals, etc., which should be legally protected before being sold in a franchise package.

Job Franchise – Where the franchise owner is a hands-on owner-operator rather than a manager, usually linked with van-based services such as maintenance.

Joint Venture Franchise – Where the franchisor also takes a financial stake in the project – often in international franchise agreements.

Know-how – The sum of the franchisor's secrets of doing business, also referred to as the 'intellectual property'.

Managment Franchise – A franchise in which the owner manages the operation and co-ordinates employees to do the actual work.

Master Franchise – The systems and brand of a large territory licence – a country or region.

Master Franchisor – The entity which grants Master Franchises to others – this is usually used in international contexts.

Management Service Fees (MSF) – Fees due to the franchisor, often based upon total turnover.

Operations Manual – The detailed document or 'bible', which describes every item of the business system and work procedures.

Profit & Loss (P&L) Projections – The calculations, based on the franchisor's, pilot's and franchise owners' experiences, which try to predict how soon franchise owners can expect a return on their investment, year-to-year turnover and profits.

Pilot Operation – An independent operation which tests the franchise concept and incorporates actual financial, organisational and logistical pressures to be faced by franchise owners in different areas.

Renewal – Refers to the legal provisions in the Franchise Agreement for renewing or not renewing the franchise for a further term of years.

Re-Sale – Refers to a franchised area already established by a franchise owner, that is offered for sale because the original franchise owner wants to realise his investment, move on, or simply retire. More expensive to buy than a 'virgin' franchise area, but with the advantages of an ongoing customer base, referrals, goodwill and income from day one.

Return On Investment (ROI) – The calculations or expectations that franchise owners work on to assess when they can 'break even' on their initial investment in the franchise and start earning profits.

Sub-Franchise Owner – A subordinate level of franchise owner to a regional franchise owner or area developer, usually appointed after the regional or area franchise has set up a training and support infrastructure for the territory.

Term – Refers to the agreed period of years (eg five, 10, 15) for which a franchise is granted through the Agreement.

Termination – Refers to the legal provisions by which either party in the relationship may terminate the contract, e.g. for breach of contract.

Territory/Area – The 'exclusive' portion of land, on a national, regional, county or postcode basis, which is allocated to franchise owners as part of the franchise package.

...fancy a slice of a £600,000,000 pie?

FILM IT SAVE IT PROVE IT

The UK inventory business is worth an estimated £600 million each year. The Video Inventory Agency has a market leading product putting its franchise owners in the best possible position to profit from this growing industry.

The Video Inventory Agency Franchise :

- Can be run from home
- Has low set up costs
- Has low overheads
- Provides an in-demand professional service
- Has the potential to earn an exceptionally high income
- Will grow and grow with repeat business
- Is flexible: working hours to suit
- Is fully scaleable

If you're looking for a genuine way to make a substantial income in an ethical and respectable way – becoming one of our franchise owners could be right for you.

The work involves producing high quality video inventories for the residential lettings market in order to protect landlords against damage that may be caused by tenants. We have developed the market leading product and streamlined business model enabling our franchise owners to replicate our business in an extremely profitable way.

There is no need for typing, video production or any other special skills. You will be taught all you need to know and our central production facility will actually produce the inventories for you, allowing you to concentrate on acquiring clients, making the videos and generating income.

Initial Investment Required: £7,000 + VAT.

Summary:

You will receive everything you need to set up and run your own inventory business in a professional manner including:
- Easy to use software including a CRM system to run your business professionally
- Full technical support
- An intensive two-day classroom training course
- Practical sales training day
- Intensive sales and marketing campaign by head office to launch your business
- Home study and on the job training
- accreditation by the Institute Of Video Inventory Professionals
- Operations and Business Development Manuals and DVDs giving you step by step guidance for all areas of your business and proven sales strategies
- A starter pack containing stationery and marketing materials
- Regular on-going training days
- Work supplied by head office for your area
- Your own customised website, hosted for you and your own email address

Tiffany Brooking
Assistant Editor
The UK Franchise Directory

Frequently Asked Questions

Established individuals from the franchise industry share their knowledge and experience to answer some of the most common franchising questions.

Question: Do I need previous experience in business to buy a franchise?

No, previous experience in business is not necessary to buy a franchise. Of course, some businesses are more complex to get to grips with than others but all reputable franchisors should provide a comprehensive training package that includes the basics of running a business as well as any core skills required for the specific franchise.

The benefit of being a franchise owner compared to an independent business owner is that you can draw upon the extensive business expertise and experience of the franchisor – particularly in the early days. At Autosheen, we also provide a number of business development days – delivered on a one-to-one basis by an experienced manager, on the franchise owner's territory – as part of the standard franchise package.

Paul Fennell
Managing Director
Autosheen

Question: How will the franchise help me establish the brand in my territory?

Some multi-national brands – McDonald's for example – will be instantly recognisable, others less so but, however big or small, a good franchisor will invest in helping you establish their brand – now your brand also – in your own chosen territory.

This question should feature prominently on your checklist when you meet the franchisor. What are their plans for your launch in your local market place? Will there be a press release? Will there be an advertising campaign? What other media may be involved? – website, social and business networks and other.

A good franchisor will recommend the best networking events to attend, at which exhibitions to take stands, in which trade publications to advertise.

In short, a good franchisor will do all they can to ensure your business is a success and plays an important part in their own strategy for growth. The best franchise is when the franchisor and franchise owner work in partnership together.

Godfrey Lancashire
Managing Director
London House International

Question: What are the advantages of investing in a franchise over starting a business for yourself?

One of the key advantages of buying a franchise is that you will be buying into a proven business model, the name and brand will be already established.

Statistics show that so many people fail in business when they try to go it alone.

One of the other advantages of buying a franchise is that you will be able to start your business very

Sandra Venables
Managing Director
Well Polished

Question: How safe is my investment with a franchise?

Your investment in a franchise is considerably safer than an investment in a stand-alone business start-up. Independent evidence gathered by the bfa and NatWest Bank shows that 90 per cent of UK franchises are profitable and many high street banks maintain that over 90 per cent are successful after two years, compared to only 40 per cent of other self-employed business start-ups.

This is because good franchises offer a proven business model, a strong brand and support from experienced business professionals. It goes without saying, that your investment is safer still if the franchise has been in operation for a number of years, has an established network of successful franchise owners and has demonstrated resilience to recession.

It is also worth noting that a great franchise can provide not only a safer investment, but also a considerably better return than many other investment opportunities.

At ChipsAway, some franchise owners have enjoyed an excellent living for many years, then achieved a good return on their initial investment when their franchise has been sold on.

However, there are no guarantees. Building any business requires hard work and commitment in order to succeed.

Lloyd Evans
Chief Executive
ChipsAway

quickly after completing your training. As well as full training, you will also receive ongoing support thereafter.

When going it alone in business you can sometimes feel very isolated. One of the other advantages of buying a franchise is that as well as ongoing support and training you will receive you will also have the benefit of being able to network with other franchise owners in the group.

Question: How do franchisors assess the suitability of prospective franchise owners?

Franchising is a powerful blend of the best elements of 'big' and 'small' business. It is an effective mixture of conformity and individuality allowing the franchise owner the opportunity to build a genuine business and a capital asset while diligently following the proven systems laid down by the franchisor.

Good franchising is a marriage of two parties with different skill sets but with a common purpose – business development. To this end, franchisors look for high work ethic, ambition, people skills (good communicators), willingness to follow a proven system and good organisational ability plus specific skills that relate to their own particular business/industry.

These may include IT, sales, marketing, education and finance. However, in my experience the specific skills are less important than work ethic, people skills and organisational ability as the franchisor will be training the specific skills required to run their system.

If a franchise owner doesn't have the right 'ethos' then no matter how good the specific skill training, they will almost certainly be unsuitable for life as a franchise owner.

Nigel Toplis **Managing Director** Recognition Express

Franchise Owner Advice

Question: How can I get a realistic idea of how much it will cost to set the franchise up?

At Ovenclean we hold open days where prospective franchise owners are invited to visit our head office to take a look at our operation at close quarters.

These events are free of charge, very informal and are designed to provide detailed information about how the franchise works, including set up costs, typical overhead and operational costs, as well as illustrations showing how profitable the franchise can be.

Julian Minwalla
Chief Executive
Ovenclean

Question: How would you describe the long-term relationship between a franchisor and a franchise owner?

At Minster our franchise owners have been in partnership with us for an average of 12 years. Both we, and our franchise owners, prefer this long term, stable relationship. For this to endure, we work hard to make sure that there is an ongoing, mutually beneficial financial interest for both parties. It is definitely a win-win relationship. This is why we take a great deal of time and care in selecting our franchise owners in the first place. We believe the relationship has to work for both parties throughout — mutual trust is imperative in sustaining the relationship.

Mike Parker
Managing Director
Minster Services Group

Question: How will buying a franchise affect my work/life balance?

If managed correctly, our management franchise is a key to your freedom. A management franchise gives you the opportunity to take back control of your life. Managed correctly, you can arrange your workload around family, hobbies and interests.

Pat Thompson **Franchise Recruitment Manager** Caremark

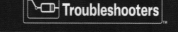

TECHNOLOGY SOLVED

LOCAL SERVICE - GLOBAL STRENGTH

From an IT background?
Want to reap the rewards of self-employment?

FRANCHISE OPPORTUNITIES

We have been in operation since 1997 and we now have over 450 outlets around the world, with over 35 in the UK.

"Your Business.... our support."

"Our solutions... your success!"

Our franchise success is based on helping you create the business that best suits your skills, experience and desires. You may wish to operate a business from a home base, handling most of the technical work yourself. Or you may wish to start from a service centre, managing technical staff to handle the day to day work.

Both options work well and, in practice, some Computer Troubleshooters start as a home operation, then expand into a service centre.

We find the potential market for on-site computer services is huge. Almost all small businesses and home offices use computers and depend on them to be working properly. They do not have the skills, time nor the desire to carry out their own computer service, repairs, and upgrades which puts us at the core of one of the fastest growing industries in the world.

To find out more and request more information, visit

www.computertroubleshooters.co.uk

CELEBRATING 10 Years of Service 1997-2007

Computer Troubleshooters DATA BACKUP

Derin Ibrahim
Online Editor
The Franchise Magazine

Is a Master Franchise right for you?

Owning a Master Franchise is very different to being a franchise owner, often requiring a much higher level of dedication but also producing higher results.

The commitment needed to be a Master Franchise Owner is much greater than that of a single unit franchise owner.

One of the main reasons for this is that a Master Franchise Owner will possess a much larger business than a franchise owner. Whereas franchise owners normally open one location and will perhaps build their business by opening a second unit, a Master Franchise Owner will own the franchise network for an entire country.

To ensure that the owner of a Master Franchise is prepared to launch multiple units, the franchisor will usually specify a minimum number of locations to be opened within a specific timescale in the agreement.

Due to the Master Franchise Owner's obligation to open a number of locations, they will normally own and operate a pilot location and then recruit a network of franchise owners to operate further locations. The Master Franchise Owner will be

responsible for managing the franchise network and will usually have to provide support and training to franchise owners (although sometimes this is done by the franchisor), as well as being responsible for recruiting quality franchise owners to the network.

Part of the franchisor's role is to ensure that the Master Franchise Owner has all the skills, knowledge and back-up needed to provide effective training and support to its franchise owners. To prepare Master Franchise Owners for this, the franchisor usually provides them with thorough training that ensures they are competent in all aspects of the business.

Normally a Master Franchise Owner is sought by foreign brands looking to expand their franchise into a new country. As a result, the Master Franchise Owner will be bringing an entirely new brand into their market. Before a franchisor

makes a Master Franchise available, it will have ensured its concept is successfully franchised throughout its own country and will sometimes initially start franchising abroad themselves to ensure the concept works internationally.

More often than not, although the basics of the franchise model are kept, when a franchise is entering a new market small adaptations are made to ensure that it suits the market. The Master Franchise Owner will usually have some influence on these changes and, as a result, will have more control and say into how the franchise is operated than a single unit franchise owner would have.

Additionally, a Master Franchise provides more opportunity to establish a growing business. This is because a Master Franchise Agreement often only states the minimum number of locations to be opened, which enables the Master Franchise owner to establish as many locations as they feel will be successful within their territory.

Not only is a Master Franchise more expensive than a single unit franchise, franchisors are also more restrictive in the type of candidates they want to apply. This is because a franchisor will want to make sure the Master Franchise Owner has the financial backing, experience and qualifications needed to establish and support a growing franchise network.

The higher investment levels and skill sets most franchisors look for in Master Franchise Owner candidates, means that they are usually owned by already established companies, highly experienced entrepreneurs or business partnerships .

Although the demands on a Master Franchise owner are much greater than that of a franchise owner, there are many benefits to owning a Master Franchise including a greater say in the franchise model and ability for business expansion. Therefore, for the right business or entrepreneur, owning a Master Franchise could be the new business opportunity they are looking for.

For further information
t: 01603 620301
e: enquiries@fdsltd.com
w: theukfd.net

Check...before Cheque!

Check
Checklist
Check
Checklist
Check

Check
Checklist

Use this checklist to assist you in performing your due diligence on your shortlist of prospective franchise investments

The Franchise Owner Prospectus should contain...

- Business background of Directors and key Executives
- Track record of the company
- Description of the franchise
- Breakdown of the initial investment required
- Details of other payments due to the franchisor
- Guidance on raising finance
- Requirements for franchise owner's participation
- Terms for termination/renewal of agreement
- Number and success rates of existing franchise owners
- Franchisor's site selection/approval rights
- Overview of guaranteed training and support
- Report on the performance of the pilot operation
- Financial statement from the franchisor
- Details of the franchisor's professional advisers

What to find out from the franchisor...

- Financial health and track record of the company
- The company's franchising history
- Results of the pilot operation
- Current number of franchise owners
- Permission to talk to existing franchise owners
- Company's main source of earnings
- Value, appeal and long-term viability of product/service
- Head office commitment to support
- Full details of the initial training programme
- Additional training costs to the franchise owner
- Total size of the franchise investment requirement
- Realistic estimate of working capital needed
- Bank and other references
- Territorial practices and exclusivity terms
- National and regional advertising practices
- Exclusivity of product supply contracts
- Franchisor's margins on product supply
- Target obligations
- Realistic franchise owner profit and loss figures
- Management service fees or royalty payments
- Restrictions on franchise owner's operations
- Franchisor's launch assistance programme
- A sample of the Franchise Agreement

Be wary if the franchisor...

- Tries to get you to sign a deposit agreement to reserve a territory
- Does not offer an automatic right to renew your agreement
- Has a very short-term contract
- Pressures you to "act now" before the cost goes up
- Tries to trade you up to a higher fee
- Demands large front end licence fee
- Promises huge profits with thin investments
- Promises "easy sales"
- Promises profits by sub-franchising
- Promises large income working from home
- Fails to give statistics on sales and profits
- Evades identifying Directors or principals
- Has no data on financial track record
- Cannot give plans for future development
- Has incomprehensible contract or vague territories
- Is vague about support and training
- Has a name similar to a well known business
- Is ignorant of competition
- Has weak advertising
- Avoids detailing your financial obligations
- Tries to meet only in a hotel or has poor head office premises
- Is evasive about access to existing franchise owners

The Franchise Agreement must cover...

- Description of exact training and support offered
- Precise price, commissions and rental fees involved
- Precise boundaries of the franchise territory
- Obligations to the franchisor
- Rights to renew or extend beyond original term
- Your rights to sell/transfer ownership of your franchise
- Terms and conditions for terminating contract
- Heir's rights in the event of your death

Start your own business with a **CENTURY 21 property franchise**

The CENTURY 21® United Kingdom franchise system offers you the opportunity to become an estate and letting agency professional and run your own business.

Did you know that the UK franchise industry is now estimated to be worth £11.8 billion and that property franchises remain the largest sector? With Franchise Europe currently ranking CENTURY 21, 15th in it's top 500 European franchise listing, you want to be joining forces with the world's largest estate agency network.

The CENTURY 21® System was created in 1971. Century 21 Real Estate LLC is the franchisor of the world's largest residential real estate sales organisation, providing comprehensive training, management, administrative and marketing support for the CENTURY 21 System. The System is comprised of more than 7,700 independently owned and operated franchised broker offices and 117,000 sales associates in 68 countries and territories worldwide.

People just like YOU have already started a business with our franchise opportunity

What should you do next?

Contact CENTURY 21 UK now to let us know you're interested. We can arrange an informal meeting to discuss our opportunities in more detail and assist you in your decision making process.

Call 0870 21 11 399 or register your interest at www.century21uk.com/franchise

Looking to own a franchise?
Want to take the next step?

Talk to Franchise Development Services (FDS), the organisation that has helped over **10,000** people to achieve their ambitions by owning and operating a franchise.

We recommend that you subscribe to *The Franchise Magazine* – today's most sought after publication promoting Business Format Franchises.

For subscription enquiries to
The Franchise Magazine
call 01603 620301

Alternatively for more information visit:
www.TheFranchiseMagazine.net
www.TheUKFranchiseDirectory.net

Looking to expand your business by franchising?

Take advantage of FDS's experience, gained since 1981, to guide you through how to successfully franchise your business.

FDS/bfa Affiliated franchise consultants will provide you with **FREE** initial advice and guidance by telephone or by visiting any of our UK offices.

FDS has already helped over **1,000** companies to successfully franchise their business nationwide and worldwide including many bfa members.

For more information on how we can assist you, contact FDS on:

t: 01603 620301
e: enquiries@fdsltd.com
w. fdsfranchise.com

Franchise Services

Professor Roy Seaman CFE
Managing Director
Franchise Development Services Ltd

10 reasons to franchise your business

If you own a business which could replicate its success on a national scale, developing a franchise could offer the most effective route to capturing the UK market. Here are 10 advantages that franchising provides over direct expansion.

1. Faster National Expansion

Once you have established your business as a franchise, your network has the potential to grow quickly with the franchise owners' capital funding the new outlets.

The overheads and expenses associated with opening company-owned outlets are replaced by the franchise recruitment, training and launch assistance at a lower cost.

2. Better Motivated Operators

By deciding to franchise your growing business, you are able to benefit from the franchise owners' ambition, energy and commitment to the business and its standards.

Franchise owners are more motivated and effective than a salaried manager, because they have a vested interest within the business.

3. Get The Edge On Competition

Customers are often attracted to a new idea and will stay with a brand if the product or service is as good as, or better than, that supplied by their previous provider. By quickly expanding into new geographical areas, you are well placed, providing your product or service is good enough, to take your competitors' customers and keep them.

4. Effective Quality Controls

Franchising is all about following a system. As all of your franchise owners are following the same system, customers throughout the network should receive the same high quality service, irrespective of location. That way the customers will always know what to expect from your brand and that encourages loyalty.

5. Rationalises Management

Running a franchise system requires less management than a

company-owned chain of outlets, since hiring, training, motivating and retaining competent staff are all functions handled by the franchise owner, not the franchisor.

This means you can get a better edge on competitors unable to operate with a compact management database because they need to spend more on this element.

6. Knowledge From Franchise Owners

When you expand your business into new areas it is essential for you to conduct extensive research.

However, when you expand through franchising the responsibility for evaluating a new territory is passed on to franchise owners.

They may already possess local business knowledge and by using their expertise you have a clearer insight into the local market.

This practice is particularly useful when expanding into foreign markets.

7. Group Purchasing Strength

Centralised buying enables your entire network to benefit from volume discounts that an independent trader is unable to obtain. This means franchised outlets are in a better position to offer competitive prices, which will help to increase your market share.

8. A Dedicated Distribution Network

If you are a manufacturer or service provider, establishing the sales function of your business as a franchise operation provides you with a distribution network entirely focused on the supply of your products or service to customers.

9. Marketing Power

As your network develops, all of your outlets can benefit from the group's marketing initiatives, at both a regional and national level.

A positive network spirit will encourage franchise owners to help each other through referrals as your customers become increasingly familiar with your brand, expanding on a national level.

10. Improved Profitability

Return on investment is likely to be higher for a business that has opted to expand through franchising.

This is because less capital is employed and the franchisor's profits are generated on a much lower capital investment.

So although the revenue received from franchised units is logically less than from 100 per cent company-owned outlets, a higher percentage of the revenue is actual profit.

For further information
t: 01603 620301
e: enquiries@fdsltd.com
w: fdsfranchise.com

Gordon Patterson
Franchise Consultant

How to franchise your business

Are you planning on expanding your business and looking for the most effective way to do so? Then franchising could well be the answer.

Developing a franchise is a challenging undertaking and only advisable when armed with a wealth of practical experience and the best Franchise Consultant you can find. You must engage those with a proven experience and the best track record of success.

Overall success in franchising is not based on a small number of factors, but a combination of many criteria – applied at the right time, in the right way and in the right place.

Accessing the franchise wisdom of more experienced parties is your insurance against having to retread these steps further down the line – a costly and difficult endeavour if franchise owners are already signed up, especially if the Franchise Agreement needs amending.

Following an exploratory discussion and having been satisfied in principle that the business concept is sound and franchiseable, your Franchise Consultant will implement the three-phase strategy for success.

Phase 1 – On-site Evaluation Of Client's Business Concept Meeting Objectives:

- Full appreciation of core/related business activities
- Securing data on the entire business method
- Securing relevant financial data
- Brainstorming ideas on possible franchise structure
- Understanding client aims plus management resources
- Securing data for a franchise development programme

The agreed work programme is then implemented over a three to four week period, generates an Action Document comprising detailed guidelines for franchising the business.

Action Document:
- Key conclusions for successful franchising
- Key elements and itemised costs of franchise package
- Recommendation on licence fee to be charged
- Financial projections for franchise owner territories

- Critical assumptions underlying these projections
- Type of franchisor support structure needed
- Ongoing fee structure between franchisor and franchise owner
- SWOT Analysis on franchising the business
- Recommendations and ideal plan of action clearly identifying the best way to franchise the business

Another meeting follows to present and discuss the contents, and clarify the best way forward. The first phase will have produced an outline skeleton for structuring the franchise. The next phase puts flesh on the bones.

Phase 2 – Preparing The Infrastructure

This second phase adheres to a work programme to produce the infrastructure for successful franchise development.
Work Programme:
- Intellectual property rights protection
- Identifying support services
- The franchise package
- Preparing financial statements

- Fixing initial and ongoing fee structure
- Production of an attractive franchise prospectus
- Producing the franchise information memorandum
- Producing the franchise manual
- Producing the legal documentation
- Designing franchise owner training programme
- Finalising corporate image elements
- Strategy for franchise owner recruitment
- Procedure for handling franchise owner recruitment

During this vital phase, your Franchise Consultant will work with specialist franchise solicitors, trademark attorneys, accountants, PR practitioners, franchise advertising and editorial personnel, corporate design experts and other professionals to ensure the creation of an attractive and professional franchise offering.

Objectives:
- Credible and professional corporate image
- Clear and inviting franchise prospectus
- Legal agreement fair to both parties but leaving you in control
- Franchise manuals for the entire business
- Territories benefiting both franchisor and franchise owners

After the second phase, the new business format should be ready for a professional and confident launch as an attractive Business Format Franchise.

Phase 3 – Franchise Owner Recruitment

This involves marketing your franchise to secure quality prospects to own and operate the franchise. Consolidating the first phase of franchise owners is vital to laying the solid foundations for franchising success.

It cannot be stressed enough the importance of selecting parties of the right calibre rather than those just with the capital to invest. You must select marketing companies which can design eye-catching advertising, in order to portray the opportunity accurately and effectively to attract quality prospects.

FDS has its own media that can generate quality prospects. The combination of advertising, editorial and websites has enabled many clients to succeed.

Having generated enquiries, your Franchise Consultant will then teach your management team how to invest time and patience in handling your enquiries correctly. It is all too easy to invest in promotions and then mishandle the resulting enquiries – for example by using ill-informed call handlers, answering machines or sending out inappropriate promotional material.

For further information
t: 01603 620301
e: enquiries@fdsltd.com
w: fdsfranchise.com

Richard Langrick
FranMatch Executive
Franchise Development Services Ltd

Specialist franchise owner recruitment is an investment not a cost

Richard Langrick, who looks after FranMatch the specialist recruitment division of Franchise Development Services, explains why.

Recruitment can be a time consuming and thankless task, involving as it does many fruitless calls and dead ends, often in the evening or at the weekend, but is an essential part of any company's growth and development, and can lead to costly mistakes if not handled properly by professionals.

Franchise owner recruitment is even more important than staff recruitment, as mistakes are costly to rectify and disgruntled franchise owners can soon destroy a franchisor's good name.

To get the best results, franchisors should advertise in publications that genuinely aspiring franchise owners read, and then follow up each and every lead – no matter how time consuming or what time of day or night the applicant is available.

FranMatch, the franchise owner recruitment division of Franchise Development Services (FDS), will take care of every step of the recruitment process – from writing the advertisement, through to arranging the meetings – ensuring only properly qualified, financially secure applicants are presented to the franchisor.

This saves a busy franchisor many hours of calling, sifting through applications, and time consuming administration keeping track of all applicants.

On the FranMatch system, applicants view advertisements in FDS's publications, or online, and are invited to fill in a simple form, which generates an initial contact email and brief details about the franchise opportunity.

The applicant will be contacted by a FranMatch Executive, who will conduct a preliminary phone interview to establish the suitability of the applicant. They will then arrange for more detailed information to be sent and for an application form to be completed.

From this information and, if the applicant is considered right for the franchise, the Franmatch Executive will discuss the applicant with the franchisor, and then arrange a meeting.

Similarly, if a potential franchise owner needs advice and guidance on selecting the most suitable franchise, then the FranMatch Executive can help with general advice, or more specific advice on particular franchises.

FranMatch is run by experienced recruiters like myself, who have worked in and understand the franchise market for many years and are ever mindful of the laws concerning discrimination and data protection.

This specialist service ensures that every lead is professionally handled, and leaves the franchisor to get on with what he does best – running his business.

FranMatch Explained

Traditionally franchisors have had two choices for their franchise recruitment strategy: build an in-house recruitment team, which can be costly, or share the responsibility of recruitment at Director level, which can detract from your other business duties.

FDS offers franchisors a third option that saves time and money.

FranMatch generates and manages leads for you using leading publications, websites and methodology.

As well as putting together your advertising campaign we design and implement a structured lead management service.

The FranMatch service appeals to both the established and new franchisor, allowing them to utilise their time management in other areas of their franchise development.

Provided your company has realistic franchise owner recruitment goals, a budget in place and the desire to work with us as part of your team, then we should have the ability to succeed together.

For further information
t: 01603 620301
e: franmatch@fdsltd.com
w: fdsfranchise.com

FDS FranMatch
Optimise your franchise
owner recruitment process

Traditionally franchisors have had two choices for their franchise recruitment strategy: build an in-house recruitment team, which can be costly, or share the responsibility of recruitment at Director level, which can detract from your other business duties. FDS offers franchisors a third option that saves time and money!

FranMatch generates and manages leads for you using leading publications, websites and methodology. As well as putting together your advertising campaign, we design and implement a structured lead management service.

The FranMatch service appeals to the established and new franchisors allowing them to utilise their time management in other areas of their franchise development.

Provided that your company has realistic franchise owner recruitment goals, a budget in place and the desire to work with us as part of your team, then we should have the ability to succeed together.

Take the next step and get your franchise owner recruitment campaign to a higher level.

For further information
please call 01603 620301, email franmatch@fdsltd.com or visit www.franmatch.net.

Ken Young
Regional Director
FDS Midlands

How to market your franchise

Using the media wisely is key to getting your franchise opportunity noticed by potential franchise owners, whether it is in print, the internet or at exhibitions.

No matter how attractive your franchise may be in terms of potential profitability and lifestyle opportunity, you will never attract sufficient franchise owner enquiries unless its attractions are clearly explained to the maximum possible number of people within your target market.

That means your first job is to carefully analyse your franchise in order to understand exactly what its most attractive features are – not for its customers or for yourself, the franchisor – but for any potential franchise owner.

You, therefore, need to put yourself into the shoes of that potential franchise owner and to identify the benefits of your total franchise proposition from his or her perspective, essentially answering the question: "Why should I invest my hard-earned savings in this particular venture?".

Once you have found answers to this question, you will have a good solid basis for marketing your franchise. Look at all the reasons you have come up with, select the most compelling ones (no more than five or six) and then find exactly the right words and phrases to express each of them as clearly and succinctly as possible. These are the messages you will be repeating time and time again in all your future marketing activities.

What media should you use to convey your marketing messages? The answer may depend on the size of budget you have available and will almost certainly vary as your franchise network progresses through the different stages of its growth. The main options include using your own website, third-party franchise recruitment sites, appearing at exhibitions and advertising in specialist magazines, directories and newspapers.

The internet is certainly a powerful force in today's market. There are numerous websites offering franchise sales, so it pays to do your research. Before making your decision, ask the operators for performance statistics, check the quality of other franchise opportunities on their sites – and perhaps even contact a few of these yourself to see if they have been pleased with the results.

The websites that attract most visitors are those associated with a well-known franchise publication or linked with a reputable franchising consultancy. Specialist franchise magazines are usually credited with generating a particularly high quality of leads because they are bought and read almost exclusively by people who are seriously interested in acquiring a franchise.

You should not entirely restrict your advertising to specialist franchise web and printed publications. You can also try out those websites and trade magazines, which target your own particular industry. By using this avenue, your franchise opportunity will be promoted to people who already have skills and experience in those areas that you need – an advantage which could help them considerably during the early stages.

National and local franchise exhibitions can provide an excellent platform for finding franchise owners and in generally building up

awareness of your brand – especially if the organiser arranges high quality press coverage for the event. For established franchisors, exhibitions also offer the possibility of bringing along existing successful franchise owners who can share their experiences and enthusiasm with the visitors.

As your network grows, you may also wish to encourage referrals from your existing franchise owners by means of a recommendation scheme. Many successful franchisors use such schemes and who better to promote your franchise than somebody who already owns one and is satisfied with his or her investment?

Having selected your marketing methods, it is important to make sure that you have the means to deal with the resultant enquiries in a professional and timely manner.

That means correct training for everybody in your organisation who is likely to handle those enquiries either by phone or email.

As a general rule, all franchise enquiries should receive an initial response within 24 hours. Since that initial response will normally include sending a copy of your Franchise Prospectus to the enquirer, you will need to make sure that you have adequate printed supplies for posting and/or a suitable electronic version for emailing. You should also be sure to follow up by phone a few days after the Franchise Prospectus has been received. This is your opportunity to answer any questions the prospect may have and for you to obtain any further information you may need to assess his or her suitability as a franchise owner.

Most importantly, you need to devise a simple system for 'tracking' the progress of each prospect from the first time he or she contacts you right through to the final outcome, be it positive or negative. As well as prompting you as to when the next action is due for each prospect, this record will highlight which methods of marketing are actually producing the best results for you.

If there is a weakness in your franchise structure or in the way it has been presented, the information on your tracking system will also help you to identify where that weakness lies. You can then correct it and move forward to further improve your recruitment performance.

For further information
t: 01603 620 301
e: enquiries@fdsltd.com
w: fdsfranchise.com

Tom Endean
Marketing Manager
British Franchise Association (bfa)

How the bfa can help franchisors

It has been said many times that franchising is far more successful than other businesses start-ups.

Franchising is a very successful way of helping good businesses grow and become more tenacious through bringing on good enterprising individuals, willing to invest into the brand both in terms of their money and hard work.

However, all of this is based on it being done well and, unfortunately, not every franchisor is set up correctly to deliver what it needs to.

In 2010, the British Franchise Association (bfa) ran a survey with its members to see what they felt were the main reasons for becoming members. The most important was the credibility that comes with membership. Closely following was the knowledge that you were building your business in the right way. As a franchisor these are two important factors that will go a long way in realising the successes that franchising can deliver.

Established in 1977, the bfa is the only voluntary self-regulatory body for the UK franchise sector. Its aim is to promote ethical franchising practice in the

UK and help the industry develop credibility, influence and favourable circumstance for growth.

It does this with a standards based approach to membership of the association. In addition, the bfa works to increase the awareness of ethical franchising by communicating with government, academia, the media and the UK public on what constitutes franchising best practice.

As a result, one of the bfa's main jobs is to help potential franchise owners recognise the good, the bad, and the ugly for what they are. Another is to help businesses involved in franchising to secure their own position among the 'good' operators.

Membership of the bfa is divided into three levels of franchisor membership, plus Affiliate membership for professional advisors.

The franchisor members have to meet the standards set by the bfa in order to establish that their franchise represents a fair, ethical and disclosed opportunity. The standards are adopted from

the *European Franchise Federation (EFF) Code of Ethics* and are set out in *The bfa Ethics of Franchising*.

Although the credibility of membership and the associated opportunity to promote an ethical and proper approach to franchising is one of the most obvious benefits to franchisors joining the bfa, there are also many other aspect of the membership. These include platforms to share best practice, raise profile, make new contacts and influence your business environment.

For those who are looking to franchise their business, or are already franchising, looking into bfa membership is a highly recommended route to becoming an established franchise brand.

The full bfa membership benefits can be broken down into four main areas:

Growth And Support
- Gain from bfa accredited status and the ethics and standards that it represents
- Gain free franchise owner and client enquiries through your listing on the bfa website, which

receives over 11 million hits per year and directs 120,000 visitors to the members' websites every year
- Access discounted exhibition space at the bfa accredited franchise exhibitions
- Access discounted advertising in industry and national press
- Gain eligibility for the national bfa Franchisor of the Year Awards and Franchisee of the Year Awards, providing high profile PR and huge industry recognition
- Access cost effective dispute resolution procedures
- Benefit from membership support via the bfa central office and a dedicated Business Development Managers

Market Profile
- Benefit from new levels of promotion to potential customers through the Proud to Franchise initiative
- Raise your profile by submitting news stories for consideration in the bfa's Newsline publication
- Access bfa events for new networking opportunities

- Be considered for speaking opportunities across the UK
- Upload news stories and case studies to the bfa website for the public and media to see
- Gain profile and opportunities through association with bfa PR activities

Knowledge And Skills
- Receive free subscription to Newsline; the bi-monthly bfa news publication
- Access valuable knowledge sharing and guidance through the bfa forums
- Gain regular updates on news and events direct to your desktop
- Receive regular technical bulletins on best practice and guidance for your business
- Access to exclusive bfa training programmes and seminars

Influencing And Lobbying
- Be part of the authoritative voice of franchising; lobbying UK and European governments in the interests of UK franchising

Benefiting Your Franchise Owners
In addition to the benefits above for the franchisor, membership to the bfa also has a number of intrinsic benefits for your franchise owners.

For a start, being an accredited member will help your franchise owners get finance in the first place, as the specialist banks in the industry will look positively on accreditation of the brand. These benefits will then continue through the life of the franchise owner and even at the point at which a franchise owner may want to sell their business.

For a franchise owner who is looking to sell their business, being part of a brand that is bfa accredited means that potential buyers will have more confidence and in many cases a better sale can be achieved.

For more information about the bfa, its role and the benefits of membership call **01865 379 892** or visit **www.thebfa.org**

Tony Urwin
Regional Director
FDS North

Going global

With the prospects of domestic business development remaining gloomy, the benefits of looking further afield may never have been brighter.

The benefits of franchising on a national level are already well established. It enables companies to grow successfully by sharing the expansion costs with a countrywide network of highly-motivated franchise owners legally bound to operate within pre-determined standards and service levels. However, when domestic opportunities are limited by a depressed marketplace, franchising overseas can be a particularly effective means of expanding and bringing a whole new dimension to a brand.

Reduced Risk

Entering a foreign market can be a huge leap into unknown waters. However, franchising allows you to lower the financial risk thanks to investors who share your vision for the development of your brand in a new location. A franchise owner has a genuine commitment to the success of the business that can be lacking in remotely-based employees. With their own investment at stake, they're also far more likely to hire the right people and instill the correct company ethics.

Remote Operation

You will still have a business to run in the UK, so franchising will allow the new overseas operation to run effectively at arm's length, while enabling you to control the fundamental aspects of the brand promise. Franchising gives you the opportunity to recruit a franchise owner you trust to run your business exactly as you would run it yourself.

Local Knowledge

Knowing the cultural and commercial peculiarities of the new location is invaluable and central to the ultimate success of the brand. Through franchising, the process of appropriately adapting the business for the local market is transferred to the franchise owner. This presents you with huge savings, as the costs of alternative advertising materials etc, are

borne by the franchise owner (although your approval is still required).

Network Expansion

Your Master Franchise Owner will recruit, train and support a network of sub-franchise owners. You will then benefit from a percentage of the turnover of the entire network – without the need to hold their hands on an individual basis. Naturally, an international expansion plan is a major step for your business to take, and there are several factors to consider before you make the move.

Trademarks

It is vital that you secure the use of your trademarks in all your target countries before you begin marketing your franchise. Just as it is impossible to franchise a brand in the UK without owning the trademark, you must ensure that registration is in place overseas also.

Control

You will need to find methods of

tracking important information such as sales data through robust monitoring systems – and you will need to build these into the franchise package from the outset. This will allow you to keep a close eye on the performance of the business and ensure you're receiving the correct payments from your franchise owner.

Legal Protection

Your Franchise Agreement will need to be adapted to suit legislation in the new trading location.

Ensure you select a lawyer with international franchise experience and they have contacts with legal professionals in the Master Franchise country. A solid Franchise Agreement that protects your interests is fundamental to the global success of your brand.

Support

As with any franchise network, you will need to provide your franchise owner with a level of support that justifies their Management Service Fee payments to you. This may well

include regular visits – so you will need to ensure your UK business can continue to operate when key personnel are absent.

Flexibility

You and your team should be prepared to learn and adapt to different cultures and ways of doing business.

International franchising is undoubtedly a great way to expand rapidly and cost-effectively with reduced risk. At a time when businesses are being forced to take drastic steps to protect their operations, franchising allows you to grow on an international scale while your competitors pull up the drawbridge. Any risk can be reduced even further if you take expert advice from the outset and ensure your business and brand are well protected.

For further information
t: 01603 620301
e: enquiries@fdsltd.com
w: fdsfranchise.com

Franchisor Advice

Debra Hiddleston
Trademark Attorney
ip21 Ltd

The real cost of *not* registering your trademark

It is tempting for cost conscious businesses to defer registering their trademarks, but what is the real cost, and therefore loss, to a business of not registering a brand identity or trademark?

There is no legal obligation to register a trademark before using it, indeed some businesses do not, but they often count the cost later. Without the benefit of a Registered Trademark, businesses are limited in the action they can bring against others who may be profiting by using their valuable, but unregistered brand identity. They are also limited in the defences they can use when accused of acts of infringement from owners of later-filed Registered Trademarks.

For franchisors, or potential franchisors, professional trade mark registration is crucial for the protection of valuable brands and, in the long run, cheaper. The very essence of franchising is allowing others to use your brand identity in return for a payment. Unless the brands are properly protected, the business model is at serious risk. On the other side of the fence, all franchise owners should also make sure that the brands they buy into are adequately protected – a strong and protected brand is a significant part of what you're paying for.

Use of an unregistered mark might prevent someone else registering a similar mark; at least in the UK. But if unsuccessful, a business could be restrained from expanding both in the products and services being provided and the geographical scope of where these might be purchased. Worst still, the business might have to fight off an infringement claim, leading to time and money being spent on avoidable legal advice. The cost to a business could be very high.

The enforcement of unregistered trademark rights is provided via the common law tort of 'passing-off' in the UK, which provides a remedy where a business has been trading under an unregistered trademark for many years and a rival business starts using the same or similar mark.

In its basic form, passing-off is a misrepresentation of the origin of goods or services – for example by the use of the brand name or logo – causing confusion in the mind of a consumer and leading to damage to a business having a reputation or goodwill in the brand.

Bringing a passing-off action can be very costly, and equally uncertain in its outcome due to the fact that owners of unregistered rights have to prove that they have a goodwill in the mark, and that misrepresentation and damage have occurred to their business. As a result, passing-off cannot be used to protect a trademark that is new, with little reputation, or where no trade in the UK has taken place.

In contrast, it is much easier to take legal action based upon a Registered Trademark, and if counterfeit goods are involved, Trading Standards and the Customs authorities would be quick to assist. With a registered trademark, the owner has a five-year period following registration to put it into use in the market, i.e. sell goods or services under the mark. It is therefore very important to make sure that a registered trademark older than five years has been used in trade before threatening infringement proceedings.

Can you save money by filing a trademark application yourself? Many people try, and some companies offer a DIY filing service, offering no advice, and with applicants doing much of the work themselves. From our experience, there are so many pitfalls with the drafting and filing of self-filed applications that these applications rarely give adequate protection for the goods and services the mark is to be used on. This leads to complications later when a rival business uses the mark on goods that are not protected by the registered mark. In the worst cases the applications are simply invalid because they do not cover the goods they were intended to cover.

Aside from the infringement complications, it is often the case that upon examination an application is objected to by the Examiner that the mark lacks distinctiveness, or that it describes the goods or services to be covered. The skill of a Trademark Attorney is invaluable here as overcoming objections is an integral part of an Attorney's job. On receiving such objections, the DIY filer often hands the application to an Attorney rather than try to respond themselves. If the specification has been poorly drafted the cost of putting the application into order and gaining registration can be higher than if the application was filed by a professional in the first place. Sometimes, defects in a self-filed trademark application simply cannot be put right, and a new application will have to be made. Not only does this further increase the costs, but it also delays the date when the valuable brands have protection.

Good advice and service really is an essential investment: businesses would not consider doing their own conveyancing or accountancy work. A DIY solution might make a modest saving, but if things go wrong, the rights at the heart of the whole business model could be in trouble if the application fails.

The good news is that an application to register a trademark can be filed at any time, even several years after starting use of a trademark. Although greater problems might be encountered from having to navigate around other people's registrations, there is no absolute bar to registration of a mark you've already used. So, if your marks aren't yet registered, act today. Don't rely on unregistered rights, and don't try to do-it-yourself. Get experienced professional assistance.

IP
TWENTYONE

For further information
t: 0203 327 1310
e: franchise@ip21.co.uk
w: ip21.co.uk/franchise

Graham Barlow
Managing Director
Tech4T

The importance of correctly designed territories

When franchising your business or buying into a franchise, you need to determine if your territories are protected.

If protected territories are part of your business model and your territories are not defined in a systematic, fair and consistent way, legal implications and issues could follow.

From a financial perspective, having the correct number of right sized territories, each optimised to maximise sales potential for the franchise owner, will help ensure your franchise business has the greatest chance of success.

So Where Do You Start?

First you need to establish the profile of the end customer of your products or services. A profile is the set of characteristics that differentiates one group of people from another and that define the kind of individuals more likely to acquire your offering.

Once you understand your customer profile, or perhaps multiple profiles if you have several products that each appeal to a different audience, the next step is

to conduct market research and acquire a demographic breakdown of the wider geographical area you wish to franchise. This information can be used to identify 'hot spots' – areas where there are high concentrations of the kind of people you need to target.

You must also understand your competitors – who they are, where they operate, their strengths and their weaknesses, and how your products or services will be positioned against theirs.

Another important consideration is to understand the sales process your franchise owners will adopt to sell your product or services. This will help determine the required size of the franchise owners sales force, the time needed to close each sale and, in essence, how many opportunities the franchise and each sales person within it will be able to manage.

The Territory Planning Process

Armed with the aforementioned

information, the challenge is to now create a territory infrastructure that is not only right sized for your business, but one where territories are appealing and straightforward to sell. Territories that are not too large in that they may never be fully exploited, and not too small in that the franchise owner runs out of opportunities within a short timescale.

Demographic data – perhaps business counts, location data, and any other information needed to undertake the design and balancing of territories – needs to be sourced and matched against the appropriate level of postal geography to define the boundaries of the territory.

For instance, in the UK the postcode system breaks down into around 125 postcode areas, 3,000 postcode districts, 11,000 postcode sectors and 1.75 million unit postcodes, each containing around 17 households.

Choosing the appropriate postcode 'building block' approach is crucial as otherwise it will be impossible to generate properly balanced territories.

Applying the data

Next comes the tricky part, applying the data, the selling rules, the competition, etc., with the geography and drive times to produce a set of equal territories – in terms of opportunities and accessibility.

These will form the basis of an agreement with your new franchise owner. This requires specialist data, analysis and mapping skills and having available technologies of the right kind.

The balancing process is more of an art rather than a science, and while technology plays a large part, a considerable amount of manual intervention is needed to keep each individual territory free from obstacles such as lakes, rivers with no crossings, and from having an unfair amount of driving to reach potential customers.

In conclusion, if your franchise operates a territorial model, getting your territory design right will be crucial if you want to maximise the value from your business.

With more than 20 years of experience, Tech4T specialises in data, targeting and franchise territory design and optimisation.

For further information
t: 01733 890790
e: info@tech4t.co.uk
w: tech4t.co.uk

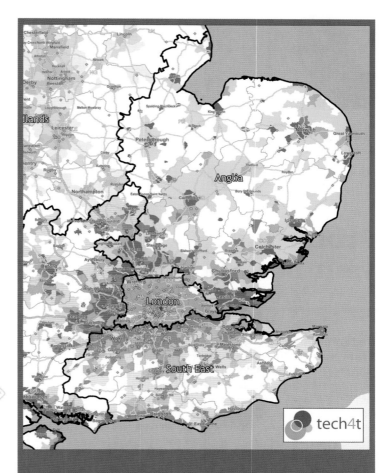

Get more value from your franchise – seven tips

- Profile your customers; check there is sufficient market potential
- Use a territory design delivering equal opportunity to each franchise owner
- Analyse and compare territory performance to steer business decisions
- Use your website to show franchise territory availability
- Source the right prospect lists and data
- Ensure all marketing collateral invites the prospect to provide their contact details
- Manage your data, your sales and your business with the right single customer view CRM/ERP solution

Al Craig
Associate
Brand Protect

Protecting your brand

An effective approach to Intellectual Property protection and licensing is critical to the success of your franchise business.

Understanding Brand Value

Your brand is the way that you identify your business to others. It can be a name, slogan, logo, distinctive corporate colours – or even a combination of all these elements.

Your brand represents a promise to your customers and symbolises the personality of your product, service or company.

As your customers learn to identify your brand with consistently positive experiences, the value of your brand will grow.

Your brand can be your most important asset – ask Coca Cola (their brand is worth £45 billion) or McDonald's (brand valuation of £32 billion).

From the point of view of a franchisor it is vital to secure protection for your brand and to maintain careful control over how it is used by franchise owners in order to ensure that this value is not degraded.

From the franchise owner's viewpoint, access to a strong and well-protected brand together with the materials, knowledge and methods of a proven business model can provide a fast track to achieving success and recognition in the marketplace.

Building Strong Brands

Registration of a brand as a trademark creates property. Like all property, trademarks need to be built on strong foundations and must be looked after during their lifetime to ensure they continue to deliver value to your business.

People engaged in branding often seek to develop specific expectations associated with the brand experience, creating the impression that a brand has certain qualities or characteristics that make it special or unique.

A brand with a good reputation attached to it becomes one of the most valuable properties that a company can own.

Descriptive vs Invented Names

There are two common forms of brand name. Let's call them 'Type 1' and 'Type 2'.

- Type 1 is where the brand name describes the business offer – examples being 'Brand Protect' for brand protection or 'franchise directory' for franchising resources.
- Type 2 brand names are unrelated to the offer and could be the owner's name or a fabricated word – well known examples being Disney or Kodak.

The advantages of Type 1 are that it is generally easier and, therefore, cheaper to explain your offer to the customer. However, the disadvantage is that there are more challenges in making your mark distinctive from the competition and, therefore, in protecting it.

A Type 2 trademark owner needs to educate the public about

the products it sells (Kodak by itself means nothing without educating the public that it is to do with photos). This type of trademark costs more to establish, initially due to the higher market education costs, but in the long run the trademark may be more valuable and much more easily protected.

Identifying Valuable IP

The most obvious assets to protect are branding elements such as names, logos and distinctive colour combinations. However, you may also need to consider further forms of intellectual property (IP) such as patentable technologies, database information, and copyright protected materials (e.g. training materials and day-to-day materials such as checklists and timesheets).

These further types of IP fall outside the scope of your brand but are a similar sort of asset. The various elements of IP that are involved in your business represent the crown jewels of your franchise and should be carefully guarded in order to protect your business as a whole.

Protecting Your Assets

There are a great many ways in which the various types of IP can be protected. The best approach for a particular situation will depend on specific details such as the nature of the franchise operation, available financial resources, the geographical regions to be covered and the expected timeline for expansion.

It is almost always better to apply for the stronger protection available through registering your IP than having to rely on unregistered protection or non-disclosure agreements.

Although it is sometimes

possible to save costs at an early stage by relying on (weaker) unregistered protection or by making the applications for registered protection yourself, this very often leads to legal issues, which are then difficult or expensive put right.

Some very common mistakes include:

- Failure to carry out proper checks for conflicting IP (e.g. similar brands).
- Failure to identify the full extent of the IP which should be protected.
- Failure to identify the most cost effective route to achieving registered protection.

Using IP Rights

Identifying and protecting your IP is only half the story. The form of your licence then needs to take account of where and what type of IP you own (which is where the value of the IP lies) as well as how it should be used and protected.

While there are many IP firms who can assist in obtaining registered protection, there are few who can offer expertise and experience that is specifically geared to the needs of franchise clients. You need to ensure that your advisors are experienced in every step of the process.

Brand Protect

Brand Protect is a niche firm offering advice and assistance on all aspects of branding law – especially those of concern to franchisors.

With our breadth of knowledge we are able to advise not only on the creation of IP but also on how to retain and use it. We regularly fight for the rights of franchisors and our clients rely on us to give

> "The various elements of Intellectual Property that are involved in your business represent the crown jewels of your franchise and should be carefully guarded."

them best advice on all aspects of IP law in this country and abroad.

At Brand Protect, we pride ourselves in investing our time to build relationships with clients so that we understand the specific details of your franchise model, your resources and your business plan.

We are experienced in working with a great many franchises, both large and small. This means that we can tailor IP protection and other strategies to your specific needs and that we can match our services to your growth.

Our team can help you at the earliest stages of development and when the time is right we can also assist you in protecting your franchise worldwide.

BRAND PROTECT

For further information
t: 01869 346160
e: advice@bptm.co.uk
w: www.bptm.co.uk

Richard Sanderson
General Manager
alphaTALK

Connect to a smoother way to run your franchise

Whatever size your business, having virtual telephony services will not only increase your business' efficiency but also its value to prospective franchise owners.

Double-dip recession, economic-downturn, credit crunch and the 'period of austerity'. These are some of the phrases used to describe the current state of our nation. Whichever phrase you use, the bottom line is that everyone is tightening their belts in the face of limited finances.

What this means for many businesses is that they have to learn to be more innovative with limited resources, without compromising their ability to deliver an impeccable service to their clients.

Virtual telephony services are essential to many organisations whether it be multi-national companies, local SMEs, regional businesses or even nationally recognised franchise brands. If you are reading this you are probably thinking: "What has this got to do with me?" The answer is simple. Irrespective of your company size, location and sector, there are a number of services which can add significant value to your business.

Features such as recording,

virtual receptionist, call forwarding, call queuing and voicemail, for example, can play an important role in your franchise success.

Since 1996, alphaTALK has helped many companies integrate modern telephony solutions into their business including national franchise brands.

Entry level packages can offer hi-tech features, which have traditionally been out of reach for many small businesses. Therefore, you no longer need thousands of pounds of investment in software and hardware to obtain these modern communication facilities.

Ask yourself, are you paying for adverts with no way of monitoring their effectiveness?

In-depth call analysis, reports and statistics allow you to monitor each and every telemarketing number you use in advertisements – vital information when deciding whether to renew them. Thousands of pounds can be saved eliminating inefficient advertisements.

alphaTALK has many clients who operate nationally and require a local presence for their

customers. We have enabled them to do that through our nationwide availability of local area numbers.

For example, in situations where Birmingham-based clients whose customers are located in London, for these companies, we have provided 0207 London numbers for their customers to call, which connect to the company's call centre in Birmingham. Our ranges of numbers are particularly useful for companies who want to be able to transfer their numbers instantly

between destinations and operate in multiple regions locally. We can also provide highly memorable numbers for radio, TV or serious marketing campaigns.

Chemdry and Stagecoach Theatre Arts are just two examples of leading nationwide franchisors that have benefitted from alphaTALK's custom franchise packages.

With over 5,000 customers signed up to our telecommunications services, the customer base is tremendously broad. With companies coming from a wide variety of different backgrounds and professions, alphaTALK prides itself on the ability to cater for the needs of these leading individuals and companies.

Managing Director of alphaTALK, Zafar Majid, claims that his company has been helping franchisors save money in times of boom and bust.

"Our advanced call analysis and statistical reports allow customers to monitor their incoming calls from the various adverts that they may have placed," he explains.

"This allows them to focus upon adverts that have not worked, thus helping them to save thousands of pounds in ineffective financial commitments that in other cases may have gone unnoticed.

"This truly is an invaluable service at a comparatively negligible cost. It has become even more imperative to save money in this current climate."

alphaTALK has impressive testimonials from many of its long-standing customers.

Frances May, Principal and Director of StageCoach Theatre Arts says: "We have been customers of alphaTALK since 2004 and in that time have been 100 per cent satisfied by their service. We originally changed our 0800 service to alphaTALK because their costs were the most competitive by far. Over the past six years we have had no reason to contact them with any queries, concerns or complaints of their service, which has been second-to-none."

Allan Simmons, Director of ChemDry, concurs: "We have been customers of alphaTALK since 2003 for our main incoming business on the 0800 freephone number. It cannot be emphasised enough that this number is the main focus of our marketing and incoming calls.

"Over the many years we have been with alphaTALK they have given us an excellent service. I particularly like the speed of their response in the event of any queries relating to my account."

Entry level packages can cost as little as £10 per month.

For further information
t: 0845 021 2000
e: franchise@alphatalk.com
w: www.alphatalk.com

Anglia & London FDS Team

FDS Anglia & London is highly experienced in all aspects of franchising, for potential and established franchisors whether looking for UK or international expansion. Our focus is on your business and your ambitions, and we always tailor our solutions to your need. We not only offer consultancy, but business advice, with a full franchise owner recruitment and marketing function.

Paul Hague

Paul has been a consultant with FDS since 1993 and during that time has worked with numerous clients both nationally and internationally, from one man bands to multi-nationals in a large range of industry sectors.

Nick Williams

Nick joined FDS in 2000 with a brief to help business owners evaluate the franchise development potential. Nick works with established franchisors in expanding their networks and in facilitating international Master Franchises.

"We view FDS as long-term partners for advice on all aspects of franchising, currently consulting them for international growth, and can recommend them without hesitation."
Hugh Man, Franchising Director of CeX

"During his two years as our mentor, Paul Hague taught us everything there is to know about starting a franchise and quite simply we wouldn't be where we are today without all his invaluable help."
Tony Williams, Managing Director of Countrywide Signs

Other brands we work with:

FOR MORE INFORMATION CONTACT OUR HEAD OFFICE:

call: 01603 620 301   **web:** www.fdsfranchise.com
email: enquiries@fdsltd.com
address: Franchise House, 56 Surrey Street, Norwich, NR1 3FD

South East FDS Regional Director

How can FDS South East help you

Potential Franchisor: For companies looking at franchising as a method for expanding their business effectively and profitably, FDS South East provides an intelligent evaluation of your potential for franchising and works with you to implement a carefully structured franchise development programme.

Existing Franchisor: We can provide assistance in several different areas including franchise healthchecks, media promotion, franchise owner recruitment support and international expansion.

Malcolm Porter
FDS South East is dedicated to serving the needs of the franchise community across Surrey, Sussex and Kent, providing assistance on everything from an initial evaluation of your business through to helping you recruit top quality franchise owners.

"I have worked with FDS over many years on a number of projects. Their knowledge of the franchise sector and what it takes to recruit franchise owners is excellent, as are their media both published and online. I have constantly recruited high quality franchise owners through working with FDS."
Simon Dalziel, Franchise Director of Bluebird Care

"Malcolm Porter helped us with the strategic implementation of our second tier franchise offering, which opened an array of new Granite Transformations units. Malcolm offers no-nonsense solutions which gets results and we found him a pleasure to work with."
Danny Hanlon, Chief Operating Officer (Europe) of
Granite Transformations

Other brands we work with:

FOR MORE INFORMATION

t: 0845 372 2010
e: malcolm.porter@fdssoutheast.co.uk
w: www.fdssoutheast.com

North & Scotland FDS Team

Franchise Development Services North specialises in the development and ongoing support of successful franchise systems. Serving Northern England and Scotland, FDS North is the North's gateway to sustainable business growth through franchising.

Tony Urwin
A leading figure in the UK franchising industry, Tony managed the franchising efforts of Clarks Shoes in the UK and Disney in the Middle East before establishing FDS North in 1999. Under his direction, FDS North has developed a sterling reputation as the North's premier franchise management consultancy.

"We were put in touch with FDS North Franchise Consultant Tony Urwin back in 2007 and we cannot praise him enough! Tony and his team at FDS North are not only extremely professional and knowledgeable, they always deliver on time and have given us some fantastic ideas about how we can improve the business and generate lead flow."
Sandra Venables, Founder of Well Polished

"Tony helped us to set up our franchise system in 2005. He repeatedly stressed the importance of long-term thinking, and was committed to developing a business model and franchise offering that would be "sustainably" profitable. Six years later, our business is thriving, our network is strong, and our prospects are very bright indeed. If you're looking to franchise your business, you want Tony developing your system."
Keith Roberts, Managing Director of All Trades Network

Other brands we work with:

FOR MORE INFORMATION

t: 0161 926 9882
e: tony@fdsnorth.com
w: www.fdsnorth.com
address: Atlantic House, Alantic Street, Broadheath, Altrincham, WA14 5NQ

Midlands & Wales FDS Regional Director

Franchise Development Services Midlands and Wales has been providing franchise consultancy and recruitment services to clients throughout Central England and Wales for over 10 years.

Ken Young

Ken is a graduate of Leeds University and also holds a post-graduate qualification in business studies. Since 1999 he has successfully owned and operated Lichfield-based FDS Midlands, providing franchise consultancy and recruitment services to clients throughout Central England and Wales. Ken was previously responsible for the UK franchise division of global logistics giant TNT Express.

"FDS Midlands was always happy to work at the pace we wanted. We first agreed the strategy plan and then rolled out the franchise infrastructure step by step. FDS provided particular help in those areas where we ourselves were weakest. Even after completion of the work, Ken continues to take a real interest in the progress of our franchise business, which is now progressing well in line with our expectations."

Alan Thomson, Managing Director of Adept Cleaning Services Ltd

"When we decided to franchise CleanMy we needed expert advice and guidance to help us through the process. We found exactly that with FDS Midlands as well as an extremely thorough and dedicated approach. Ken quickly identified our requirements and paid particular attention to our need for clarity throughout the consultancy process. As a result, I would strongly recommend FDS services to anybody serious about franchising their business."

Ben Williams, Managing Director of CleanMy Ltd

Other brands we work with:

FOR MORE INFORMATION

t: 01603 620 301
e: enquiries@fdsltd.com
address: 28 Footherley Road, Shenstone, Lichfield, Staffs, WS14 0NJ

Southern

Gordon Patterson has assisted UK and international franchisors in the development of their franchise networks for some 25 years, building a reputation as one of the UK's leading franchise consultancies.

Gordon Patterson
For more than 25 years Gordon has gathered a vast knowledge of franchising and contributed to the franchise success story of many brands, building a reputation as one of the UK's leading franchise consultants.

"Some time after launching our London House franchise we commisioned FDS to provide consultancy services. It was an extremely beneficial exercise to our company. Our only regret was that we did not do it sooner."
Godfrey Lancashire, Founder and Managing Director of London House International

"We launched the Northwood franchise through The Franchise Magazine in September 1999. Since then, it has strongly contributed to providing us with quality prospects that have resulted in franchise owners."
Andy Goodson, Founder of Northwood

Some other brands we have consulted for:

FOR MORE INFORMATION

t: 0118 974 5115   Web: www.fdsfranchise.com
e: gordon@fdsfranchise.com
address: Maple Grove, Bradfield, Reading, Berkshire, RG7 6DH

The Franchise Services Showcase

Are you a franchisor? Or are you looking to franchise your business? If so, you are likely to require a number of key products and services to help you along the way.

This section showcases the leading suppliers in the franchise market with a proven track record of delivering high quality services and an affordble price.

Financial Services
Anglia Finance
The finance solution to the franchise market

Do you want to run your own business but a lack of cash is stopping you? Well at Anglia Finance we can help you raise that important finance and turn your dreams into a reality.

Once you've made the decision to run a business you want to move fast, as the banking sector is notoriously slow and requires constant chasing. At Anglia Finance we take all the stress away by approaching the banks on your behalf, dealing with the decision makers you struggle to get hold of and turn around decisions faster than if you approach the banks yourself. We also negotiate the best rates!

By using Anglia Finance you stand the best chance of turning your dream into a reality. We are more likely to get lending agreed than approaching the banks yourself and we are here to assist you realise your goals.

So for all your business financial needs, from purchasing your first franchise right through to buying equipment, don't hesitate in making use of our expert services.

For further information contact Richard Chatten on **t:**01603 620301 or **e:**richardc@fdsltd.com

---

Financial Services
Lloyds TSB
Whatever your franchising needs
Lloyds TSB Franchise Unit can help you

The Lloyds TSB Franchise Unit is the first point of contact for enquiries about becoming a franchise owner or individuals looking to franchise their own business. Our trained Franchise Managers are on hand to help. They have undertaken a training programme in conjunction with the bfa and sector professionals and they are available throughout the UK.

For those who are in the early stage of reviewing franchise opportunities, our FREE guide is an essential read. It contains a list of 30 key questions you should be asking a franchisor to ensure that you make an informed decision about your options. We have also negotiated preferential terms for you to get your legal agreement independently checked by an experienced franchise solicitor.

Our specialists are on hand to offer guidance and support to anyone considering franchising as a way of developing their existing business.

Since 1981 Franchise Development Services has helped over 10,000 people choose their franchise.

Call us today for free advice before you make your final decision:

01603 620 301

Food & Beverages

Actively recruiting franchise owners

The food and beverage business sector is the most well known for franchise opportunities. Some of the UK's and world's largest companies operate in this sector and belong to the fast food, quick service and restaurant franchise industries which actively dominate many high streets throughout the UK. Franchise opportunities include **Auntie Anne's, McDonald's, Perfect Pizza** and **Pizza Hut.**

bfa
ASSOCIATE

Perfect Pizza Ltd

Summary of Operation: Perfect Pizza is one of the UK's leading pizza delivery and takeaway businesses. Established in 1982, the company now has more than 110 stores across the UK, with the largest concentration in the Midlands and South of England. Perfect Pizza plans to open a further 100 stores. The relaunched website clearly demonstrates Perfect Pizza's commitment to growth and harnessing technology in support of its continued success. Since the relaunch of the website, there has been a dramatic increase in sales which looks set to continue.

Ideal Franchise Owner Profile: Still an entrepreneur and wants the security of a franchise brand.

Cost of Franchise: £120,000 + VAT

Franchise Owner Contact: Roger Ahearn

Year Company Established: 1982

Number of Company Outlets: 0
Number of Franchised Outlets: 112
Number of Franchise Owners Planned: 200

Overseas Operations Existing: No
Overseas Operations Planned: In the future
Management Service Fees: 10%

Breakdown of Package: Full information provided within the franchise brochure.

Training Provided: Food safety, health & safety, management, in-store training which covers all aspects of the franchise over a two week period.
Training Location: Head office and regionally.

Support Services: Full ongoing operational support through a dedicated operations team.

Areas of Priority Development: England and Wales.

More Information: theukfd.net/21265182

Perfect Pizza Ltd
Gailey Park, Gravelly Way,
Standeford, Wolverhampton,
WV10 7BW

t: 07824 338 720
f: 01372 363728
e: rogerahearn@perfectpizza.co.uk
w: www.perfectpizza.co.uk

Auntie Anne's – Freshly Baked Ltd
PO Box 888, Aylesbury Vale, HP22 9HB

Telephone: 01844 273226
Fax: 01844 273227
Email: newfranchising@auntieannes.co.uk
Website: www.auntieannes.co.uk

Summary of Operation: Snack food retailer selling sweet and savoury hand-rolled pretzels as well as hot and cold beverages. Franchise owners operate an Auntie Anne's store or kiosk.

Ideal Franchise Owner Profile: Auntie Anne's pretzels is looking for franchise owners who enjoy working in a customer facing environment and understand the importance of providing an excellent level of customer service.

Cost of Franchise: £97,500 + VAT

Franchise Owner Contact: Max Burton

Year Company Established: 2003
Year of First Franchise Owner: 2003

Number of Franchised Outlets: 12

Number of Franchise Owners Planned: 100

Overseas Operations Existing: USA 900 stores and 300 locations in 23 other international territories.

Management Service Fees: 8% MSF + 3% marketing

Breakdown of Package: Initial franchise fee, including training in USA £16,000; build out, shop fit and legal's £66,000, initial stock, rent deposit and first quarter rent £17,500.

Financial Assistance Available: Several major banks.

Training Provided: Two weeks initial plus launch plus ongoing at UK HQ and on-site.

Training Location: USA and UK on-site.

Areas of Priority Development: UK and Ireland.

More Information: theukfd.net/85107622

bfa Full Member
McDonald's
11-59 High Road, East Finchley,
London, N2 8AW

Telephone: 020 8700 7000
Website: www.mcdonalds.co.uk/franchising

Summary of Operation: McDonald's is one of only a handful of brands that commands instant recognition throughout the world. With over 31,000 restaurants in over 120 countries, serving over 50 million people everyday, McDonald's is by far the world's largest food service company.

Ideal Franchise Owner Profile: High personal integrity; entrepreneurial spirit; ability to manage people and finances; be an effective on-premise owner operator post full training and possess the financial resources.

Cost of Franchise: Ranging from £125,000 - £325,000 + VAT

Franchise Owner Contact: Joe Zammuto

Year Company Established: 1974
Year of First Franchise Owner: 1986

Number of Company Outlets: 500
Number of Franchised Outlets: 700

Overseas Operations Existing: AOR
Overseas Operations Planned: AOR

Management Service Fees: Rent (typically ranging from 10% -15%), MSF 5% and marketing contribution 4.5%.

Breakdown of Package: £30,000 franchise fee.

Financial Assistance Available: All major banks.
Training Provided: Nine months
Training Location: Both restaurant and office based.

Support Services: Personal franchising consultant and full range of national departments.

More Information: theukfd.net/84564683

Pizza Hut (UK) Ltd

One Imperial Place, Elstree Way, Borehamwood, WD6 1JN

Telephone: 020 8732 9000
Fax: 020 8732 9002
Email: franchise.mail@pizzahut.co.uk
Website: www.pizzahutfranchise.co.uk

Summary of Operation: Pizza Hut (UK) Ltd is a pizza restaurant and home delivery company.

Ideal Franchise Owner Profile: Ambitious, dedicated individuals with a passion for customer service and a drive to succeed. They should be willing and able to expand to multiple sites in the short-medium term.

Cost of Franchise: £185,000-£215,000 + VAT

Franchise Owner Contact: Ben Phillips

Year Company Established: 1973 (In the UK)

Year of First Franchise Owner: 2001

Number of Company Outlets: 510
Number of Franchised Outlets: 198

Overseas Operations Existing: Worldwide
Overseas Operations Planned: Worldwide

Management Service Fees: 6%

Breakdown of Package: AOR

Training Provided: Comprehensive bespoke training given.

Training Location: Nationwide

Support Services: Full support provided day to day by a Franchise Business Manager and from specialist support functions across all areas of your business including marketing, new product development, acquisitions, training and more.

Areas of Priority Development: North England with further areas to be announced throughout the year.

More Information: theukfd.net/75707082

5aDayBox

Telephone: 01380 860 968
Website: www.5adaybox.co.uk
Summary of Operation: 5aDayBox operates a hugely popular home delivery box scheme. We source fresh produce direct from farmers and growers – local to our depots! With a 5aDayBox Box you will get a huge range of high quality fruit, vegetables and salads delivered straight to your door.
More Information: theukfd.net/37969890

Amorino

Telephone: 07595 675 021
Website: www.amorino.fr
Summary of Operation: Ice cream parlours.
More Information: theukfd.net/22175576

Apetito Limited

Telephone: 01225 756 071
Website: www.apetito.co.uk
Summary of Operation: Apetito is a leading supplier of frozen food and catering solutions. We provide hospital food, local authority community meals and care home food.
More Information: theukfd.net/86502112

Arbuckles American Diners

Summary of Operation: Restaurants serving classic American food.
More Information: theukfd.net/87684736

Archers Jersey Ice Cream

Telephone: 01325 300 336; 01325 254 433
Website: www.archersjerseyicecream.com
Summary of Operation: Archer's Jersey Ice Cream is a highly successful family business which has operated since 2004. John and Sue Archer opened the parlour on their farm at Walworth Gate and use milk from their award winning pedigree Jersey herd.
More Information: theukfd.net/83122020

Bagel Factory Ltd

Telephone: 020 7407 7616
Website: www.bagelfactory.co.uk
Summary of Operation: Freshly baked bagels. To complement our filled bagels, Bagel Factory offers Coffee Co. speciality coffees and our Second Cup filter coffee offering our customers a free refill! We also have a range of fresh juices and soup (in season) and cakes and fresh-baked muffins.
More Information: theukfd.net/45436428

Baguette Express
Telephone: 0845 070 4360
Website: www.baguette-express.co.uk
Summary of Operation: Sandwich shop franchise. Baguette Express provides an alternative approach to the expanding world of healthy snacking. Run by brothers Robin and Billy Stenhouse, Baguette Express has stores in Scotland, England and Northern Ireland and aims to become the largest independent snack business in the UK within the next five years.
More Information: theukfd.net/44756518

Baguette n Go
Telephone: 01750 725 567
Website: www.baguettengo.com
Summary of Operation: Sandwich shop franchise offering offering a wide selection of the finest quality ingredients.
More Information: theukfd.net/50997654

Barfoots of Botley Ltd
Telephone: 01243 268 811
Website: www.barfoots.co.uk
Summary of Operation: Sweetcorn, vegetable supply chain and food service specialists.
More Information: theukfd.net/65720157

Basilico Ltd
Telephone: 0800 028 3531
Website: www.basilico.co.uk
Summary of Operation: Truly delicious pizzas using only the highest quality ingredients, baked in a traditional Italian wood fired brick oven.
More Information: theukfd.net/50154826

Baskin Robbins
Telephone: 07894 095 249
Website: www.baskinrobbins.co.uk
Summary of Operation: Baskin Robbins is a chain of ice cream speciality stores, cafes and kiosks. The format enables franchise owners to offer everything in ice cream.
More Information: theukfd.net/37248366

Bavarian Beerhouse
Telephone: 0844 330 2005
Website: www.bavarian-beerhouse.com
Summary of Operation: Traditional Bavarian restaurant.
More Information: theukfd.net/31457580

BBs Coffee & Muffins Ltd
Telephone: 020 8758 1234
Website: www.bbscoffeeandmuffins.com
Summary of Operation: Coffee shop manufacturing and retailing hot and cold beverages, muffins and baguettes.
More Information: theukfd.net/40830281

Ben & Jerry Homemade Ltd
Telephone: 01753 834034
Website: www.benjerry.co.uk
Summary of Operation: Ice cream manufacturers and distributers.
More Information: theukfd.net/30400135

Bitesize Vending Ltd
Telephone: 01202 269 524
Website: www.bitesizevending.com
Summary of Operation: Promotion and marketing of confectionary products.
More Information: theukfd.net/75581762

Bob's Cornutopia
Telephone: 01243 268 811
Website: www.bobscornutopia.com
Summary of Operation: Food service specialists.
More Information: theukfd.net/00222476

Boost Juice
Website: www.boostjuicebars.com
Summary of Operation: Juice and smoothies bar.
More Information: theukfd.net/32874768

Brady's Fresh Fish Restaurant
Telephone: 020 8877 9599
Website: www.bradysfish.co.uk
Summary of Operation: Fresh fish food.
More Information: theukfd.net/28625398

Brampton Pie Company
Telephone: 01480 356 020
Website: www.bramptonpie.co.uk
Summary of Operation: The Brampton Pie Company are award winning makers of the famous Brampton Pie.
More Information: theukfd.net/70001740

Burger King Ltd
Telephone: 01753 500 000
Website: www.burgerking.co.uk
Summary of Operation: Burger restaurants – eat in and take away.
More Information: theukfd.net/28736016

Burger Star

Telephone: 01452 862 099
Website: www.burgerstar.com
Summary of Operation: Fast food restaurants, burgers, chicken and pizza etc.
More Information: theukfd.net/43718339

C House Italia Coffee - UK

Telephone: +39 035 691 553
Website: www.chouseitalia.it
Summary of Operation: Coffee shop.
More Information: theukfd.net/7164768

Cafe Nino

Telephone: 0845 607 0116 - 01276 804 479
Website: www.cafenino.com
Summary of Operation: Upmarket coffee and food concept.
More Information: theukfd.net/47687148

Cafe2U

Telephone: 0845 644 4708
Website: www.cafe2u.co.uk
Summary of Operation: Cafe2U is a premier mobile coffee franchise system.
More Information: theukfd.net/33502386

Caffe Latino

Telephone: 020 8429 6861
Website: www.caffe-latino.com
Summary of Operation: Caffé Latino is the new standard of Coffee House in the UK. We totally focus our efforts on the perfect espresso every time.
More Information: theukfd.net/37051076

Carluccios

Telephone: 020 7580 3050
Website: www.carluccios.com
Summary of Operation: We have explored the length and breadth of Italy to find the best ingredients from every region. We work with family and artisanal producers who make delicious products in traditional ways, with care.
More Information: theukfd.net/68936417

Charisnack

Telephone: 01392 360 600
Website: www.charisnack.co.uk
Summary of Operation: Delivering a superb selection of healthier snacks and smoothies directly into the workplace.
More Information: theukfd.net/50002386

Charity Sweet Boxes

Telephone: 01323 741 077
Website: www.sweetsellers.com
Summary of Operation: Charity Sweet Boxes work as a partner to Bliss - national charity for the new born, raising much needed money for them by selling charity branded sweets and healthy snacks.
More Information: theukfd.net/70484245

Cherry Tree

Telephone: 01308 458 111
Website: www.cherrytreeproduce.co.uk
Summary of Operation: We manufacture an extensive range of premium quality preserves and confectionery.
More Information: theukfd.net/13629867

Chicken Cottage International

Telephone: 0208 683 3553
Website: www.chicken-cottage.co.uk
Summary of Operation: Our menu includes: original recipe chicken, delicious chicken wraps, chicken grilled, bbq chicken and crunchy chicken.
More Information: theukfd.net/08301567

Chicko's Grilled Chicken

Telephone: 01293 400 013
Website: www.chickos.co.uk
Summary of Operation: Chicko's chicken is not deep fat fried or bread crumbed but first seasoned with a marinade of fresh lemon and herbs and then flame grilled to perfection from fresh for a tastier, healthier chicken.
More Information: theukfd.net/20154944

Chilli Banana (Franchising) Ltd

Telephone: 01625 530 095
Website: www.chillibanana.co.uk
Summary of Operation: High quality Thai restaurants with relaxed atmosphere. Authentic Thai food freshly prepared by fully trained chefs to our own recipes.
More Information: theukfd.net/56455245

Chocolate Fountain Heaven

Telephone: 0870 850 1876
Website: www.chocolatefountainheaven.co.uk
Summary of Operation: As the longest running chocolate fountain hire company, Chocolate Fountain Heaven have attended in excess of 5,000 events throughout England and Jersey.
More Information: theukfd.net/87477568

Chunky Chicken
Telephone: 079 718 66 680
Website: www.chunkychicken.com
Summary of Operation: Chunky Chicken serves high-quality, cooked to order food, available for takeout, delivery and dine-in.
More Information: theukfd.net/60691634

Coffee King
Telephone: 0844 243 7844
Website: www.coffee-king.me
Summary of Operation: Coffee King's espresso vans deliver the best freshly ground Fairtrade espresso coffee to your door.
More Information: theukfd.net/65007242

Coffee Republic Trading Ltd
Telephone: 020 7828 5800
Website: www.coffeerepublic.co.uk
Summary of Operation: Re-inventing the way the British enjoy coffee by bringing together freshly made food with what the press has described as Britain's 'best cappuccino'.
More Information: theukfd.net/48317344

COOK Trading Ltd
Telephone: 01732 759 000
Website: www.cookfood.net
Summary of Operation: Frozen meals that look and taste like they have been home-cooked.
More Information: theukfd.net/55456877

Cooper8 Ltd
Telephone: 01424 422 784
Website: www.cooper8.co.uk
Summary of Operation: Catering.
More Information: theukfd.net/34281745

Costa Ltd
Telephone: 01582 424 2200
Website: www.costa.co.uk
Summary of Operation: Leading coffee brand retailing own coffee including the 'Frescato' range and hearty breakfasts to light snacks.
More Information: theukfd.net/52114837

Crêpe Affaire
Telephone: 020 7375 0376
Website: www.crepeaffaire.com
Summary of Operation: Crêpeaffaire is a place where you can enjoy freshly prepared crêpes whatever your craving, at any time of the day.
More Information: theukfd.net/59256479

Dairy Crest Ltd
Telephone: 01252 366 815
Website: www.dairycrestfranchise.co.uk
Summary of Operation: Distribution of milk and dairy products and soft drinks.
More Information: theukfd.net/05866363

Dallas Chicken & Ribs
Telephone: 020 8684 4899
Website: www.dallaschicken.co.uk
Summary of Operation: Fast food takeaway outlets.
More Information: theukfd.net/84545531

Delifrance UK Ltd
Website: www.delifrance.com
Summary of Operation: French-style retail outlet for bakery and other fast food products.
More Information: theukfd.net/12888870

Dinky Deli
Telephone: 023 9241 5000
Website: www.dinkydeli.com
Summary of Operation: Delivering confectionery snacks and soft drinks to small workplace sites with a hygenic self-service box. Slim line compact vending equipment.
More Information: theukfd.net/26161272

Domino's Pizza PLC
Telephone: 01908 580 657
Website: www.dominos.uk.com
Summary of Operation: One of the leading players in the fast-growing pizza delivery market with 616 stores across the UK and Ireland. Domino's Pizza has a singular focus - the home delivery of pizza, freshly-made to order with high quality ingredients.
More Information: theukfd.net/58868322

Double Dutch Pancake Bar Ltd
Website: www.doubledutchpancakebar.com
Summary of Operation: Double Dutch pancake bars offer the perfect catering solution for any business or private event.
More Information: theukfd.net/28748108

Drinkmaster Ltd
Website: www.drinkmaster.com
Summary of Operation: Sales and delivery of beverage systems to commercial premises dispensing equipment.
More Information: theukfd.net/78227266

Dunkin Brands (UK)
Telephone: 07894 095 249
Website: www.dunkinbrands.com
Summary of Operation: Quick-service restaurant franchisor whose brands include Dunkin' Donuts and Baskin-Robbins.
More Information: theukfd.net/37697213

Earles Direct
Telephone: 01270 500 968
Website: www.earles-direct.co.uk
Summary of Operation: Earle's is the most advanced mobile food concept on the market at this present time.
More Information: theukfd.net/32129647

Easy Food Ltd
Telephone: 0844 477 3456
Website: www.easyfood.co.uk
Summary of Operation: Easyfood is simply 'ordering food made easy'. With the ability to do almost anything on the internet, ordering your local take away has never been so easy.
More Information: theukfd.net/82927704

Easyjuice
Telephone: 01903 410 318
Website: www.easyjuice.co.uk
Summary of Operation: Our pure fruit smoothie solution takes the worry out of starting out in business for yourself.
More Information: theukfd.net/41602860

Easypizza UK Ltd
Telephone: 0871 210 2000
Website: www.easypizza.com
Summary of Operation: Pizza online ordering and delivery franchise.
More Information: theukfd.net/80384552

eCuisine
Telephone: 01253 362 490
Website: www.eatitnow.co.uk
Summary of Operation: Takeaway food online ordering.
More Information: theukfd.net/15291210

Espresso Soul
Telephone: 02890 327 474
Website: www.espressosoul.co.uk
Summary of Operation: Coffee machines and supplies.
More Information: theukfd.net/08317427

Esquires Coffee Houses
Telephone: 020 7251 5166
Website: www.esquirescoffee.co.uk
Summary of Operation: Coffee house providing speciality coffees and iced beverages, range of premium food items in a special environment.
More Information: theukfd.net/16664320

Euphoria Smoothies
Telephone: 0151 353 0126
Website: www.euphoriasmoothies.com
Summary of Operation: Euphoria Smoothies offer free consultation for people who want to open their own smoothie store.
More Information: theukfd.net/01547566

Everards Brewery Ltd
Telephone: 0116 201 4181
Website: www.everards.co.uk
Summary of Operation: Independent family owned brewery.
More Information: theukfd.net/57670243

Famous Moes
Telephone: 01273 676867
Website: www.Famousmoes.com
Summary of Operation: Offers online pizza ordering and delivery service.
More Information: theukfd.net/76023833

Favorite Fried Chicken Ltd
Telephone: 01255 222 568
Website: www.favorite.co.uk
Summary of Operation: Quick service restaurants and express chicken take-away.
More Information: theukfd.net/84572682

Frankies Fish Bar
Telephone: 0161 445 3300
Website: www.frankiesfishbar.co.uk
Summary of Operation: At Frankies we pride ourselves on the basic philosophy of good old fashioned fish and chips. To us this means authenticity assurance and rigorous attention to obtain the finest quality ingredients at source.
More Information: theukfd.net/42133469

Fruity Smoothie
Telephone: 01392 823 937
Website: www.fruitysmoothie.co.uk
Summary of Operation: Mobile smoothie and wholesome foods.
More Information: theukfd.net/29369883

Good Stuff Foods Ltd
Telephone: 07908 718 822
Summary of Operation: Distributer of fine foods.
More Information: theukfd.net/25959030

Haagen-Dazs Cafe
Telephone: 0800 125 556
Website: www.genmills.com
Summary of Operation: Ice cream parlours.
More Information: theukfd.net/12524552

Heavenly Smoothies
Telephone: 0845 467 0725
Website: www.heavenlysmoothies.co.uk
Summary of Operation: High quality, easy to make smoothies for the trade such as cafes, pubs, food and drink outlets. We give our franchise owners all the training you need, so no previous experience necessary except enthusiasm for smoothies.
More Information: theukfd.net/32245525

Hell Pizza
Telephone: 08456 666 999
Website: www.hellpizza.co.uk
Summary of Operation: Fresh from taking New Zealand by storm, Hell Pizza has successfully set up a pilot store in London. We are now looking for franchise owners to open up a Hell store in the UK.
More Information: theukfd.net/22713244

Henry J. Beans Group PLC
Telephone: 020 7352 9255
Website: www.henryjbeans.com
Summary of Operation: An American style bar and grill, operating from breakfast till late night.
More Information: theukfd.net/08663066

Hudson's Coffee House
Telephone: 01212 369009
Website: www.hudsonsfood.com
Summary of Operation: Hudsons coffee house, cafes, snack bars and tea rooms.
More Information: theukfd.net/13504338

I Love Candy
Telephone: 0141 337 33 99
Website: www.ilovecandystore.com
Summary of Operation: I Love Candy is a sweet shop with a twist, specialising in sweets from days gone by and Scottish favourites too. We also have a super handmade range of vintage scottish treats.
More Information: theukfd.net/81519117

JAGS Catering Co
Telephone: 029 2061 3333
Website: www.jagscatering.co.uk/contact.html
Summary of Operation: Catering franchise.
More Information: theukfd.net/93185333

Jaldi Jaldi
Telephone: 01274 571 861
Website: www.jaldijaldi.co.uk
Summary of Operation: Indian fast food takeaways.
More Information: theukfd.net/47221910

Jasper's Corporate Catering Ltd
Telephone: 0121 622 2043
Website: www.japsers-franchise.co.uk
Summary of Operation: An expert catering service for B2B clients throughout the UK. With thousands of meetings being held every day your service is in high demand. You'll produce food from fresh ingredients and deliver in branded refrigerated vehicles.
More Information: theukfd.net/04525125

Jim Garrahys Fudge Kitchen
Telephone: 01303 864 400
Website: www.fudgekitchen.co.uk
Summary of Operation: Online and retail based fudge creations.
More Information: theukfd.net/52099574

Juice Fix
Telephone: 0845 6860 555
Website: www.juicefix.co.uk
Summary of Operation: A dynamic health food and fresh juice franchise offering a variety of different start up opportunities.
More Information: theukfd.net/99360706

Juice Zone
Telephone: 01293 548 151
Website: www.juicezone.com
Summary of Operation: Healthy food and drink franchise operation.
More Information: theukfd.net/32477102

Jumbucks the Aussie Pie Company
Telephone: 0844 4773 250
Website: www.jumbucks.co.uk
Summary of Operation: Australian Pie company. A range of gourmet Jaffle Pies and conventional cafe products supplied with a bespoke premises.
More Information: theukfd.net/83337100

Kentish Man Catering Company
Telephone: 07976 895129
Summary of Operation: Supply sandwiches, paninis, wraps, baguettes and pasta salads.
More Information: theukfd.net/15417078

KFC
Telephone: 01483 717 000
Website: www.yum.com
Summary of Operation: Operator of fast food restaurants.
More Information: theukfd.net/22271134

La Baguette du Jour
Telephone: 01792 790701
Website: www.la-baguette.co.uk
Summary of Operation: Distinctive sandwich cafe and expresso bar specialising in a premium range of made-to-order sandwiches.
More Information: theukfd.net/45656712

Le Petit Four Francais Ltd
Website: www.lp4.co.uk
Summary of Operation: French style café-bakery and take away.
More Information: theukfd.net/62230331

Mahmoods
Telephone: 01274 722 686
Website: www.mahmoods.biz
Summary of Operation: Fast food restaurant.
More Information: theukfd.net/14113258

Marble Slab Creamery
Telephone: 01382 200 225
Website: www.marbleslabuk.com
Summary of Operation: Ice cream retail.
More Information: theukfd.net/75666941

Mibod Ltd
Telephone: 0845 094 0036
Website: www.mibod-eu.com
Summary of Operation: We specialise in supplying healthy food and snacks either by vending machine or wholsale.
More Information: theukfd.net/37822865

Millie's Cookies
Telephone: 020 7543 3441
Website: www.milliescookies.com
Summary of Operation: Manufacture and retail of freshly baked cookies and muffins.
More Information: theukfd.net/20609854

Minter's Fine Foods
Telephone: 01477 505 867
Website: www.mintersfinefoods.co.uk
Summary of Operation: A quality range of award winning fine foods, many of which are handmade.
More Information: theukfd.net/53981211

Mitchells & Butlers PLC
Telephone: 0121 498 5900
Website: www.mbplc.com
Summary of Operation: Pub retail.
More Information: theukfd.net/22678378

Mongolian Barbeque Ltd
Telephone: 020 8330 7333
Website: www.themongolianbarbeque.co.uk
Summary of Operation: A unique participation restaurant using fresh ingredients cooked before the customer. A destination restaurant appealing to large groups as well as couples.
More Information: theukfd.net/73415536

Mr Cod Franchise UK
Telephone: 01747 860 176
Website: www.mrcod.com
Summary of Operation: Fast food fish and chicken takeaway and restaurant.
More Information: theukfd.net/37824551

Muffin Break
Telephone: 01223 308 781
Website: www.muffinbreak.co.uk
Summary of Operation: Cafe and bakery retail system located in busy shopping centres, specialising in espresso coffees and freshly baked goods on site.
More Information: theukfd.net/65607273

Natural Welsh Water Ltd
Telephone: 01691 700 000
Website: www.coldwatercoolers.co.uk
Summary of Operation: Water cooler products.
More Information: theukfd.net/66234873

Nosh
Telephone: 07776 166 277
Website: www.noshretail.com
Summary of Operation: Nosh was created with the ambition of making the best hot and cold wholesome food, prepared daily in our kitchens. Our aim is to give handmade quality and freshness at sensible prices.
More Information: theukfd.net/59367935

Oakhouse Foods Ltd
Telephone: 01225 899 820
Website: www.oakhousefoods.co.uk
Summary of Operation: Home delivery of high quality frozen ready made meals, groceries and homeware.
More Information: theukfd.net/41322650

O'Briens (UK) Ltd
Telephone: 0141 222 2600
Website: www.obriensonline.com
Summary of Operation: Sandwich cafe with locations all over the UK.
More Information: theukfd.net/51077742

Oggy Oggy Pasty Co.
Telephone: 01603 873 364
Website: www.oggyoggy.com
Summary of Operation: Oggy Oggy offer mobile van and shop-bakery based franchises supplying high quality, freshly baked Cornish pasties and other food and drink lines.
More Information: theukfd.net/28174285

Oil & Vinegar (UK) Ltd
Website: www.oilvinegar.com
Summary of Operation: An exciting new retail franchise offering cullinary gifts from all over the world with 35 franchises in four European countries and currently 12 in the UK.
More Information: theukfd.net/55178177

Papa John's (GB) Ltd
Telephone: 01932 574368
Website: www.papajohns.co.uk
Summary of Operation: One of America's leading pizza delivery and takeaway companies. Has developed an exciting new format for the UK to exploit it's 'Better Ingredients, Better Pizza' quality positioning.
More Information: theukfd.net/37077687

Papa-Doms (UK) Ltd
Telephone: 0161 926 9882
Website: www.papa-doms.com
Summary of Operation: Restaurant.
More Information: theukfd.net/46566932

Pastiche Bistro Ltd
Telephone: 01785 222 241
Website: www.pastichebistro.co.uk
Summary of Operation: Distinctive bistro.
More Information: theukfd.net/11665716

Percolapps
Telephone: 01297 552 159
Website: www.percolapps.com
Summary of Operation: Percolapps provide mobile coffee barista vans to service your workforce or event.
More Information: theukfd.net/28054687

Phat Pasty Co.
Telephone: 01908 217 257
Website: www.phatpasty.com
Summary of Operation: Combining freshly baked traditional Cornish pasties, high quality homemade sandwiches, baguettes, salads and soups and delivering with our unique brand and our distinctive Phat van.
More Information: theukfd.net/73446483

Pistachios In The Park
Telephone: 020 8852 5381
Website: www.pistachiosinthepark.org.uk
Summary of Operation: Cafes, healthy food and selling of wooden educational, musical toys.
More Information: theukfd.net/49163413

Pizza Express Franchising Ltd
Telephone: 08453 899 489
Website: www.pizzaexpress.com
Summary of Operation: Pizza restaurants.
More Information: theukfd.net/72546781

Pizza Gogo Ltd
Telephone: 01708 551 414
Website: www.pizzagogo.co.uk
Summary of Operation: Established in 1987, Pizza GoGo now has 90 outlets and expanding all the time.
More Information: theukfd.net/10864407

Poppins Restaurants
Website: www.poppinsrestaurants.co.uk
Summary of Operation: Popular family restaurant chain in the UK.
More Information: theukfd.net/06377573

Puccino's Ltd
Telephone: 0845 872 4699
Website: www.puccinos.com
Summary of Operation: Puccino's Limited was founded in 1995 in response to a gap in the market for good quality coffee and ancillary products at travel locations.
More Information: theukfd.net/84078804

Punch Taverns

Website: www.punchtaverns.com
Summary of Operation: Pub group.
More Information: theukfd.net/74112715

Pure Waffle Ltd

Telephone: 020 7629 0546
Website: www.purewaffle.co.uk
Summary of Operation: Pure Waffle prides itself in its light, freshly made waffles.
More Information: theukfd.net/76865875

Quick Crepes Ltd

Telephone: 01225 783 050
Website: www.quickcrepes.com
Summary of Operation: Mobile crepe franchise business.
More Information: theukfd.net/44636377

Quiznos Corporation UK Ltd

Telephone: 01273 771 196
Website: www.quiznosuk.co.uk
Summary of Operation: Italian American toasted sub sandwich store, providing an alternative, healthy fast food option.
More Information: theukfd.net/66555057

Red Veg Ltd

Telephone: 01273 679 910
Website: www.redveg.com
Summary of Operation: RedVeg provides vegetarian fast food. It's different and affordable with a global menu from independently created recipes.
More Information: theukfd.net/28517882

Reload

Telephone: 0141 552 3998
Website: www.healthfuelstop.com
Summary of Operation: Reload originated in New Zealand and is fast becoming a global, revolutionary and innovative fast food outlet and prides itself on offering something unique in the fast food industry.
More Information: theukfd.net/64557547

Revive Juice Bars Ltd

Telephone: 0845 555 2015
Website: www.revivejuicebars.com
Summary of Operation: Revive provide their customers with Europe's most comprehensive range of made to order fruit drinks.
More Information: theukfd.net/81070314

Rice Faster Food Franchising

Telephone: 0161 244 5540
Website: www.ricemanchester.com
Summary of Operation: Oriental influenced world cuisine.
More Information: theukfd.net/89336744

Riverford Organic Vegetables Ltd

Telephone: 01803 762 073
Website: www.riverford.co.uk
Summary of Operation: Through the box scheme – delivered and serviced by a network of franchise owners – we supply customers with fresh produce directly from our farms.
More Information: Turn to page 27 or visit theukfd.net/65801741

Rockys Fast Food Ltd

Telephone: 020 8577 0034
Website: www.rockysfastfood.com
Summary of Operation: Fast food outlets.
More Information: theukfd.net/77505230

Rollover Ltd

Telephone: 01753 575 558
Website: www.rolloverhotdogs.com
Summary of Operation: Rollover is the UK's leading hot dog company, providing equipment and consumables such as hot dogs and other hot snacks to suit every customer's needs.
More Information: theukfd.net/03781108

Roly's Fudge

Telephone: 01363 84778
Website: www.rolysfudge.co.uk.
Summary of Operation: Produces fudge for weddings, wholesale and retail etc.
More Information: theukfd.net/71181325

Sacks Restaurant

Telephone: 01271 373 930
Website: www.sacks-franchise.co.uk
Summary of Operation: Sacks outside food and drinks served all day, to eat in or take out. Specialising in jacket poatoes, baguettes, tortilla wraps and ciabatta.
More Information: theukfd.net/68727405

Sam's Chicken

Telephone: 020 8591 4546
Website: www.samschicken.com
Summary of Operation: Chicken takeaway.
More Information: theukfd.net/40477830

Scottish & Newcastle Pub Company
Telephone: 07884 113 465
Website: www.s-npubcompany.co.uk
Summary of Operation: Scottish & Newcastle Pub Company is the leased pub division of Heineken UK and operates over 2,000 pubs in partnership with individual business people throughout the UK. We manage pubs on behalf of a number of leading financial partners, all of whom leave it to us to develop the pubs in conjunction with our lessees.
More Information: theukfd.net/79956009

ShakeAway
Telephone: 01202 310 402
Website: www.shakeaway.com
Summary of Operation: Milkshake takeaway.
More Information: theukfd.net/9799080

Snak Appeal
Website: www.snakappeal.com
Summary of Operation: Charity snack boxes.
More Information: theukfd.net/97812575

So Asia
Telephone: 01276 29138
Website: www.so-asia.com
Summary of Operation: Unique oriental buffet style restaurant that offers quality, variety and value for money authentic dishes from across Asia.
More Information: theukfd.net/57225355

SOHO Coffee Co. Ltd
Telephone: 01242 250 692
Website: www.sohocoffee.co.uk
Summary of Operation: Gorgeous food, healthy choices and coffee.
More Information: theukfd.net/98477808

Southern Fried Chicken
Telephone: 0118 944 1100
Website: www.southernfriedchicken.com
Summary of Operation: Fresh chicken based quick service restaurant with a full menu range that includes wrap, salads and piri piri, desserts and breakfasts.
More Information: theukfd.net/76276725

Spud U Like Ltd
Telephone: 020 8830 2424
Website: www.spudulike.co.uk
Summary of Operation: Fast food restaurants based on baked potatoes with various fillings.
More Information: theukfd.net/23218433

Subway (UK & Ireland)
Telephone: 01223 550 820
Website: www.subway.co.uk
Summary of Operation: Fast food sandwich outlets. The Subway chain offers an exceptional franchise opportunity which provides franchise owners with the tools and knowledge to run their own successful business.
More Information: theukfd.net/65051670

Sugacane Ltd
Telephone: 01629 815 540
Website: www.sugacane.co.uk
Summary of Operation: One of the largest specialists sweet shops in the UK.
More Information: theukfd.net/47806764

Superfish
Telephone: 020 8979 6600
Website: www.superfishuk.co.uk
Summary of Operation: Fish and chip restaurant.
More Information: theukfd.net/3866084

Sussex Farmhouse Meals
Telephone: 01903 820057
Website: www.sussexfarmhousemeals.co.uk
Summary of Operation: Sale and delivery of tasty prepared high quality meals to the elderly.
More Information: theukfd.net/08708300

Sweet Appeal Ltd
Telephone: 0845 055 8176
Website: www.sweetappeal.co.uk
Summary of Operation: Sweet Appeal is a social venture established to work with charity fundraising and marketing, in the most ethical way possible for the benefit of all involved.
More Information: theukfd.net/75510267

TacoTico.com
Telephone: 0203 178 6862
Website: www.leeslawfirm.net
Summary of Operation: Taco Tico is home to the best fresh, great tasting Mexican food you can find.
More Information: theukfd.net/52707772

Taste
Telephone: 01708 727 288
Website: www.tastesfresh.com
Summary of Operation: Serving quality food that is healthier than the fast food norm.
More Information: theukfd.net/28862680

Texas Chicken

Telephone: 020 8213 3120
Website: www.texaschicken.co.uk
Summary of Operation: Fast food franchise opportunity offering both restaurant and takeaway outlets and serving chicken, fries, side dishes and accompaniments.
More Information: theukfd.net/21288483

The Eggfree Cake Box

Telephone: 020 8470 2652
Website: www.eggfreecake.co.uk
Summary of Operation: Egg free cakes.
More Information: theukfd.net/47960046

The Farmshed Ltd

Telephone: 08458 333 135
Website: www.thefarmshed.co.uk
Summary of Operation: We are a small, family run business providing our customers with the best selection of organic British produce available, from farm fresh fruit and veg to organically reared meat and sustainably sourced fish – all delivered to your door in returnable boxes.
More Information: theukfd.net/29676174

The Frying Squad

Telephone: 02891 857 990
Website: www.fryingsquad.com
Summary of Operation: The Frying Squad offers value and choice to motorists and passers-by with quality fast food for busy people.
More Information: theukfd.net/68271406

The Grazing Cow Snack Company Ltd

Telephone: 01223 894 370
Website: www.thegrazingcow.co.uk
Summary of Operation: We at the Grazing Cow Snack Company have worked with premium brands such as Douwe Egberts, Cadbury, Tetley and Premier Foods to introduce a new range of 'In-Cup' hot drinks for the out-of-home market, (which includes the workplace) combined with a vast range of snacks.
More Information: theukfd.net/62043324

The Happy Plaice Franchise Ltd

Telephone: 0800 2182 408
Website: www.thehappyplaice.co.uk
Summary of Operation: Fish and chip van franchise.
More Information: theukfd.net/96413874

The Original Chocolate Fountain

Telephone: 01420 479 995
Website: www.theoriginalchocolatefountain.com
Summary of Operation: Hire and operation of Chocolate Fountain entertainment.
More Information: theukfd.net/51635875

The Real Ale Shop

Telephone: 01328 710 810
Website: www.therealaleshop.co.uk
Summary of Operation: The Real Ale Shop is unique because of its location in the beautiful rural setting of a classic North Norfolk malting barley farm which supplies the brewers with malt, their prime ingredient.
More Information: theukfd.net/85123171

The Roast Inn

Telephone: 01748 831 370
Summary of Operation: The Roast Inn provides quality catering for events and private functions. The vehicle is fully equipped and fresh food is cooked on the van for each event. The service provides freshly prepared roast joints, as well as breakfast buns, burgers, daily specials, cold food and snacks.
More Information: theukfd.net/18749833

The Streat Franchising Ltd

Telephone: 02890 42 42 80
Website: www.thestreat.com
Summary of Operation: Fast food, restaurant and catering.
More Information: theukfd.net/77825872

The Vending Revolution Ltd (Snack-a-Can)

Telephone: 01778 420 077
Website: www.vendingrevolution.com
Summary of Operation: Our Snack-a-Can franchise is a simple, proven, highly profitable, cash business. Ideal as a part-time venture or to build into a seriously large business.
More Information: theukfd.net/55348992

Thomas Green Ltd

Telephone: 01765 609 337
Website: www.thomasgreen.com
Summary of Operation: Retail franchise opportunity focused on creating a network of British grocery shops throughout Europe.
More Information: theukfd.net/72721566

Thorntons PLC
Telephone: 0845 075 0056
Website: www.thorntons.co.uk
Summary of Operation: Confectionery manufacturer and retailer.
More Information: theukfd.net/42867046

Tiffinbites (V8 Gourmet Group)
Telephone: 020 8438 4990
Website: www.tiffinbites.com
Summary of Operation: Indian restaurants.
More Information: theukfd.net/9756743

Tossed Partners
Telephone: 020 7289 2516
Website: www.tosseduk.com
Summary of Operation: Healthy food.
More Information: theukfd.net/23082325

Usmoothie
Telephone: 0870 042 0700
Website: www.usmoothie.co.uk
Summary of Operation: Usmoothie is an official Blendtec distributor in the UK.
More Information: theukfd.net/03008512

Vendsetters
Telephone: 023 9241 5000
Summary of Operation: Delivering fresh sandwiches, pastries and fresh bean to cup coffee to the work place via specialised chilled vehicle and chilled vending machines in association with Ginsters.
More Information: theukfd.net/50142018

Water Cooler World
Telephone: 01691 688 999
Website: www.watercoolerworld.co.uk
Summary of Operation: The Water Cooler World is the franchised brand of the successful office and domestic water retailer, Natural Welsh Water. Having served their home territory for several years and in response to the demands of the growing customer base, Natural Welsh Water are now awarding franchises to selected applicants throughout the UK.
More Information: theukfd.net/36963646

Watsons Bakeries
Telephone: 01483 285 219
Website: www.watsonsbakeries.co.uk
Summary of Operation: Bakery.
More Information: theukfd.net/16593494

Whistlestop And Amigo Specialist Brands Ssp
Summary of Operation: We are truly the food travel experts, skilled in combining global reach with a distinctive local touch.
More Information: theukfd.net/27134140

Wiltshire Farm Foods
Telephone: 01225 756 085
Website: www.wiltshirefarmfoods.com
Summary of Operation: Wiltshire Farm Foods is the UK's leading meals delivery service. Our meals are prepared in Trowbridge, Wiltshire, frozen the moment they are cooked, and delivered across the UK and Northern Ireland through a network of local outlets.
More Information: theukfd.net/81767288

Wimpy International Ltd
Telephone: 01628 891 655
Website: www.wimpy.uk.com
Summary of Operation: Fast food franchising.
More Information: theukfd.net/32232062

Yellow River Cafe
Website: www.yellowrivercafes.co.uk
Summary of Operation: Southern England chain of Chinese restaurants.
More Information: theukfd.net/18238868

Yo! Sushi UK Ltd
Telephone: 020 7841 0700
Website: www.yosushi.com
Summary of Operation: Retailing of classic and gourmet Sushi using a conveyor belt in an innovative high-tech restaurant environment.
More Information: theukfd.net/47565036

Yo-tribe UK Ltd
Telephone: 07876 563 687
Website: www.yogurtlandia.com
Summary of Operation: Yoghurt bars.
More Information: theukfd.net/18184410

Yogen Fruz
Summary of Operation: Cafes serving a wide variety of frozen yoghurt, fruit products and now also bagels.
More Information: theukfd.net/78107066

Shortlist

_____   _____
_____   _____
_____   _____
_____   _____
_____   _____
_____   _____
_____   _____
_____   _____
_____   _____
_____   _____
_____   _____
_____   _____
_____   _____
_____   _____

Franchise Tips

Take full advantage of the training provided

Comprehensive training opens up the availability of a franchise opportunity to a much wider population of potential franchise owners, enabling the franchisor to select the best candidates in terms of commitment, drive and enthusiasm for the business rather than searching for relevant experience.

For the franchise owner, initial and ongoing training provides an opportunity to expand the horizons of your occupation and develop new specialised knowledge in areas you may never have operated in before.

Retail

   INDIA JANE

Actively recruiting franchise owners

Retail franchising in the UK requires a higher level of investment, however the rewards are there for strong brands with quality products or services. These franchises can include electrical shops, new and secondhand product shops and clothing retailers. Franchise opportunities include **Cash & Cheque Express, Cash Converters, CeX, India Jane, Marvin's Menswear** and **The Zip Yard.**

bfa
FULL MEMBER

Cash Converters

Summary of Operation: One of the UK's leading retailers of pre-owned and graded goods and financial services providers, has transformed the concept of buying and selling second-hand goods. Since its launch in Australia in 1984 the company has grown enormously with more than 190 stores in the UK, 620 stores worldwide and is the largest of its kind in the world.

Ideal Franchise Owner Profile: Determined, hard working, committed, and a desire to succeed and reap the rewards.

Cost of Franchise: £110,000 + VAT plus financing

Franchise Owner Contact: Sharon Shannon

Year Company Established: International 1984, UK 1996

Year of First Franchise Owner: 1991

Number of Company Outlets: 45

Number of Franchised Outlets: 145

Number of Franchise Owners Planned: Unlimited

Overseas Operations Existing: Worldwide

Overseas Operations Planned: AOR

Management Service Fees: £362 per week

Breakdown of Package: Franchise fee, opening stock, shopfit, IT costs, pre-opening costs and working capital.

Financial Assistance Available: Yes – relationships in place with several high street banks and specialised lenders.

Training Provided: Bespoke 10-week schedule alongside personal Training Manager.

Training Location: In-store, in-house workshops and head office.

Support Services: Business Development Manager, Regional Training Manager, stock, logistics as well as marketing and PR support.

Areas of Priority Development: England, Scotland and Wales.

More Information: theukfd.net/81774273

Cash Converters House, Gentlemen's Field, Westmill Road, Ware, SG12 0EF

t: 01920 485 696
f: 01920 485 695
e: franchise.enquiry@cashconverters.net
w: www.cashconverters.co.uk

CeX – Complete Entertainment Exchange

Summary of Operation: Retailer of second-hand electronic and digital entertainment products. We trade in videogames, DVDs, mobile phones, digital electronics, computing, vision products and music CDs.

Ideal Franchise Owner Profile: Retail and management experience preferred. An interest and working knowledge of some or all of the products we deal in. Hard working people with a passion for giving the best service to our customers, someone who will dedicate themselves full time into the business.

Cost of Franchise: £200,000-£250,000 + VAT

CeX – Complete Entertainment Exchange CeX Support Centre, The Old Brewery, 132a St Albans Road, Watford, WD24 4AE

e: uk.franchising@webuy.com
w: www.webuy.com

Franchise Owner Contact: Martin Hawthorne, Alan Wilkinson, Frank Orchard.
Year Company Established: 1992
Year of First Franchise Owner: 2006

Number of Company Outlets: 55
Number of Franchised Outlets: 71
Number of Franchise Owners Planned: 150+
Overseas Operations Existing: Currently operating corporate stores in Spain and the USA.
Overseas Operations Planned: Franchise stores in Spain and the USA, Republic of Ireland and India
Management Service Fees: 8%

Breakdown of Package: £20,000 license fee and £10,000 training and opening support fee includes free training for life for franchise owners and employees.

Projected Turnover:
1st Year: £900,000   **2nd Year:** £1,100,000
3rd Year: £1,300,000
Projected Profit:
1st Year: £60,000   **2nd Year:** £75,000
3rd Year: £90,000

Financial Assistance Available: Accreditation with major banks

Training Provided: Yes – minimum of 400 hours
Training Location: Coventry for basic training and a local corporate store for ongoing training.
Support Services: Initial training and ongoing procedure updates. Stock and pricing advice from experts. Ongoing support including intranet and B services. Hands-on store identification, design and outfit. Bespoke EPOS designed especially for buying, selling and exchanging goods.

Areas of Priority Development: All UK, particular focus on Scotland and Wales

More Information: theukfd.net/20618366

Marvin's Menswear

Summary of Operation: Retail outlet for men's fashion wear, aimed for high street selling.

Ideal Franchise Owner Profile: Looking for an outgoing business driven individual, willing to build on our existing business format franchise. A background in marketing and sales is essential with the ability to direct a team.

Cost of Franchise: £200,000 + VAT
Franchise Owner Contact: Roy Summers
Year Company Established: 1995
Year of First Franchise Owner: 1995

Number of Company Outlets: 1
Number of Franchised Outlets: 3
Number of Franchise Owners Planned: 40

Overseas Operations Existing: None
Overseas Operations Planned: Europe

Management Service Fees: 7.5%

Breakdown of Package: Turnkey programme including training, shopfit and launch.

Projected Turnover:
1st Year: £400,000
2nd Year: £500,000
3rd Year: £600,000

Projected Profit:
1st Year: Break even
2nd Year: £80,000
3rd Year: £120,000

Financial Assistance Available: No

Training Provided: Initial and ongoing
Training Location: Norwich
Support Services: Location visits monthly.

Areas of Priority Development: London, Birmingham and Manchester.

More Information: theukfd.net/87063851

**Marvin's Menswear
Cedar Holdings, Ipswich Road,
Tasburgh, Norwich, NR15 1NS**

t: 01508 470 686
e: roysummers@hotmail.co.uk

The Zip Yard

Summary of Operation: Stores offering all types of garment alterations.

Ideal Franchise Owner Profile: Ambitious, customer-driven, well organised and keen to follow a proven business system.

Cost of Franchise: £40,000 + VAT

Franchise Owner Contact: Janet Matthews

Year Company Established: 2005

Year of First Franchise Owner: 2006

Number of Company Outlets: 0

Number of Franchised Outlets: 16

Number of Franchise Owners Planned: 100

Overseas Operations Existing: Ireland

Overseas Operations Planned: AOR

Management Service Fees: 8%

Breakdown of Package: Licence to trade, two weeks intensive training, marketing launch package and marketing collateral, website, hands-on operational support, shop fitting, opening stock, bespoke till and epos system, manuals and ongoing business support.

Financial Assistance Available: Major banks.

Training Provided: Full two-week programme of training covering systems, customer service, operations and marketing etc.

Training Location: Head office in Leicester.

Support Services: Marketing support, ongoing training and product development.

Areas of Priority Development: Throughout the UK.

More Information: theukfd.net/84249730

**The Zip Yard
Unit 2, Cartwright Way, Forest Business Park, Bardon, Coalville, LE67 1UB**

t: 01530 513 307
f: 01530 513 309
e: jmatthews@thezipyard.co.uk
w: www.thezipyard.co.uk

Cash & Cheque Express
Ashford House, 45, Church Road, Ashford, TW15 2TY

Telephone: 01923 606158
Fax: 01784 250876
Email: david@cashandchequeexpress.co.uk
Website: www.cashandchequeexpress.co.uk

Summary of Operation: Cash & Cheque Express stores offer a wide range of services, from buying and selling quality pre-loved goods to providing fast and convenient ways of raising short term cash. You will also find us a great place to buy your foreign currency and send money worldwide through Western Union.

Cost of Franchise: From £60,000 + VAT plus financing.

Franchise Owner Contact: David Wheeler

Year Company Established: 2005
Year of First Franchise Owner: 2006
Number of Company Outlets: 2
Number of Franchised Outlets: 13
Number of Franchise Owners Planned: 80

Overseas Operations Existing: No
Overseas Operations Planned: Europe

Management Service Fees: £150 per week

Breakdown of Package: Initial licence fee, shop fitting, training, stock and working capital.

Financial Assistance Available: Yes

Training Provided: Full
Training Location: At store locations and head office corporate store.

Support Services: Initial and ongoing marketing support, staff training, plus introduction of new 'bolt-on' initiatives.

Areas of Priority Development: England, Scotland and Wales.

More Information: theukfd.net/08168228

INDIA JANE

India Jane
2 Chase Road, London, NW10 6HZ

Telephone: 01603 620301
Email: franmatch@fdsltd.com

Summary of Operation: Retailer of furniture and accessories of high quality and design.

Ideal Franchise Owner Profile: Hard working, well disciplined, enthusiastic, honest with integrity and a determination to succeed! An affinity with good design and a passion for the product and the concept of an India Jane franchise. Adequate business funding, organisational and communication skills and the ability to work as part of a team.

Cost of Franchise: £25,000 + shop fitting, stock and working capital.

Franchise Owner Contact: Richard Langrick
Year Company Established: 1991
Year of First Franchise Owner: 2009
Number of Company Outlets: 2
Number of Franchised Outlets: 2
Number of Franchise Owners Planned: 20

Overseas Operations Existing: None
Overseas Operations Planned: Ireland
Management Service Fees: 5% + 1.5% National Marketing Levy.

Breakdown of Package: Franchise Licence with sole rights to operate an India Jane stand alone branded retail business in the territory. Rights to use the India Jane Trade Mark, know-how, Operations Manuals and business systems. Store design and fitout assistance, premises and location evaluation, store planning and design.

Financial Assistance Available: N/A
Training Provided: Head office training centre, training store, franchise owner's own store – pre and post opening.
Training Location: London
Areas of Priority Development: Edinburgh, Chester, York, Leeds, Cheltenham, Bath, Exeter, Windsor, Guildford, Bournemouth and Canterbury.

More information: theukfd.net/37425074

Dream Doors
Unit 22, Heritage Business Park, Heritage Way, Gosport, PO12 4BG

Telephone: 02392 604 630
Email: recruitment@dreamdoorsltd.co.uk
Website: www.dreamdoorsfranchise.co.uk

Summary of Operation: Dream Doors is a showroom-based management and sales franchise. Franchise owners sell made-to-measure kitchen doors, worktops, sinks and appliances. A Dream Doors' kitchen facelift saves customers time, money and upheaval when compared to a complete re-fit.

Ideal Franchise Owner Profile: Proactive and self driven people. Kitchen experience is not necessary as we help recruit an installation team.

Cost of Franchise: £23,825 + VAT
Franchise Owner Contact: Troy Tappenden
Financial Assistance Available: Barclays, HSBC, Lloyds TSB and NatWest.

More Information: theukfd.net/42251004

Abbeyfield VE Ltd
Telephone: 0115 988 2109
Summary of Operation: Abbeyfield is a retail optician franchise.
More Information: theukfd.net/85693061

ABC Music
Website: www.abcmusic.co.uk
Summary of Operation: Musical instrument retailer.
More Information: theukfd.net/12746425

Ableworld
Telephone: 01270 627 185
Website: www.ableworld.co.uk
Summary of Operation: Ableworld are the largest mobility and stairlift retailers in the North West.
More Information: theukfd.net/86817869

Action Bikes
Telephone: 01273 605 160
Website: www.action-bikes.com
Summary of Operation: Action Bikes from a core business established in the 1930's is today the largest independent bicycle retailer in the UK.
More Information: theukfd.net/25453148

Aftershock PLC
Telephone: 020 8965 3898
Website: www.aftershockplc.com
Summary of Operation: Aftershock is a luxury British brand and is one of the leading designers, retailers and manufacturers of exquisite handcrafted womenswear and accessories.
More Information: theukfd.net/71146052

All Fired Up Ceramics Cafe
Telephone: 08444 992 820
Website: www.allfiredupceramics.co.uk
Summary of Operation: Ceramics painting, coffee shops, cards and gifts.
More Information: theukfd.net/02021271

Amaze Blinds & Curtains Ltd
Telephone: 01553 777 770
Website: www.amazeblindsandcurtains.net
Summary of Operation: Supplier of window blinds, curtains, curtain poles and wall papers etc.
More Information: theukfd.net/21341818

Art 4 Fun Ltd
Telephone: 020 7794 0800
Website: www.Art4Fun.com
Summary of Operation: Contemporary shops and cafes where the customer creates original designs by painting onto ceramic, wood, glass, paper, silk, fabric items, or make amosaic. No artistic skills or experience necessary. Workshops are also offered.
More Information: theukfd.net/53003435

Austin Reed
Telephone: 020 7534 7766
Website: www.austinreed.co.uk
Summary of Operation: Mens and womens clothing retail shops.
More Information: theukfd.net/53028022

Autopaint International
Telephone: 0151 549 1409
Summary of Operation: Your one stop shop for all your classic car refinishing requirements.
More Information: theukfd.net/00014857

b.young
Telephone: 020 7631 1602
Website: www.byoung.com
Summary of Operation: Fashion retailer.
More Information: theukfd.net/34552302

Bang & Olufsen
Telephone: 0118 969 2288
Summary of Operation: Retail television and hi-fi.
More Information: theukfd.net/24881585

Bargain Booze Ltd
Telephone: 0845 345 0001
Website: www.bargainbooze.co.uk
Summary of Operation: UK off-licence chain.
More Information: theukfd.net/22700714

BHS International
Telephone: 020 7319 8437
Website: www.bhs.co.uk
Summary of Operation: Retailer for the whole family and the home across a wide range of products.
More Information: theukfd.net/70861217

Blazes Fireplace & Heating Centres Ltd
Telephone: 01282 831 176
Website: www.blazes.co.uk
Summary of Operation: Retail sale and installation of fires, fireplaces and central heating products from high street showrooms.
More Information: theukfd.net/60152728

Blue Spirit UK
Telephone: 02870 321 115
Website: www.bluespirit.uk.com
Summary of Operation: The largest international retail jewellery franchise.
More Information: theukfd.net/16035015

Bo Concept TCR
Telephone: 020 7843 6900
Website: www.boconcept.com
Summary of Operation: Furniture retail shops.
More Information: theukfd.net/08467321

Box 2 Ltd
Telephone: 01444 882 727
Website: www.box2.co.uk
Summary of Operation: Ladies fashion for sizes 16-30 (for the larger lady).
More Information: theukfd.net/50414106

British Blinds
Telephone: 01274 717 952
Website: www.britishblinds.co.uk
Summary of Operation: Selling and fitting window blinds to consumers and business customers.
More Information: theukfd.net/51148252

Burberry Ltd
Telephone: 020 7806 1328
Website: www.uk.burberry.com
Summary of Operation: Luxury clothing brand with a worldwide distribution network.
More Information: theukfd.net/23762333

C & J Clark International Ltd
Telephone: 01458 842 471
Website: www.clarks.com
Summary of Operation: Clarks brand footwear retail stores following company owned retail operation formats.
More Information: theukfd.net/15502440

Calendar Club
Telephone: 01392 207 001
Website: www.calendarclub.co.uk
Summary of Operation: Calendar retailer.
More Information: theukfd.net/86056946

Card Group Greetings
Telephone: 020 8758 9159
Website: www.cardgroup.com
Summary of Operation: CardGroup Greetings is a hugely successful organisation established in 41 countries. With a well-structured and established franchise format, it won the 2004/5 Swedish franchise associations 'best franchise of the year'. The exclusive products of cards, bags, wrap etc are best sellers in their category and are sold through retail outlets on a consignment basis.
More Information: theukfd.net/82316845

Cards For You Greetings Ltd
Telephone: 01902 623 520
Website: www.cards-for-you.co.uk
Summary of Operation: Franchise owners supply greeting cards to retailers on a sale or return basis. The franchise owner will supply a display stand if required by the retailer. After four to six weeks the franchise owner returns to the store to restock the display and invoice the retailer only for the cards that have been sold.
More Information: theukfd.net/47574603

Cartridge City (Franchising) Ltd
Telephone: 07841 843 380
Website: www.cartridgecity.co.uk
Summary of Operation: Retailing of computer ink refills and related services.
More Information: theukfd.net/27280154

Cash Generator
Telephone: 01204 574 444
Website: www.cashgenerator.co.uk
Summary of Operation: Cash Generator is a nationwide high street retailer of pre-owned and new products. Its 130+ Buy, Sell & Loan stores have multiple income streams, which maximise profitability and safety. One in three franchise owners have opened additional outlets such was the success of their first store.
More Information: theukfd.net/22510830

CD Franchise
Telephone: 0845 463 2273
Website: www.cdfranchise.co.uk
Summary of Operation: Online CD sales.
More Information: theukfd.net/8923767

Chevron Texaco Ltd
Telephone: 020 7719 3000
Summary of Operation: Petrol forecourt retailing.
More Information: theukfd.net/67252664

CHIPS Franchise Ltd
Telephone: 01642 227 348
Website: www.chipsworld.co.uk
Summary of Operation: CHIPS video games stores buy, sell, trade new and second hand consoles, video games, DVDs and accessories.
More Information: theukfd.net/42511151

Clarks International
Telephone: 01458 842 470
Website: www.clarks.com
Summary of Operation: Retail shoe shops.
More Information: theukfd.net/90725844

Cloebelle
Telephone: 01458 241 385
Website: www.cloebelle.co.uk
Summary of Operation: Jewellery retail.
More Information: theukfd.net/19299242

Dancia International - The Dancers Shop
Telephone: 01273 414455
Website: www.dancia.co.uk
Summary of Operation: Premises based retail dancewear shops selling childrens shoes, garments and accessories for ballet, tap ballroom, salsa etc plus keep-fit, gym and skate wear.
More Information: theukfd.net/77608684

Debenhams
Website: www.debenhams.com
Summary of Operation: High street retailer with stores all over the UK.
More Information: theukfd.net/83342802

Dixons Stores Group
Telephone: 01727 203 055
Website: www.dixons.co.uk
Summary of Operation: One of the largest consumer electronics retailers in Europe.
More Information: theukfd.net/19898193

Doors & Doors
Telephone: 01895 638 900
Website: www.doorsanddoors.co.uk
Summary of Operation: A specialist retail business, operating in the home improvement market, selling doors and 'everything for doors'.
More Information: theukfd.net/21407381

e-racking
Telephone: 01274 662 912
Website: www.e-racking.com
Summary of Operation: e-racking is the revolutionary online tool for instant drawings and quotations for pallet racking, office shelving and industrial shelving products.
More Information: theukfd.net/00153205

Esprit (GB) Ltd
Telephone: 020 7406 1400
Website: www.esprit.com
Summary of Operation: Retail high street fashion shops.
More Information: theukfd.net/56522463

Felicity Hat Hire
Telephone: 01772 742 428
Website: www.felicity.co.uk
Summary of Operation: Felicity hat hire shops hire fabulous hats from the world's top designers for a fraction of the retail cost. A comprehensive support package is offered to franchise owners.
More Information: theukfd.net/08505024

FingerPrint Jewellery
Telephone: 0845 652 6012
Website: www.fingerprint-jewellery.co.uk
Summary of Operation: FingerPrint Jewellery is an established, thriving and innovative business which produces the highe quality jewellery.
More Information: theukfd.net/15618939

French Connection
Telephone: 07825 056 589
Website: www.frenchconnection.com
Summary of Operation: Fashionable clothing retailer.
More Information: theukfd.net/04475732

GEMS
Telephone: 02886 766 110
Website: www.gemsthefranchise.com
Summary of Operation: An established quality jewellery retail chain.
More Information: theukfd.net/88667011

Get Ahead Hats
Telephone: 01254 889 574
Website: www.getaheadhats.co.uk
Summary of Operation: Ladies hat hire.
More Information: theukfd.net/48442507

Go Mobile
Telephone: 01327 304 225
Website: www.gomobileuk.com
Summary of Operation: One of the largest independent mobile phone retailers in the UK, now part of 100+ retail stores nationwide.
More Information: theukfd.net/46244495

G-Star
Telephone: 020 7939 0930
Website: www.g-star.com
Summary of Operation: Denim retail.
More Information: theukfd.net/70704619

H & M Hennes Ltd
Telephone: 020 7323 2211
Website: www.hm.com
Summary of Operation: Offers clothing for men, women and children.
More Information: theukfd.net/07703641

Hamleys
Telephone: 020 7479 7363
Website: www.hamleys.co.uk
Summary of Operation: Toy shop.
More Information: theukfd.net/22212793

Hobgoblin Music
Telephone: 01903 203 399
Website: www.hobgoblin.com
Summary of Operation: Music stores.
More Information: theukfd.net/26134510

Horsatack
Telephone: 01295 226 851
Website: www.horsatack.co.uk
Summary of Operation: Horse saddlery and horse riding supplies retailer.
More Information: theukfd.net/53429974

Hotter Shoes
Telephone: 0800 525 893
Website: www.hotter.com
Summary of Operation: Comfortable shoes for men and women from the makers of the 'Comfort Concept' range of footwear.
More Information: theukfd.net/11288712

Inkbox
Telephone: 01493 652 875
Website: www.inkboxonline.co.uk
Summary of Operation: Inkjet cartridge shops.
More Information: theukfd.net/72181780

In-toto
Telephone: 01924 487 900
Website: www.intoto.co.uk
Summary of Operation: In-toto is the UK's largest kitchen franchise retailing high quality German kitchens.
More Information: theukfd.net/36573414

Jeffery West
Telephone: 020 7730 9606
Website: www.jeffery-west.co.uk
Summary of Operation: Luxury mens footwear.
More Information: theukfd.net/85325433

Karen Millen Ltd
Telephone: 020 7452 1000
Website: www.karenmillen.co.uk
Summary of Operation: Retail womens fashion, including eye wear and cosmetics.
More Information: theukfd.net/55434286

Ladies That Do
Telephone: 01403 268 636
Website: www.ladiesthatdo.co.uk
Summary of Operation: Ladies domestic cleaning.
More Information: theukfd.net/91406113

Lance James
Telephone: 01227 219 800
Website: www.lancejames.co.uk
Summary of Operation: Jewellery retailer.
More Information: theukfd.net/13252539

Laura Ashley
Telephone: 020 7880 5100
Website: www.lauraashley.com
Summary of Operation: Home furniture and ladies fashion retailer.
More Information: theukfd.net/08511114

Leightons Franchises Ltd
Telephone: 01252 823 400
Website: www.leightonsopticians.co.uk
Summary of Operation: Optical retailers.
More Information: theukfd.net/05118435

Levi Strauss
Website: www.levistrauss.com
Summary of Operation: Retailing of clothing.
More Information: theukfd.net/82630073

Lillywhites/Sports Direct
Telephone: 020 7730 9606
Website: www.sportsdirect.com
Summary of Operation: Sports retailer
More Information: theukfd.net/67927181

Little Impressions UK Ltd
Telephone: 01903 230 515
Website: www.little-impressions.com
Summary of Operation: Little Impressions is a casting technique to create a lasting 3D image of childrens hands and feet in perfect detail.
More Information: theukfd.net/83002183

Living Clean
Telephone: 01603 492 820 /219 966
Website: www.livingclean.co.uk
Summary of Operation: Environmentally friendly cleaning products and services.
More Information: theukfd.net/56706213

Mamas & Papas
Telephone: 01484 438 200
Website: www.mamasandpapas.com
Summary of Operation: A leading brand for prams, pushchairs, car seats, cots, highchairs, nursery furniture, bedding and toys.
More Information: theukfd.net/26384550

Mexx
Telephone: 020 7292 7973
Website: www.mexx.co.uk
Summary of Operation: Extensive range of fashion apparel for women, men and children.
More Information: theukfd.net/26580381

Mini Melts UK Ltd
Telephone: 0115 989 0230
Website: www.minimeltsdirect.co.uk
Summary of Operation: Premium novelty ice cream company.
More Information: theukfd.net/26538475

Minit UK PLC
Telephone: 0115 981 1629
Summary of Operation: Multi-service retailer trading as MINIT solutions, SupaSnaps and Sketchley.
More Information: theukfd.net/67058175

Monsoon Accessorize Ltd
Telephone: 020 3372 3000
Website: www.monsoon.co.uk
Summary of Operation: Monsoon Accessorize brings you the latest fashion and accessories for women, children and your home.
More Information: theukfd.net/35253232

Moshulu Colours
Telephone: 01404 540 770
Website: www.moshulu.co.uk
Summary of Operation: Quality sandals, shoes, boots and slippers.
More Information: theukfd.net/58225266

Mothercare
Telephone: 01923 241 000
Website: www.mothercare.com
Summary of Operation: Mothercare is synonymous with children and parenting with a reputation for specialism, quality, safety and innovation in providing products and services for mothers, mothers-to-be, babies and young children.
More Information: theukfd.net/32301410

Mudfish Trading
Telephone: 01677 427 177
Website: www.mudfish.co.uk
Summary of Operation: The only confectionery franchisor to attain full member status of the bfa. Franchise owners supply local retailers in their own exclusive area.
More Information: theukfd.net/76728853

Murco Petroleum Ltd
Telephone: 01727 892 400
Website: www.murco.co.uk/welcome.htm
Summary of Operation: Petrol forecourt retailing.
More Information: theukfd.net/15645454

Natuzzi
Telephone: 01322 312 550
Website: www.natuzzi.co.uk
Summary of Operation: Natuzzi produces over 400 different models in casual contemporary, modern and classic styles, at all price points, in all versions.
More Information: theukfd.net/20547038

Neck & Neck
Telephone: 020 8660 3111
Website: www.neckandneck.com
Summary of Operation: Fashion retailer franchise operation.
More Information: theukfd.net/86453033

Nevada Bob's Golf
Telephone: 01923 222 370
Website: www.nevadabobs.co.uk
Summary of Operation: Nevada Bob's is the largest and only worldwide golf retailer with franchises covering Europe.
More Information: theukfd.net/22665852

New Look Retailers Ltd
Telephone: 01305 765 000
Website: www.newlookgroup.com
Summary of Operation: Retail fashion high street brand.
More Information: theukfd.net/6357265

Next Franchise
Telephone: 0845 456 7777
Website: www.next.co.uk
Summary of Operation: Latest fashion for women, men, children and homeware.
More Information: theukfd.net/44806365

NOA NOA
Telephone: 01737 246 652
Website: www.noanoareigate.com
Summary of Operation: NOA NOA opened in 2007 and introduced a whole new range of NOA NOA clothing and style to the ladies of Reigate and the surrounding areas.
More Information: theukfd.net/82508339

O2 (UK) Ltd
Telephone: 0800 902 0202
Website: www.o2.co.uk
Summary of Operation: Retail shops in the mobile phone industry.
More Information: theukfd.net/64482273

Olio & Farina
Telephone: 07930 546 064
Website: www.olioefarina.com
Summary of Operation: O&F retail and cafe specialise in the selection and retail of top quality Italian food and design kitchenware for personal use and as gifts.
More Information: theukfd.net/87272735

Optika/Clulow Group
Telephone: 020 8515 6700
Website: www.davidclulow.com
Summary of Operation: Complete fashionable eyewear within a high street retail operation.
More Information: theukfd.net/81065606

Orange
Telephone: 07812 241 432
Website: www.orange.co.uk
Summary of Operation: The Orange retail franchise offers a full range of mobile communications and fixed and mobile broadband solutions.
More Information: theukfd.net/97685857

Pauline May Ltd
Telephone: 01535 661 362
Website: www.paulinemay.com
Summary of Operation: Suppliers of clothing to the elderly, predominantly in care homes, but also via mailorder and to individuals who are housebound.
More Information: theukfd.net/25314826

PC Friend
Telephone: 0800 328 5072
Website: www.pcfriend-online.com
Summary of Operation: Retailer of PC peripherals.
More Information: theukfd.net/80207818

Pinks Franchising
Telephone: 020 8343 3666
Website: www.pinksflorists.com
Summary of Operation: Retail florists with online sales.
More Information: theukfd.net/20617672

Pooh Corner Ltd
Telephone: 01892 770 456
Website: www.pooh-country.co.uk
Summary of Operation: Offers a wide variety of items from plush to games to clothing.
More Information: theukfd.net/40391304

Powerhouse Fitness
Telephone: 0141 951 4477
Website: www.powerhousefitness.co.uk
Summary of Operation: Providing high-quality exercise equipment and fitness products as well as wide range of sports nutrition.
More Information: theukfd.net/45530728

Pronuptia (UK) Ltd
Telephone: 01273 563 006
Website: www.pronuptia.co.uk
Summary of Operation: Bridal gowns.
More Information: theukfd.net/55061431

Pumpkin Patch
Telephone: 0800 458 8914
Website: www.pumpkinpatch.co.uk
Summary of Operation: Children's clothes retail.
More Information: theukfd.net/55327858

Punky Fish
Telephone: 020 7730 9606
Website: www.punkyfish.com
Summary of Operation: Clothing retail.
More Information: theukfd.net/27392855

Quiz Clothing
Telephone: 0141 569 1544
Website: www.quizclothing.co.uk
Summary of Operation: Quiz supplies womens fashion clothes and girls clothes for stylish females.
More Information: theukfd.net/16134461

Rainbow Room International
Telephone: 0141 221 0400
Website: www.rainbowroominternational.com
Summary of Operation: Hair and beauty group selling unique hair products and gift vouchers.
More Information: theukfd.net/10429453

Raleigh Cycle Centre (Franchising) Ltd (CycleLife)
Telephone: 01903 505 155
Website: www.raleigh.co.uk
Summary of Operation: Cycle retailing.
More Information: theukfd.net/45523237

Ramsdens4Cash
Telephone: 01642 579 975
Website: www.johnramsden.com
Summary of Operation: Pawnbroking, cheque cashing and allied services.
More Information: theukfd.net/34132436

Rohan Designs Ltd
Telephone: 01908 517 900
Website: www.rohan.co.uk
Summary of Operation: Rohan is a quality outdoor clothing retail franchise. Franchise owners have the opportunity to operate their own Rohan retail outlet.
More Information: theukfd.net/64206060

Royal Yachting
Telephone: 020 8920 3431
Website: www.royalyachting.net
Summary of Operation: Boat sales and hire.
More Information: theukfd.net/22463621

Rye International Ltd
Telephone: 01243 585 779
Website:
Summary of Operation: Rye International was formed in the early 90's as an import and export merchants, specialising in general cargo on a global basis.
More Information: theukfd.net/88581641

S'coolwear For Less
Telephone: 01462 812 819
Website: www.schoolwearforless.com
Summary of Operation: Retailer of school uniforms and school clothing.
More Information: theukfd.net/50188873

Seven Oaks Sound and Vision
Telephone: 01494 431 290
Website: www.sevenoaksfranchising.co.uk
Summary of Operation: Specialist independent Hi-Fi retailer.
More Information: theukfd.net/61274070

Shared Earth
Telephone: 01904 655 314
Website: www.sharedearth.co.uk
Summary of Operation: One of the UK's largest Fair Trade retailer, specialising in eco-products.
More Information: theukfd.net/36428600

Shoes Glorious Shoes
Telephone: 01202 659 595
Website: www.shoesgloriousshoes.co.uk
Summary of Operation: Mobile shoe boutique selling shoes, boots and handbags through shoe parties in the home and other events.
More Information: theukfd.net/76883772

Silverdaze (UK) Ltd
Telephone: 01372 374 800
Website: www.silverdazeuk.com
Summary of Operation: A unique jewellery franchise company.
More Information: theukfd.net/38650223

Taylor of Old Bond Street
Telephone: 020 7930 5321
Website: www.tayloroldbondst.co.uk
Summary of Operation: Full range of luxury shaving and skin products for gentlemen including soaps, face and body creams, razors, mirrors and manicure items.
More Information: theukfd.net/81094714

The Inkdrop Franchise Company Ltd
Telephone: 01902 798 900
Website: www.theinkdropshop.co.uk
Summary of Operation: At The Inkdrop you can buy ink jet and laser cartridges online or from our growing network of high street shops, cutting the cost of printing by up to 60%.
More Information: theukfd.net/47078025

The Magic Custard Company Ltd
Telephone: 0845 601 7081
Website: www.magiccustard.com
Summary of Operation: Babies hands and feet casts.
More Information: theukfd.net/60014781

The White Company
Telephone: 020 8799 6773
Website: www.thewhitecompany.com
Summary of Operation: White linen, tablewear, furniture, accessories and gift shop.
More Information: theukfd.net/48476746

Trespass Franchise Ltd
Telephone: 0141 568 8000
Website: www.trespass.co.uk
Summary of Operation: Retail of outdoor and sports fashion clothing and accessories.
More Information: theukfd.net/72188182

Two Feet For Kids
Telephone: 0161 929 1394
Website: www.twofeet.biz
Summary of Operation: Mobile children's shoe sales and fitting.
More Information: theukfd.net/91524707

United Carpets
Telephone: 01709 732 666
Website: www.unitedcarpetsandbeds.com
Summary of Operation: Sales of carpet, laminates, vinyls and beds. Generally out of town locations in 'warehouse style' outlets of between 5-10,000 sq ft.
More Information: theukfd.net/67082733

Vom Fass Concessions Ltd
Telephone: 0870 750 0962
Website: www.vomfassfranchise.com
Summary of Operation: Retailer of premium liqueurs, spirits, wines, oils and vinegars straight from the cask in a unique environment in which they can taste before they purchase.
More Information: theukfd.net/31565043

Whittard of Chelsea
Telephone: 01993 893 700
Website: www.whittard.co.uk
Summary of Operation: Shop at Whittard of Chelsea for the finest teas and coffees chocolate drinks, instant teas and, tea and coffee related gifts.
More Information: theukfd.net/22474265

Workwear For Less
Telephone: 01462 812 819
Website: www.workwearforless.co.uk
Summary of Operation: Retailer of work wear, uniforms etc.
More Information: theukfd.net/83143021

SERVICES | Automotive

etyres

Actively recruiting franchise owners

Franchises in this sector are opportunities related to cars, vans and automobiles. Many of these franchises are van-based opportunities and can be home-based franchises. Investment levels are lower and many tend to be low cost franchise opportunities. Franchise opportunities include **etyres**.

etyres

Summary of Operation: Local exclusive territory of the UK's #1 online tyre retailer. Visit our website to view our recruitment movie www.etyres.co.uk/franchisemovie.

Ideal Franchise Owner: Practical, hard working individuals with good customer service skills.

Cost of Franchise: £35,000 + VAT

Franchise Owner Contact: Richard Langrick

Year Company Established: 1992

Year of First Franchise Owner: 1996

Number of Company Outlets: 0

Number of Franchised Outlets: 90

Number of Franchise Owners Planned: 120

Overseas Operations Existing: None

Overseas Operations Planned: Yes, initially in Europe.

Management Service Fees: MSF 5%, National Marketing Levy 1% of turnover.

Breakdown of Package: Franchise Licence and training. Computer equipment, corporate dress, initial stock, vehicle deposit and launch programme.

Projected Turnover:
1st Year: £200,000 **2nd Year:** £350,000
3rd Year: £600,000

Projected Profit:
1st Year: £28,000 **2nd Year:** £40,000
3rd Year: £60,000

Financial Assistance Available: All major banks.

Training Provided: One week at head office for accounts, sales and marketing. One week operational skills at training outlet. Further training and mentoring within own territory.

Training Location: Cambridge and Milton Keynes.

Support Services: Comprehensive support from National Accounts team.

Areas of Priority Development: Key areas available.

More information: theukfd.net/72041476

etyres
Lower Court 3, Copley Hill Farm Business Park, Cambridge Road, Babraham, Cambridge, CB22 3GN

t: 01603 620301
e: franmatch@fdsltd.com

Alloy Wheel Repair Specialist
Telephone: 01684 291 900
Website: www.awrswheelrepair.com
Summary of Operation: Mobile wheel repair company offering both mobile and remanufacturing services.
More Information: theukfd.net/73854863

Anniversary Cars
Telephone: 01244 880 302
Website: www.anniversarycars.co.uk
Summary of Operation: Provide a personal, professional chauffeur service for special occasions.
More Information: theukfd.net/92755446

Armaplate
Telephone: 0845 838 0700
Website: www.armaplate.com
Summary of Operation: Vehicle protection systems.
More Information: theukfd.net/11527268

Autoease
Telephone: 0870 122 3229
Website: www.autoease.co.uk
Summary of Operation: Automotive services.
More Information: theukfd.net/18043181

Autoglym
Telephone: 01462 677 766
Website: www.autoglym.com
Summary of Operation: Autoglym produces professional motor vehicle care products.
More Information: theukfd.net/03456446

Autosheen PCC Ltd
Telephone: 0800 131 3301
Website: www.autosheenpcc.com
Summary of Operation: Autosheen is a successful mobile specialist vehicle and marine valeting franchise.
More Information: theukfd.net/14120400

Autosmart International Ltd
Telephone: 01543 482 926
Website: www.startautosmart.co.uk
Summary of Operation: Autosmart, bfa Franchisor of the Year 2008, is also the UK's largest manufacturer and supplier of professional vehicle cleaning products.
More Information: theukfd.net/50553172

Autovalet Services UK Ltd
Telephone: 0845 166 4156
Website: www.autovaletservices.com
Summary of Operation: The original founders of car cleaning and valeting services, Autovalet is the country's leading provider of these services within the UK.
More Information: theukfd.net/69220479

Avis Europe PLC
Telephone: 0844 544 5314
Website: www.avis.co.uk
Summary of Operation: Car hire and rental.
More Information: theukfd.net/80300087

AWG Windscreens Ltd
Telephone: 01553 770 999
Website: www.awg-windscreens.co.uk
Summary of Operation: Replacement and repair of all vehicle glass, windscreens and fitting or repair of sunroofs.
More Information: theukfd.net/65608442

Beaverscreens Franchise Ltd
Telephone: 07850 456 696
Website: www.beaverscreens.co.uk
Summary of Operation: Beaverscreens provides a totally innovative repair service for car windscreens, headlights, interior trim and carpeting.
More Information: theukfd.net/17628160

Black Code Ltd
Telephone: 0845 643 6898
Website: www.black-code.co.uk
Summary of Operation: Vehicle re-mapping specialists for cars, vans and motorbikes.
More Information: theukfd.net/78681133

BMI Hose (UK) Ltd
Telephone: 01902 867 800
Website: www.bmiuk.co.uk
Summary of Operation: BMI is one of the UK's second largest supplier of emergency hydraulic repair services.
More Information: theukfd.net/92538605

British School Of Motoring (BSM)
Telephone: 01922 721 313
Website: www.bsm.co.uk
Summary of Operation: Driving schools.
More Information: theukfd.net/76728530

Franchise Listings

CAM Riderr
Telephone: 0845 83 83 766
Website: www.camrider.com
Summary of Operation: CAM Rider is an award winning company; it has been in existence since 1977 and was originally part of a large County Council Road Safety Department.
More Information: theukfd.net/87512623

Car Audio Centre
Telephone: 0115 975 8600
Website: www.caraudiocentre.co.uk
Summary of Operation: Car audio.
More Information: theukfd.net/60205607

Car Brokers Direct
Telephone: 01494 717 427
Website: www.carbrokersdirect.co.uk
Summary of Operation: Cheap new and secondhand cars.
More Information: theukfd.net/30174128

Car Medic
Telephone: 01525 375 375
Website: www.carmedic.co.uk
Summary of Operation: Mobile paint repair system for the automotive industry that is approved by all the major vehicle manufacturers.
More Information: theukfd.net/04134204

Car Park Valeting Ltd
Telephone: 020 7822 1859
Website: www.carparkvaleting.com
Summary of Operation: Professional hand carwash and valeting services to customers while shopping at supermarkets, shopping centres, etc.
More Information: theukfd.net/24042175

Carlton Premier Car Group
Telephone: 0800 622 6905
Website: www.carltonpremiercargroup.co.uk
Summary of Operation: The opportunity is in the sourcing of nearly new cars for the prestige manufacturer franchises in the motor industry.
More Information: theukfd.net/94424290

Carnoisseur
Telephone: 01582 605 600
Website: www.carnoisseur.com
Summary of Operation: Carnoisseur is a unique concept in retailing for the car enthusiast, selling over 4,000 innovative specialist accessoriess.
More Information: theukfd.net/80232030

carSPA
Telephone: 01634 717747
Website: www.carspa.uk.com
Summary of Operation: Car valeting.
More Information: theukfd.net/68510504

ChipsAway International Ltd
Telephone: 0800 731 6914
Website: www.chipsaway.co.uk
Summary of Operation: With over 15 years' experience, ChipsAway is not only one of the most successful franchises in the UK, but is also the brand leader of the automotive paintwork repair market. Operating from fully equipped mobile workshops and CarCare Centres, ChipsAway specialists provide high quality on-the-spot repairs to minor car bodywork damage, quickly and cost-effectively, restoring paintwork in a matter of hours.
More Information: theukfd.net/51113413

Classic Car Club
Telephone: 020 7490 9090
Website: www.classiccarclub.co.uk
Summary of Operation: Classic car club. Members can hire the cars.
More Information: theukfd.net/20484425

Cool Car Ltd
Telephone: 0121 314 2099
Website: www.coolcaraircon.co.uk
Summary of Operation: Car air conditioning specialists for over 20 years and providers of car air conditioning services, recharging, parts, regassing etc to the public, trade, local garages and main dealers.
More Information: theukfd.net/66089052

Colour Wizard Ltd
Telephone: 0800 849 7106
Website: www.colour-wizard.com
Summary of Operation: Specialists in SMART (Small -Medium-Area-Repair-Techniques). Repairs aimed specifically at the auto market.
More Information: theukfd.net/33964449

Dent Devils Ltd
Telephone: 01206 751 536
Website: www.dentdevils.co.uk
Summary of Operation: The UK's largest company specialising in the removal of minor dents from car body work without the need for re-painting.
More Information: theukfd.net/42665015

Dent Wizard International
Telephone: 01675 471 150
Website: www.dentwizard.com
Summary of Operation: Paintless dent removal.
More Information: theukfd.net/04204338

Dent-Technique Ltd
Telephone: 0870 850 0625
Website: www.dent-technique.com
Summary of Operation: Dent-Technique specialises in paintless dent removal, the most cost-effective and convenient way of removing dents from vehicle bodywork.
More Information: theukfd.net/84350225

Dial-a-Rad
Telephone: 01908 274 484
Website: www.dialarad.com
Summary of Operation: Automotive car radiators specialists. We supply new and reconditioned radiators to the public and trade.
More Information: theukfd.net/65041166

Easirent
Telephone: 0151 922 4991
Website: www.easirent.com
Summary of Operation: Easirent vehicle rental is a long established vehicle rental company with branches in the North, Midlands and the London area.
More Information: theukfd.net/22386206

etyres
Telephone: 01603 620301
Summary of Operation: Van based and management mobile tyre fitting business.
More Information: theukfd.net/72041476

Europcar
Telephone: 01923 81 10 00
Summary of Operation: Internationl self drive rental company. With Europcar, convenience, choice, simplicity and quality come as standard.
More Information: theukfd.net/62383230

First Self Drive
Telephone: 01603 663 233
Website: www.firstselfdrive.co.uk
Summary of Operation: An exciting opportunity within the vehicle rental industy.
More Information: theukfd.net/81741012

Fix-A-Chip Ltd
Telephone: 0800 146 619
Summary of Operation: Mobile vehicle bodywork and interior repair service to the retail and private sector.
More Information: theukfd.net/35715460

Flexilease Contract Motoring Ltd
Website: www.flexilease.co.uk
Summary of Operation: Contract hire, leasing and brokerage franchise with vehicle funding and supply solutions.
More Information: theukfd.net/73041481

Glas Weld Systems (UK) Ltd
Telephone: 01634 735 600
Website: www.glaswelduk.com
Summary of Operation: Glas Weld operates in over 40 countries worldwide and in the UK has 100 local franchised offices offering windscreen repair with over 150 trained technicians on the road.
More Information: theukfd.net/68064141

Gr Pro-Clean
Telephone: 0297 630 797
Website: www.grpro-clean.com
Summary of Operation: Fibre glass yacht detailing.
More Information: theukfd.net/83001628

Green Cleen (UK) Ltd
Telephone: 01785 282 855
Website: www.greencleen.com
Summary of Operation: Wheelie bin cleaning franchise, providing a franchise package with all of the support and training you need to be a success.
More Information: theukfd.net/20207622

Green Motion Ltd
Telephone: 0333 888 4001
Website: www.greenmotion.co.uk
Summary of Operation: Fully environmentally friendly vehicle rental company.
More Information: theukfd.net/42199634

Green Motor Sport
Telephone: 01483 763 375
Summary of Operation: Motorsport company solely devoted to environmental racing, with emphasis on research into alternative future energies.
More Information: theukfd.net/80732031

Franchise Listings

Hertz UK Ltd
Telephone: 01895 553 500
Summary of Operation: Car and van hire.
More Information: theukfd.net/20211354

HiQ
Telephone: 0121 306 6000
Website: www.goodyear.eu
Summary of Operation: Express fitting of vehicle tyres and exhausts.
More Information: theukfd.net/65871325

Hometyre Group Ltd
Telephone: 01743 861 183
Website: www.hometyre.co.uk
Summary of Operation: Mobile tyre and alignment specialists.
More Information: theukfd.net/95387278

Jumicar UK Ltd
Telephone: 07971 439 522
Website: www.ukjumicar.co.uk
Summary of Operation: Driving tracks for children.
More Information: theukfd.net/87341532

Lellers
Telephone: 01920 466 044
Website: www.lellers.co.uk
Summary of Operation: Mobile car and commercial vehicle valeting services.
More Information: theukfd.net/04287356

MCV Franchising Ltd
Telephone: 0800 781 7117
Website: www.mobilecarvaleting.co.uk
Summary of Operation: Vehicle valeting.
More Information: theukfd.net/72481045

Mikes Waterfont Trading Ltd
Telephone: 020 8994 6006
Summary of Operation: Retail shops selling scuba diving equipment.
More Information: theukfd.net/82543371

Minster Chauffeurs Ltd
Telephone: 01937 541 081
Website: www.minsterchauffeurs.com
Summary of Operation: Chauffeuring organisation offering a wide range of personal services.
More Information: theukfd.net/56515867

Mobi-Tyre
Telephone: 01743 461 223
Website: www.mobi-tyre.co.uk
Summary of Operation: Mobile tyre and battery fitting service.
More Information: theukfd.net/85750669

Mr Clutch Autocentres
Telephone: 01634 717 747
Website: www.mrclutch.com
Summary of Operation: Clutch and autocentre specialist. Offers a large range of garage repiars including clutches, MOTs, servicing, brakes, gearboxes, exhausts, cambelts, tyres and general repairs.
More Information: theukfd.net/51134268

Network Vehicles Ltd
Telephone: 0844 493 5812
Website: www.network.leaseplan.co.uk
Summary of Operation: Providing small businesses and private individuals with vehicle leasing solutions through a network of franchise owners.
More Information: theukfd.net/18056714

Optic-Kleer
Telephone: 01205 311 132
Website: www.optic-kleer.co.uk
Summary of Operation: Windscreen repair specialists.
More Information: theukfd.net/47057405

Perfection Alloys
Telephone: 0116 282 4040
Website: www.perfectionalloys.com
Summary of Operation: Alloy wheel refurbishment.
More Information: theukfd.net/31171925

Permagard (UK) Ltd
Telephone: 020 7473 0099
Website: www.permagard.info
Summary of Operation: Mobile franchise. Paint protection for aviation, marine and automotive.
More Information: theukfd.net/05651064

Pinnacle Chauffeur Transport Ltd
Telephone: 0870 752 3381
Website: www.wedriveyou.co.uk
Summary of Operation: Nationwide luxury chauffeur business.
More Information: theukfd.net/37146176

Plancars
Telephone: 01992 890 999
Website: www.plancars.com
Summary of Operation: Offering finance for aquisition of private and business cars.
More Information: theukfd.net/60711406

Practical Car & Van Rental Ltd
Website: www.practical.co.uk
Summary of Operation: Car and van rental franchise.
More Information: theukfd.net/81057483

Protex Solutions Ltd
Website: www.protexsolutions.uk.net
Summary of Operation: UK distributor and Master Franchisor for Protex Tyre Sealant in the UK and Ireland. Protex is a puncture protection system designed for all pneumatic tyres.
More Information: theukfd.net/12732100

Puncture Safe
Telephone: 0870 241 3730
Website: www.puncturesafe.co.uk
Summary of Operation: Puncture preventative and tyre life extender.
More Information: theukfd.net/02051185

Revive! Auto Innovations (UK) Ltd
Telephone: 01788 569 999
Website: www.revive-uk.com
Summary of Operation: Revive! offer a professional service providing minor paint repairs on vehicles. With no gimmicks or gadgets, Revive! provides its franchise owners with the most comprehensive training and business support to take them from a man in a van to a multi-van business owner.
More Information: theukfd.net/75580414

Safeway Motoring School
Website: www.safewayuk.com
Summary of Operation: Motoring school.
More Information: theukfd.net/43587340

scooterMAN Ltd
Telephone: 0333 666 1999
Website: www.scooterman.co.uk
Summary of Operation: scooterMAN provides a personal chauffeur to drive you and your car home.
More Information: theukfd.net/86567085

Shell Petroleum
Telephone: 020 7934 1234
Website: www.shell.com
Summary of Operation: Shell service stations, convenience stores.
More Information: theukfd.net/58886662

Smart Alloy
Telephone: 0800 1077 926.
Website: www.smartalloyfranchise.co.uk
Summary of Operation: Smart Alloy offer UK wide accredited training on SMART repairs. Learn the procedures and techniques for tackling car scratches and bumper scuffs repairs with our state of the art water based paint system.
More Information: theukfd.net/12808309

SMART Tech GB Ltd
Telephone: 01639 820 888
Website: www.smarttechgb.co.uk
Summary of Operation: Specialists in alloy wheel repair.
More Information: theukfd.net/32674069

Smart Wise (UK) Ltd
Telephone: 0800 1077 926
Website: www.smartwise.com
Summary of Operation: Alloy wheel repair franchise.
More Information: theukfd.net/31608651

Superseal International Ltd
Telephone: 0870 744 3750
Website: www.punctureproof.com
Summary of Operation: The manufacture of a tyre sealant which prevents punctures and loss of tyre pressure.
More Information: theukfd.net/25436434

The Raccoon Group
Telephone: 0845 257 8757
Website: www.raccoon.co.uk
Summary of Operation: Award winning, specialist vehicle wrapping and branding company.
More Information: theukfd.net/48300154

The Wheelie Bin Cleaning Service
Telephone: 01443 806 151
Website: www.wheeliebin.co.uk
Summary of Operation: Cleaning and disinfecting wheeled refuse bins for householders and businesses.
More Information: theukfd.net/20246866

Thrifty Car Rental
Website: www.thrifty.co.uk
Summary of Operation: Car and van rental.
More Information: theukfd.net/13643376

TLS Ltd
Website: www.trimline-systems.com
Summary of Operation: Small, medium, automotive repair techniques.
More Information: theukfd.net/16343364

Touch Up Guys UK
Telephone: 01525 382 008
Website: www.touchupguys.co.uk
Summary of Operation: Vehicle SMART repair service.
More Information: theukfd.net/29582179

Towbar2U
Telephone: 01325 340 033
Website: www.towbar2u.co.uk
Summary of Operation: Mobile van based, mobile towbar fitting.
More Information: theukfd.net/67285270

Trade My Motor
Telephone: 0845 299 4999
Website: www.trademymotor.co.uk
Summary of Operation: The hassle free way for members of the public to quickly and efficiently sell their car and achieve an instant cash price.
More Information: theukfd.net/64982567

Trimline Systems
Telephone: 08701 620 625
Website: www.trimlinesystems.co.uk
Summary of Operation: The SMART solution for paintless dent removal.
More Information: theukfd.net/09871554

Tyre Protector International Ltd
Telephone: 0844 567 1010
Website: www.tyreprotector.com
Summary of Operation: Market leader in permanent puncture protection.
More Information: theukfd.net/67145872

Ultimate Tinting
Telephone: 0800 011 2630
Website: www.ultimatetinging.co.uk
Summary of Operation: Window tinting for vehicles, the home and commercial premises.
More Information: theukfd.net/83038277

Vehicle Options
Website: vehicleoptions.biz
Summary of Operation: Vehicle hire, rental and lease to both business and private users.
More Information: theukfd.net/57153023

Vehicle Strategies Club
Telephone: 05601 295 258
Website: www.vsclub.co.uk
Summary of Operation: Vehicle strategy tool.
More Information: theukfd.net/56424805

Waterless Detailers (Franchise) UK Ltd
Website: www.waterlessdetailers.co.uk
Summary of Operation: The Waterless Detailers provide a range of specialist vehicle detailing services based around technical knowledge and disciplines of the valeting trade.
More Information: theukfd.net/86086657

Waves Car Wash Ltd
Telephone: 020 7978 5000
Website: www.wavescarwash.co.uk
Summary of Operation: Hand carwash franchise.
More Information: theukfd.net/73753547

Wheel Wizard
Telephone: 0844 800 9075
Website: www.dentwizard.co.uk
Summary of Operation: UK's leading expert in the removal of alloy wheel damage, ranging from scuffs and scrapes through to rim damage and general corrosion.
More Information: theukfd.net/22990410

WheelsApproved
Telephone: 01483 728 160
Website: www.wheelsapproved.co.uk
Summary of Operation: Wheels Approved can return your alloy wheels to an 'as new' appearance. At Wheels Approved we want to provide total satisfaction.
More Information: theukfd.net/26610210

Wicked Wheels
Telephone: 0844 050 2121
Website: www.wickedwheels.co.uk
Summary of Operation: Mobile workshop specialising in refurbishing alloy wheels, servicing motor trade and private individuals.
More Information: theukfd.net/46337131

SERVICES | Business 2 Business

Actively recruiting franchise owners

Franchises in this sector provide a wide range of services to other businesses from specialised consultancy to essential products and services. Franchise opportunities include **Assured Security Shredding, Business for Breakfast, Computer Troubleshooters, Cost Centre Services, Fita-Seal, Franchise Development Services** and **Tongue Tied**.

Independent Energy Consultant

Energy 'Buying & Supplying' Excellence Awards 2010
www.energyexcellenceawards.com

Cost Centre Services Ltd

Summary of Operation: Specialising in carrying out energy billing audits, dealing with problem cases and conducting energy tenders. We provide a wide range of cost reduction and conservation solutions to businesses. You can work from home using our own highly developed online software. Finalist for the Independent Energy Consultant 2010 award.

Ideal Franchise Owner Profile: Many career backgrounds are suitable, particularly in the financial and related services industry. A real desire to help businesses is essential as is the enjoyment of providing high standards of service. A detective or analytical mentality is important, together with an organised, disciplined and confident attitude.

Cost of Franchise: £17,000 + VAT
Franchise Owner Contact: Simon Binks

Year Company Established: 2000
Year of First Franchise Owner: 2008
Number of Company Outlets: 1
Number of Franchised Outlets: 10
Number of Franchise Owners Planned: 50-60
Overseas Operations Existing: None
Overseas Operations Planned: None
Management Service Fees: 15% on actual turnover plus £160pm Admin Fee from month eight.

Breakdown of Package: Comprehensive training and startup package which includes 50 leads /

appointments generated on your behalf. Software configured, together with printing and template stationery. Training Manual, help pages, how to procedures and a complete document repository included. Ongoing support provided including option for further lead generation.

Projected Turnover:
Year 1: £60,000 **Year 2:** £90,000 **Year 3:** £120,000
Projected Profit:
Year 1: £51,000 **Year 2:** £74,000 **Year 3:** £99,000
Financial Assistance Available: Possible

Training Provided: Three day intensive course followed by online and telephone support.
Training Location: Norwich
Support Services: Total operational support.

Areas of Priority Development: Nationwide (except N. Ireland).

More information: theukfd.net/62962483

Cost Centre Services Ltd
Cavell House, Stannard Way,
St. Crispins Road,
Norwich, NR3 1YE
t: 0845 450 1446
f: 0845 450 1447
e: simon.binks@costcentreservices.com
w: www.costcentreservices.com

Franchise Development Services Ltd

Summary of Operation: Providing a full range of consultancy services to established and prospective franchisors and franchise owners. Publisher of *The Franchise Magazine, Irish Franchise Magazine, Scottish Franchise Magazine* and *The UK Franchise Directory*. Three different franchise opportunities are available; franchise consultancy sales, franchise consultancy and FranMatch.

Ideal Franchise Owner Profile: Experienced sale and marketing or management consultants with the ability to explain, sell and deliver professional advice and guidance. A clear understanding of business plans, corporate infrastructure and building business relationships.

**Franchise Development Services Ltd
Franchise House, 56 Surrey Street,
Norwich, NR1 3FD**

t: 01603 620 301
f: 01603 630 174
e: enquiries@fdsltd.com
w: www.fdsfranchise.com

Cost of Franchise: £50,000-£100,000 + VAT UK; £100,000-£250,000 International.

Franchise Owner Contact: Roy Seaman

Year Company Established: 1981
Year of First Franchise Owner: 1985

Number of Company Outlets: 1
Number of Franchised Outlets: 5
Number of Franchise Owners Planned: 10 UK and Ireland, 21 Worldwide.

Overseas Operations Existing: Spain and Australia.

Overseas Operations Planned: Portugal and other European countries, New Zealand, Canada, USA, applicants from world markets.

Management Service Fees: Details disclosed during due diligence.

Breakdown of Package: Comprehensive initial and ongoing traning covering the relevant franchise opportunity selected.

Projected Turnover: AOR

Projected Profit: AOR

Financial Assistance Available: All banks.

Training Provided: Initial four weeks, plus comprehensive ongoing as required.

Training Location: Norwich and in territory.

Support Services: Advertising, marketing and expos.

Areas of Priority Development: Nationwide.

More Information: theukfd.net/75668115

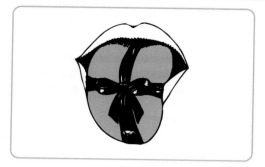

Tongue Tied Ltd

Summary of Operation: We translate, interpret, DTP (into every known software platform) and print, including digital to and from every language in the world. We also arrange complete conferences including the sound equipment, interpreter booths, and microphones etc. Therefore we can offer 'single source supply' from translation through to print.

Ideal Franchise Owner Profile: Franchise owners must have business sales and marketing skills, preferably with contacts. Individuals from all backgrounds are welcome, but they must have an excellent sales record as we provide all of the 'back office' work. Must be left to obtain business, sometimes through leads generated.

Cost of Franchise: £9,995 + VAT

Franchise Owner Contact: John Shouler

Year Company Established: 1989
Year of First Franchise Owner: 1998

Number of Company Outlets: 5
Number of Franchised Outlets: 2
Number of Franchise Owners Planned: 5

Overseas Operations Existing: 1
Overseas Operations Planned: 5

Management Service Fees: N/A

Breakdown of Package: The use of the Tongue Tied brand, backed up by ongoing training and head office telephone support and visits in the field if required. We also set up a Ltd company and provide all initial stationery.

Projected Turnover: AOR
Projected Profit: 36% ongoing

Financial Assistance Available: No

Training Provided: We provide three full days training covering marketing, selling and an introduction to an accounts package, normally Sage as the franchise is responsible for invoicing their clients.

Training Location: Sussex
Support Services: Franchise owners receive ongoing 24/7 support from our team based in Hove, East Sussex, including day-to-day telephone support from an allocated project leader. We also provide on-site field support to attend sales meetings to discuss contracted business.

Areas of Priority Development: Midlands, North East England, Scotland, West Country, East Anglia, Wales and London.

More information: theukfd.net/03713356

Tongue Tied Ltd
Waterside House,
Basin Road North, Hove, East
Sussex, BN41 1UY

t: 01273 419 999
e: sales@tongue-tied.co.uk
w: www.tongue-tied.co.uk

Assured Security Shredding Ltd

26/28 Central Avenue, West Molesey,
Surrey, KT8 2QT

Telephone: 0845 505 9999
Email: info@assuredsecurityshredding.co.uk
Website: www.assuredsecurityshredding.co.uk

Summary of Operation: Assured Security Shredding Ltd is a confidential data destruction company specialising in the destruction of confidential data, general waste paper of all grades, uniforms and counterfeit stock, computers, hard drives and disks.

Ideal Franchise Owner Profile: A strong self-motivated individual with a can do attitude willing to learn hands on and a very good understanding of customer service, who can lead by example.

Cost of Franchise: From £40,000 + VAT plus equipment
Franchise Owner Contact: Grahame Watson

Year Company Established: 1996

Number of Company Outlets: 2
Number of Franchised Outlets: 0
Number of Franchise Outlets Planned: 16
Overseas Operations Planned: Yes
Management Service Fees: Yes

Breakdown of Package: A starter pack includes uniforms, ID badges, business cards, order pads, service agreements, letter heads, compliment slips etc. NAID membership, software, full Google advertising, comprehensive training and full support package to help you in the early days.

Financial Assistance Available: Can be discussed

Training Provided: Yes
Training Location: London and franchise owner's location
Support Services: Yes

More Information: theukfd.net/22889315

Business for Breakfast Ltd

114 Innovation Forum, Salford University Business Park, Frederick Street, Salford, M6 6FP

Telephone: 0845 688 445
Email: franchising@bforb.co.uk
Website: www.bforb.co.uk

Summary of Operation: Business for Breakfast (BforB) is now the proven blueprint for running a successful business referral franchise in UK and Europe. With more than 31 franchise owners already reaping their rewards. Business for Breakfast has firmly established itself as one of the UK's leading and thriving business networking organisations.

Ideal Franchise Owner Profile: A self-motivated individual with strong desire to succeed. Approachable and willing to work with business people. Willing to learn and adapt or implement processes in their local area, with good understanding of customer service and is willing to work hard especially on the first two years of establishing and developing the business.

Cost of Franchise: From £23,000 + VAT

Franchise Owner Contact: John Fisher
Year Company Established: 2001
Year of First Franchise Owner: 2004
Number of Company Outlets: 0
Number of Franchised Outlets: 31
Number of Franchise Owners Planned: 50

Overseas Operations Existing: Czech Republic.
Overseas Operations Planned: Ireland and Australia.

Breakdown of Package: £9,500 licence fee, £3,000 training and training materials, £5,000 start-up stationery and start-up marketing materials and database. £2,500 support and mentoring.

Financial Assistance Available: NatWest and RBS.
Training Provided: One week
Training Location: Birmingham, Staffordshire, Humberside, Central London, Plymouth and Glasgow.
Areas of Priority Development: Birmingham, Central London, Scotland and Oxfordshire.

More Information: theukfd.net/46141268

Fita-Seal

The Locks, Hillmorton, Rugby, CV21 4PP

Telephone: 01788 550 100
Fax: 01788 551 839
Email: enquiries@filtagroup.co.uk
Website: www.fita-seal.co.uk

Summary of Operation: Mobile manufacture and immediate on-site fitting service for replacement fridge and freezer seals to the commercial market.

Ideal Franchise Owner Profile: Hands-on, practical with a full driving licence.

Cost of Franchise: From £14,950 + VAT plus working capital.

Franchise Owner Contact: Damian Slater

Year Company Established: 2010

Year of First Franchise Owner: 2010

Number of Company Outlets: 2
Number of Franchised Outlets: 10

Overseas Operations Existing: Italy and Poland
Overseas Operations Planned: Worldwide

Management Service Fees: AOR

Financial Assistance Available: Up to 70% lending from major banks.

Training Provided: The company training programme covers every aspect of the business.

Training Location: Head office and field based.

Support Services: The support team is always available to give advice and guidance regarding the business through the various stages of its development and as part of the ongoing mentoring programme.

Areas of Priority Development: Various

More Information: theukfd.net/84074911

---

bfa Provisional Member

BCR Associates

Brittany House, New North Road, Exeter, EX4 4EP

Telephone: 0844 880 9838
Email: phil.gaffer@bcrassociates.co.uk
Website: www.bcrassociatesfranchise.co.uk

Summary of Operation: A recession-proof management franchise specialising in identifying and cutting excess cost in UK companies' essential spend (energy, telecoms, insurance, water, business rates, finance, staff, vehicles and green services).

Training Provided: One-week intensive training, director-accompanied client meetings, ongoing director support, 'Fast Launch' package for the first 120 days of trading and marketing collateral.

Cost of Franchise: £29,950 + VAT

Franchise Owner Contact: Phil Gaffer

Financial Assistance Available: Barclays, HSBC, Lloyds TSB and NatWest.

More Information: theukfd.net/24959106

---

bfa Full Member

CerTax Accounting Ltd

Certax House, 47 Clarence Road, Chesterfield, S40 1LQ

Telephone: 01246 200 255
Email: ca@certax.co.uk
Website: www.certaxaccounting.co.uk

Summary of Operation: An accountancy and tax advisory franchise serving the needs of local business communities. With the support of professionally qualified Chartered Certified Accountants, franchise owners can build and operate their own successful accountancy and tax advisory practice.
Ideal Franchise Owner Profile: A background in accountancy is not essential although experience in dealing with numeracy is an advantage.
Cost of Franchise: £28,750 + VAT
Franchise Owner Contact: Keith Bradshaw
Financial Assistance Available: Major banks.
Support Services: Support is always available via the support helpline. Full marketing support and lead generation – 100 appointments in first year.

More Information: theukfd.net/28754533

CityLocal

24 Woodfield Road, Oadby, Leicester, LE2 4HP

Telephone: 08448 844 815
International Telephone: +44 (0) 116 215 3615
Email: franchise@citylocal.co.uk
Website: www.citylocal.co.uk

Summary of Operation: CityLocal is a cutting edge network of local sites that span every single village, town and city in the UK and Ireland. Each CityLocal franchise owner is given access to an exclusive territory to generate repeat income from effectively promoting local businesses online and offline through Google Search and local voucher distribution. Is it time to use this revolution to create a lifestyle you want!

Ideal Franchise Owner Profile: All of our franchise owners are professional business minded people and want to create a better work life balance for themselves. They enjoy meeting new people, are sociable and find it easy to develop relationships.
Cost of Franchise: £2,900 - £12,900 + VAT
Franchise Owner Contact: Zakir Daud

More information: theukfd.net/47463687

bfa Associate Member
Office Canopy Group (OCG Netstationers)

70, Bardwell Business Park, Leatherhead Road, Chessington, KT9 2NY

Telephone: 0845 372 2010
Email: malcolm.porter@fdssoutheast.co.uk

Summary of Operation: Netstationers is the fastest growing office supplies company in the UK supplying a catalogue of 60,000 common office supplies products from over 400 manufacturers. Netstationers uses the unique OCG Fusion e-procurement technology to help businesses reduce their expenditure on commodity goods such as office supplies, print and furniture etc.

Ideal Franchise Owner Profile: Well connected and experienced business people who ideally have business to business experience and strong interpersonal skills.

Cost of Franchise: £24,950 + VAT
Franchise Owner Contact: Malcolm Porter
Financial Assistance Available: AOR

More information: theukfd.net/80555817

bfa Full Member
London House International

London House, 6 The Stocks, Cosgrove, Milton Keynes, MK19 7JD

Telephone: 01908 262444
Email: info@londonhouseinternational.com
Website: www.londonhouseinternational.com

Summary of Operation: London House is a financial and commercial investigation franchise. As a London House franchise owner you will be a banking, legal and insurance consultant and investigator, providing a range of services to banks, finance houses, law firms, insurance companies and the rest of the credit industry. As a commercial investigator, your core business will be gathering information to advise clients on fraud and bad debt decisions.

Cost of Franchise: Standard: £10,750 + VAT
Premium: from £19,750 + VAT
Franchise Owner Contact: Godfrey Lancashire
Financial Assistance Available: NatWest, RBS and Lloyds TSB.

More Information: theukfd.net/42607267

Stockcheck Ltd

The Water Mill Park, Broughton Hall, Skipton, BD23 3AG

Telephone: 0870 903 0018
Fax: 0870 903 0019
Email: enquiries@stockcheck.co.uk
Website: www.stockcheck.co.uk

Summary of Operation: Specialist licensed trade stocktaking services/consultants and auditors to hotels, pubs, clubs, restaurants etc. for food and liquor operations.

Ideal Franchise Owner Profile: With a background in food and beverage operations, perhaps hotel trained management operator looking for the advantages of becoming self employed in the hospitality sector, without the disadvantages of an unsociable working life.

Cost of Franchise: from £9995 – £16,000 + VAT
Franchise Owner Contact: Mike Smith
Financial assistance available: An established franchisor for high street bank lending approval.

More information: theukfd.net/32113212

Franchise Listings

1st Class Bailiffs Ltd
Telephone: 0844 484 1450
Website: www.enforcementofficers.co.uk
Summary of Operation: Our Bailiffs UK Service is an easy and efficient way to collect your commercial rent quickly. Because there's no need for court action the Bailiffs UK Service ensures a rapid resolution at a competitive fee.
More Information: theukfd.net/60469736

40 Plus
Telephone: 01869 241 254
Website: www.40plusrecruitment.co.uk
Summary of Operation: Recruitment agency for people aged 40 plus.
More Information: theukfd.net/11832041

8020 Financial Management Ltd
Telephone: 0870 112 7320
Website: www.8020financials.com
Summary of Operation: Financial services.
More Information: theukfd.net/66231608

A1 Financials Ltd
Telephone: 01865 379 272
Website: www.a1financials.co.uk
Summary of Operation: Bookkeeping and management accounts.
More Information: theukfd.net/74243934

Abacus Franchising Company Ltd
Telephone: 08700 552 455
Website: www.abacusnetwork.co.uk
Summary of Operation: Accountancy and financial services
More Information: theukfd.net/46853871

Accelerator Ltd
Telephone: 020 7993 3117
Website: www.accsimple.com
Summary of Operation: Offer tailored 'utility' based hosted IT and telecoms solutions to small and medium businesses.
More Information: theukfd.net/34177706

Accounting Express
Telephone: 0845 0946 202
Website: www.accountingfranchise.co.uk
Summary of Operation: Provides bookkeeping and financial support services to small businesses of up to £1m turnover, backed by a powerful but simple online accountancy management system.
More Information: theukfd.net/43843607

Accounts Assist
Telephone: 01327 856 076
Website: www.accountsassist.com
Summary of Operation: Accounts Assist offers a book-keeping franchise based on the ethos of good local service at competitive prices to suit the needs of the individual client. Services offered are bookkeeping, personal tax returns, VAT returns, monthly management accounts, payroll, forecasting and business plans etc.
More Information: theukfd.net/69739916

ActionCOACH
Telephone: 01234 392 805
Website: www.actioncoach.com
Summary of Operation: Coaching business owners of small to medium sized companies to achieve massive results with the world's number one business coaching firm.
More Information: theukfd.net/67195075

Activ Click & Earn
Telephone: 0845 094 0497
Website: www.activuk.com
Summary of Operation: Activ provide essential advice for business and entrepreneur development.
More Information: theukfd.net/35788560

Activ SEO
Telephone: 0845 094 0497
Website: www.activseo.com
Summary of Operation: At Activ SEO we keep things simple, we do not confuse you or baffle you with technical jargon. We will send one of our local advisors to explain how Activ SEO can help to get more people viewing your website.
More Information: theukfd.net/52944773

Additional Resources Ltd
Telephone: 01277 822 668
Website: www.additionalresources.net
Summary of Operation: Recruitment consultancy.
More Information: theukfd.net/31600020

Adroit-e Research Technologies Ltd
Telephone: 01582 463 479
Website: www.adroit-e.co.uk
Summary of Operation: Adroit-e is a quantitative market research company and we are experts at what we do.
More Information: theukfd.net/44060353

AIMS Partnership PLC
Telephone: 020 7616 6628
Website: www.aims.co.uk
Summary of Operation: AIMS Accountants offer cost-effective accountancy for small to medium, independent businesses. As with all our clients we know you will have individual needs and a package of services will meet your requirements.
More Information: theukfd.net/99139374

ALB Accountancy (Franaccounts)
Telephone: 01403 865 742
Website: www.albaccountancy.com
Summary of Operation: Accountancy firm.
More Information: theukfd.net/71084427

AMR Group
Telephone: 01905 726 304
Website: www.amrgroup.co.uk
Summary of Operation: AMR is a market leading, national group, offering professional, unbiased and confidential recruitment solutions for people.
More Information: theukfd.net/66621274

Antal International Network
Telephone: 0870 774 5464
Website: www.antalfranchising.com
Summary of Operation: Antal is a global recruitment company. We train and support our franchise owners to set up profitable recruitment businesses specialising in placing candidates at the mid to senior income bracket.
More Information: theukfd.net/01686561

Apex Business Associates Ltd
Telephone: 01276 482 840
Website: www.apexbusiness.co.uk
Summary of Operation: Marketing consultancy.
More Information: theukfd.net/86075649

Apple Mortgages Direct Ltd
Telephone: 0161 476 2959
Summary of Operation: National mortgage brokers and packagers for both commercial and residential mortgages.
More Information: theukfd.net/47363518

APS Legal & Associates
Telephone: 0845 430 4600
Website: www.aps-legal.co.uk
Summary of Operation: APS Legal and Associates offer professional legal expertise.
More Information: theukfd.net/37810656

ASC Partnership PLC
Telephone: 020 7616 6628
Website: www.asc.co.uk
Summary of Operation: Offer businesses access to finance from lenders across the UK. We treat each person on an individual basis and work with them to get the best finance possible.
More Information: theukfd.net/78234831

Assisting in Business Ltd
Telephone: 01685 352 744
Website: www.assistinginbusiness.co.uk
Summary of Operation: Assisting in Business Limited (AiB Ltd) provides recovery assistance for clients in both the commercial and domestic markets.
More Information: theukfd.net/76924489

Assunto
Telephone: 01480 494 141
Website: www.assunto.co.uk
Summary of Operation: Assunto provides marketing, finance, administration and customer relations support to start up businesses within the office cleaning sector.
More Information: theukfd.net/87047060

Atlantic Business Resources
Telephone: 01580 200 100
Website: www.atlanticbr.co.uk
Summary of Operation: An effective cost reduction service for British businesses.
More Information: theukfd.net/06257532

Auditel
Telephone: 0800 583 3355
Website: www.auditelfranchise.co.uk
Summary of Operation: Auditel is one of the UK's leading home-based executive franchises. If you're looking for a recession-proof business opportunity, now is an excellent time to consider our cost and purchase management model.
More Information: theukfd.net/10851804

Ayton Global Research
Telephone: 01749 344 644
Website: www.aytonfranchise.co.uk
Summary of Operation: Ayton Global Research is a global business that provides a lightening-speed, accurate, safe and user-friendly online research facility.
More Information: theukfd.net/97720928

Franchise Listings

B Environmental Swisher/BE Swisher
Telephone: 0500 500 165
Website: www.swisher.co.uk
Summary of Operation: Effective long-term solutions to odour control and hygiene management based on an environmentally friendly system and products. Setting the global standard for hygiene with a unique range of products and services for residential and non residential areas.
More Information: theukfd.net/03852284

Bartercard
Telephone: 0845 219 7000
Website: www.bartercard.co.uk
Summary of Operation: Bartercard is the unchallenged UK and global leader of it's industry and is the largest and fastest growing barter network in the world. Becoming a franchise owner is the start of a very successful partnership. Bartercard combines your talents with its experience and provan systems.
More Information: theukfd.net/54667372

Big Fish
Telephone: 02392 489 653
Website: www.bigfishhooked.com
Summary of Operation: Office computer printer specialist providing supplies and service support for all makes of office printers.
More Information: theukfd.net/71202266

BigFoot
Telephone: 01329 820 572
Website: www.bigfootrecruitment.com
Summary of Operation: Recruitment for LGV drivers.
More Information: theukfd.net/34865382

Billboard Connection Ltd
Telephone: 0845 6004010
Website: www.billboardconnection.com
Summary of Operation: Outdoor advertising agency specialising in providing and managing cost effective campaigns for businesses.
More Information: theukfd.net/50244775

Bite Digital Ltd
Telephone: 0845 688 4491
Website: www.biteus.net
Summary of Operation: Web and system developer digital services.
More Information: theukfd.net/49464893

Bluemonday Recruitment UK Franchise
Telephone: 020 7025 8747
Website: www.bluemondayrecruitment.com
Summary of Operation: The bluemonday franchise opportunity is open to both accomplished recruiters and to senior-level managers who are seeking to establish their business within their sector of experience.
More Information: theukfd.net/01822711

Buffin Leadership International
Telephone: 01242 511 979
Website: www.buffin.com
Summary of Operation: Buffin Leadership International has established an international and highly successful network of professional associates, coaching facilitators and consultants who are trained personally by David Buffin.
More Information: theukfd.net/20371324

Business Doctors Ltd
Telephone: 0845 219 7077
Website: www.businessdoctors.co.uk
Summary of Operation: Help SMEs 'Achieve their Vision' by offering a free Strategic Health Check service leading to a full strategic planning, advice and implementation service. Franchise owners will provide individual health assessments, create strategies and 'get on the pitch' to help businesses grow by whatever means necessary.
More Information: theukfd.net/47263091

Business Finance Plus Ltd
Telephone: 0845 051 4588
Website: www.businessfinanceplus.co.uk
Summary of Operation: Small business finance company.
More Information: theukfd.net/37248230

Business Referral Exchange
Telephone: 01707 644 822
Website: www.brxnet.co.uk
Summary of Operation: BRX Groups help its members gain quality new business through relaxed, professional, business networking groups.
More Information: theukfd.net/52237248

Business Rescue
Telephone: 0207 917 1750
Website: www.businessrenew.co.uk
Summary of Operation: Corporate recovery and business turnaround services.
More Information: theukfd.net/70089339

canduu.mobi
Telephone: 0113 391 0527
Summary of Operation: Mobile internet directory and advertising service.
More Information: theukfd.net/05733012

Carewatch Care Services Ltd
Telephone: 01273 208 111
Website: www.carewatch-care-services.co.uk
Summary of Operation: Management franchise running a recruitment business specialising in providing care staff to a range of clients from home care to staffing care homes and hospitals.
More Information: theukfd.net/63641337

Cartridge Saver
Telephone: 01873 854 913
Website: www.cartridgesaver.co.uk
Summary of Operation: Supply of ink cartridges for computers. We provide a range of alternatives for the majority of printer manufacturers with an efficient, friendly service.
More Information: theukfd.net/56637843

Cash 22
Telephone: 020 7244 1210
Website: www.cash22.net
Summary of Operation: Credit, finance and pawn broking services.
More Information: theukfd.net/5142875

Cava Guard UK Franchise Ltd
Telephone: 01527 523100
Website: www.cavaguard.co.uk
Summary of Operation: International freight forwarding.
More Information: theukfd.net/87517505

Chamberlains Security Ltd
Telephone: 0121 553 0999
Website: www.chamberlainssecurity.com
Summary of Operation: Provision of security services to national businesses and local communities.
More Information: theukfd.net/77617526

Clarity Copiers Ltd
Website: www.clarity-copiers.co.uk
Summary of Operation: Clarity market and service colour copiers, digital copiers, facsimile and electronic systems.
More Information: theukfd.net/43617407

Clikingo
Telephone: 08451 651 515
Website: www.clikingo.com
Summary of Operation: Corporate video production and digital signage company, delivering quality, bespoke and great value.
More Information: theukfd.net/27136176

Cloud Bookkeeping
Telephone: 0203 1372 878
Website: www.cloudbookkeeping.co.uk
Summary of Operation: Cloud bookkeeping has revolutionised outsourced bookkeeping, using the latest cloud technology with online Sage software, so that the most up to date data information can be accessed by the business owner, the bookkeeper and the accountant, all at the same time if needed.
More Information: theukfd.net/79191062

CNA International
Telephone: 01676 524 653
Website: www.cna-international.com
Summary of Operation: Executive recruitment and management consultancy.
More Information: theukfd.net/87477424

Complete Financial Solutions
Telephone: 01244 533 696
Website: www.cfsfranchise.com
Summary of Operation: Business and residential financial solutions.
More Information: theukfd.net/28457262

Computer Troubleshooters UK
Telephone: 0870 974 5837
Website: www.comptroub.com
Summary of Operation: The international Computer Troubleshooters franchise network is highly regarded for its unique style of onsite computer service provided to small businesses and home offices. Each Franchise is usually run by a team of between two and four people and is often operated from a home base.
More Information: Turn to page 57 or visit theukfd.net/21322518

Concept Building Solutions Ltd
Telephone: 01772 799 750
Website: www.concept-solutions.co.uk
Summary of Operation: Manage property insurance claims on behalf of the insured.
More Information: theukfd.net/86762043

Franchise Listings

Concept Staffing Group
Telephone: 01271 321 666
Website: www.conceptstaffing.co.uk
Summary of Operation: Recruitment agency with branches across the region.
More Information: theukfd.net/50244078

Connect 2 (Franchising) Ltd
Website: www.connect2franchising.com
Summary of Operation: Mobile showroom offering business to business promotional merchandise from around the world.
More Information: theukfd.net/48043540

Coversure Insurance Services Ltd
Telephone: 0800 3081 326
Website: www.coversure.co.uk
Summary of Operation: Coversure is a leading insurance broker franchise. Coversure franchise owners operate their own insurance brokerage and have access to literally hundreds of products with leading insurers, and earn substantial commissions.
More Information: theukfd.net/84422998

Crestcom International
Telephone: 0151 944 1744
Website: www.vcoll.ac.uk
Summary of Operation: Crestcom is ranked one of the top management training organisations in the world.
More Information: theukfd.net/35018250

CrossCheque
Telephone: 0114 234 8888
Summary of Operation: Fast, efficient encashment of third party cheques.
More Information: theukfd.net/06427532

Crunchers
Telephone: 0800 59 999 59
Website: www.welovebookkeeping.co.uk
Summary of Operation: Bookkeeping for small businesses.
More Information: theukfd.net/54425614

Davis Coleman Ltd
Telephone: 01277 364 333
Website: www.daviscoleman.com
Summary of Operation: Provide a comprehensive range of services to banks, financial institutions, insurance sector and the legal profession .
More Information: theukfd.net/11545322

DCM Money Solutions
Telephone: 0800 011 2725
Website: www.dcmmoney.com
Summary of Operation: Money counselling for the general public.
More Information: theukfd.net/24211827

Driver Hire Group Services Ltd
Telephone: 0844 846 0000
Website: www.driverhire.co.uk
Summary of Operation: The UK's leading provider of temporary and permanent recruitment solutions for driving, warehousing and other logistics staff to industry and the public sector in the UK and Ireland.
More Information: theukfd.net/58867114

Drivers Direct
Telephone: 01928 572 200
Website: www.driversdirect.co.uk
Summary of Operation: Drivers Direct specialises in the recruitment and placement of temporary and permanent drivers of all classes. We pride ourselves on our ability to work closely with both our clients and applicants to ensure that we provide a quality service to both.
More Information: theukfd.net/53211678

Easy Office
Telephone: 020 7938 3504
Website: www.easyoffice.co.uk
Summary of Operation: Easy branded offices – low value office space and equipment rental.
More Information: theukfd.net/86468757

EPI International Ltd
Telephone: 01905 620 670
Website: www.epiopp.com
Summary of Operation: Exceptional opportunity to earn a multiple six figure income by becoming an EPI Business Consultant using our world-class business improvement software and methodologies and leveraging our exemplary track record.
More Information: theukfd.net/81755371

Equation Accounting Ltd (UK)
Telephone: 01305 769739
Website: www.equation-uk.co.uk
Summary of Operation: Accounting franchise operation.
More Information: theukfd.net/19642378

European Coaching Network

Telephone: 01273 897 517
Summary of Operation: Professional network for people in individual and organisation development.
More Information: theukfd.net/26763805

Everett Masson & Furby

Telephone: 01404 813 762
Website: www.emfgroup.com
Summary of Operation: For over 40 years we have specialised in selling businesses. Thousands of satisfied clients chose Everett Masson & Furby because of our business sale expertise and service.
More Information: theukfd.net/84505245

EVP Recruitment

Telephone: 078 14030 463
Website: www.evp.cc
Summary of Operation: Recruitment specialists franchise.
More Information: theukfd.net/63084737

Executive Gold Club (Holdings) Ltd

Telephone: 020 8948 6466
Website: www.execgoldclub.com
Summary of Operation: EGC specialises in marketing international event management creating business to business opportunities for its corporate and diplomatic clients. Corporate membership currently over 3,000.
More Information: theukfd.net/54578328

Executives Online

Telephone: 0845 053 1188
Website: www.executivesonline.com
Summary of Operation: Interim management and Executive recruitment utilising online technologies coupled with traditional recruitment skills.
More Information: theukfd.net/05158489

Expense Reduction Analysts Int. Ltd

Telephone: 01923 858 130
Website: www.findextraprofit.com
Summary of Operation: Since 1992, ERA has helped thousands of companies of all types and sizes find savings hidden in their non-core expense categories (such as office supplies, insurance, travel, energy, small-package freight, etc).
More Information: theukfd.net/18363252

Expense Reduction Analysts UK

Telephone: 0845 058 4771
Website: www.erauk.net
Summary of Operation: At Expense Reduction Analysts, our cost analysis experts are trained specialists at reducing their client's costs and increasing profits.
More Information: theukfd.net/06182273

FDG Resourcing Ltd

Telephone: 0800 298 5411
Website: www.fdg.co.uk
Summary of Operation: Specialised recruitment for the financial sector.
More Information: theukfd.net/46331476

Fiducia Commercial Solutions

Telephone: 01529 410747
Website: www.fiduciacommercialsolutions.co.uk
Summary of Operation: This is a unique opportunity to become a commercial lending broker using the only commercial lending sourcing system in the UK.
More Information: theukfd.net/38269767

Filta Group Chemi-Call Plus

Telephone: 01788 550 100
Website: www.filtagroup.com
Summary of Operation: A mobile distribution franchise providing a full range of chemicals, cleaning products, sundries and equipment to a wide and diverse market.
More Information: theukfd.net/11267837

Financial Solutions (Euro) Ltd

Telephone: 020 8345 5678
Website: www.financialsolutionseuro.com
Summary of Operation: Established in 2001, primarily to serve a few existing clientele needs emanating from the legal profession for services provided by one of our company directors.
More Information: theukfd.net/30513409

Fire Compliance & Safety Franchise Ltd

Telephone: 0845 8 333 930
Website: www.fcsfranchise.com
Summary of Operation: Due to changes in the law every business that employs staff and or has access by the public has to carry out a fire risk assessment. After qualifying on the training course, you will have an exclusive territory.
More Information: theukfd.net/59621767

Franchise Listings

Kream Motor Recruitment
Telephone: 0871 200 0215
Website: www.kream.net
Summary of Operation: Kream focus on automotive jobs within franchise motor dealerships in your local area.
More Information: theukfd.net/26014240

Less Tax 2 Pay
Telephone: 020 8275 3540
Website: www.lesstax2payfranchise.com
Summary of Operation: Business accountancy franchise.
More Information: theukfd.net/51333432

Lifestyle Architecture
Telephone: 01738 827 813
Website: www.lifestylearchitecture.com
Summary of Operation: Lifestyle Architecture provide practical holistic role-specifc leadership development frameworks and systems.
More Information: theukfd.net/10279856

Linguaphone Group Ltd
Telephone: 020 8687 6104
Website: www.directenglish.com
Summary of Operation: World-leading English language training that combines premium quality bilingual training materials and home study with personalised tutorials, conversation classes, online resources and social activities held at director English Centres.
More Information: theukfd.net/80377753

LMI UK
Telephone: 01628 669 888
Website: www.lmi-uk.com
Summary of Operation: LMI® operates in over 60 countries and has 40 years of experience. LMI® franchise owners have the enviable role and highly rewarding career of developing potentialileaders, managers and Individuals.
More Information: theukfd.net/54547532

Loans 2 Go
Telephone: 01706 869 722
Website: www.logbookloans2go.co.uk
Summary of Operation: Loans 2 Go is a UK based financial services company, providing short term cash flow solutions to individuals and small businesses.
More Information: theukfd.net/35950583

Locallife Site Selection
Telephone: 01702 343 411
Website: www.locallife.co.uk
Summary of Operation: Website giving tourist information. Eating out, entertainment, shopping etc. in UK towns and cities.
More Information: theukfd.net/58650567

Mail Boxes Etc (UK) Ltd / MBE
Telephone: 01608 649 239
Website: www.mbe.co.uk
Summary of Operation: Total office support - postal business and communication services for the small/medium business and general public community from high street retail outlets.
More Information: theukfd.net/50385036

Mailshot International (Franchising) Ltd
Telephone: 01923 800 422
Website: www.mailshotinternational.co.uk
Summary of Operation: Mailing and e-marketing services.
More Information: theukfd.net/00873176

Mimosa Planet UK
Telephone: 07789 251 781
Website: www.mimosaplanet.com
Summary of Operation: Management consultancy to SME and implementation of plans.
More Information: theukfd.net/77893285

Mobile5 Ltd
Telephone: 08707 743 250
Website: www.mobile5.co.uk
Summary of Operation: Best price contracts on mobiles, phones and GPS tracking for small and medium businesses.
More Information: theukfd.net/82250568

Money Advice & Planning Ltd
Telephone: 0141 891 7850
Website: www.ifafranchise.co.uk
Summary of Operation: Independent financial advisers.
More Information: theukfd.net/82468480

Money Logic
Telephone: 07793 049 001
Website: www.moneylogicuk.co.uk
Summary of Operation: Financial solutions franchise operation.
More Information: theukfd.net/39038134

Monk Marketing Franchising Ltd

Telephone: 0845 070 0826
Website: www.monkmarketing.com
Summary of Operation: Incentive gifts, promotional merchandise and corporate clothing.
More Information: theukfd.net/50231566

Morgan Digital Security Systems Ltd

Telephone: 020 8654 0599
Website: www.morgandigital.co.uk
Summary of Operation: Security products and IT solutions providers.
More Information: theukfd.net/01822518

Morgan Harvey Personnel

Telephone: 0844 811 0473
Website: www.morgan-harvey.co.uk
Summary of Operation: Morgan Harvey was established in July 2002 and has become a well know specialist recruitment agency with a first class level of service.
More Information: theukfd.net/13187258

Mortgage Options Franchising Ltd

Telephone: 0800 028 4040
Website: www.mortgageoptions.co.uk
Summary of Operation: Financial services.
More Information: theukfd.net/7171950

Motorkwik.com Ltd

Telephone: 0845 269 0826
Website: www.motorkwik.co.uk
Summary of Operation: Motorkwik.co.uk is the place to find used cars, car services and all things motoring related.
More Information: theukfd.net/94387334

MRINetwork Worldwide Ltd

Telephone: 0870 777 3900
Website: www.mrifranchising.com
Summary of Operation: A global market leader in technical managerial and executive search - noother search company matches MRI Worldwide in size or scope.
More Information: theukfd.net/70656067

New Opportunities

Telephone: 0844 884 2801
Website: www.newopps.co.uk
Summary of Operation: Provides telephone, call centre answering and marketing services.
More Information: theukfd.net/72725597

Ology Coaching Ltd

Telephone: 0845 519 0591
Website: www.ologycoaching.com
Summary of Operation: Business coaching franchise providing effective professional coaching.
More Information: theukfd.net/33624566

One 2 Three Commercial

Telephone: 01752 764 275
Website: www.one2threecommercial.co.uk
Summary of Operation: Providing guidance to businesses and individuals with financial problems via our nationwide locations.
More Information: theukfd.net/71970041

ORCA Websites

Telephone: 0845 270 1128
Website: www.orcafranchise.com
Summary of Operation: The ORCA Websites franchise is your opportunity to become a professional E-Business Consultant. Work within a thriving and recession proof sector worth over £2 billion – this is your chance to join an exciting and dynamic team of people and become a genuine E-Business consultant.
More Information: theukfd.net/84684635

PACE Partners International

Telephone: 07760 107 558
Website: www.pacepartnersinternational.com
Summary of Operation: We are offering a unique opportunity, with an unparalleled level of support. Individuals joining us can look forward to building their own very successful, highly profitable training and consultancy business based on the proven PACE system.
More Information: theukfd.net/32695088

Parkhouse Recruitment

Telephone: 01582 811 600
Website: www.parkhouse.com
Summary of Operation: Parkhouse Recruitment specialises in placing industrial, technical and engineering staff. With an established brand, infrastructure and franchise model you will be supported by a proven formula and award winning team. We have opportunities across the UK for passionate people to become our franchise partners operating their own local recruitment business.
More Information: theukfd.net/66716722

Pentagon (UK) Ltd - EuroDebt Financial Services
Telephone: 01234 836 357
Website: www.eurodebt.co.uk
Summary of Operation: EuroDebt provides debt solutions including debt management, IVA, bankruptcy and sale and rent back in the domestic marketplace.
More Information: theukfd.net/26083237

Performance Brands
Telephone: 020 7730 9606
Website: www.performance-brands.com
Summary of Operation: Performance Brands is one of the Europe's leading brand licensing and franchising agency and consultancy.
More Information: theukfd.net/73907358

Personal Career Management
Telephone: 01753 888 995
Website: www.personalcareermanagement.com
Summary of Operation: Personal Career Management are one of the UK's leading provider of outplacement services and career management programmes for individual and corporate clients.
More Information: theukfd.net/31756945

Pink Connect Ltd
Telephone: 0845 540 9393
Website: www.pinkconnect.com
Summary of Operation: Pink Connect is a national business communications company, offering a complete suite of business, office and telecoms solutions.
More Information: theukfd.net/82065307

Pirtek Ltd
Telephone: 020 8749 8444
Website: www.pirtek.co.uk
Summary of Operation: Pirtek UK are one of the leading providers of fluid transfer solutions and mobile hose replacement.
More Information: theukfd.net/55435747

Plumplanet Ltd
Telephone: 01737 554 560
Website: www.plumplanet.co.uk
Summary of Operation: Computer training and support.
More Information: theukfd.net/78102478

Priority Management (UK)
Telephone: 0115 933 3144
Website: www.prioritymanagement.com
Summary of Operation: Management services.
More Information: theukfd.net/20217043

Professional Pre-Selection Services
Website: www.pps500.co.uk
Summary of Operation: Fixed cost recruitment service using cost-effective telephone interviewing techniques for all levels and all types of business.
More Information: theukfd.net/78574754

Professional Property Searches
Website: www.ppsearches.co.uk
Summary of Operation: Provides property search information to solictiors and conveyancers.
More Information: theukfd.net/73621265

Promobikes Ltd
Telephone: 020 7978 6399
Website: www.promobikes.co.uk
Summary of Operation: Promotional bikes, vehicles.
More Information: theukfd.net/84216405

Property Inventories
Telephone: 020 7812 0489
Website: www.propertyinventories.com
Summary of Operation: We supply professional inventory services for landlords and agents across the country .
More Information: theukfd.net/50640648

Quintadena Ltd
Telephone: 0121 669 1111
Website: www.quintadena.com
Summary of Operation: Quintadena is the only company in the UK focussed exclusively upon working with the award-winning QuoteWerks Quotation Software. Quintadena supplies quotation systems based around QuoteWerks, which can be tailored to the specific needs of any business.
More Information: theukfd.net/66412982

Regus Business Centres PLC
Website: www.regus.com
Summary of Operation: Regus provide fully serviced offices in over 300 centres in 48 countries.
More Information: theukfd.net/18175462

Rig Franchising
Telephone: 020 3178 6586
Website: www.rigfranchising.co.uk
Summary of Operation: Recruitment within the security industry.
More Information: theukfd.net/86513899

RISC
Telephone: 0118 925 5979
Website: www.riscl.co.uk
Summary of Operation: RISC is a specialist recruitment consultancy.
More Information: theukfd.net/2062972

Robertson Technologies Ltd
Telephone: 0845 838 1710
Website: www.robertsontech.com
Summary of Operation: Robertson Technologies IT support franchise is a specialist in offsite data backup and computer support services at various regions in UK.
More Information: theukfd.net/48327832

Rosemary Bookkeeping
Telephone: 01442 800 147
Website: www.rosemaryfranchise.com
Summary of Operation: Rosemary Bookkeeping is an exciting franchise concept based on an outsourced bookkeeping service to businesses. Based on systems that were established in 2002, this is ideal for those looking for a profitable service business with the flexibility of working from home.
More Information: theukfd.net/23811477

Sandler Training
Telephone: 01608 611 211
Website: www.sandlerfranchising.co.uk
Summary of Operation: Sandler Training is a world leader in innovative sales and sales management training. For more than 40 years, Sandler Training has taught its distinctive, non-traditional selling system through ongoing reinforcement.
More Information: theukfd.net/79641255

ScotCall
Telephone: 07966 969 376
Website: www.scotcall.co.uk
Summary of Operation: As credit management experts since 1992, we've built our reputation on resolving financial issues and rounding up debt.
More Information: theukfd.net/24215445

SDM Financial Services Ltd
Telephone: 0871 666 1925
Website: www.sdmfinancial
Summary of Operation: Finance and credit company.
More Information: theukfd.net/03072682

Select Appointments
Telephone: 01582 811654
Website: www.select.co.uk
Summary of Operation: Recruitment agency franchise operation.
More Information: theukfd.net/78747740

ServiceMaster Commercial Cleaning
Telephone: 0116 275 9050
Website: www.servicemaster.co.uk
Summary of Operation: The provision of professional office cleaning services to businessess from local and national accounts.
More Information: theukfd.net/58678317

Smart Cartridge Ltd
Telephone: 0131 440 9845
Website: www.smart-cartridge.com
Summary of Operation: Inkjet, laser cartridge refill and remanufacture specialists. We can significantly reduce home and office printer running costs by up to 60%.
More Information: theukfd.net/42732502

Sollertia Ltd
Telephone: 0845 0946 202
Website: www.accountingfranchise.co.uk
Summary of Operation: Completely outsourced accounting and finance department services.
More Information: theukfd.net/69078570

Spettro
Telephone: 01883 621 047
Website: www.spettro.net
Summary of Operation: Building maintenance franchise operation.
More Information: theukfd.net/70466504

Spirit Control
Website: www.spiritcontrol.com
Summary of Operation: Spirit Control is a system for reducing wastage and improving the profit margins.
More Information: theukfd.net/44774134

Spoton.net
Telephone: 01803 401 060
Website: www.spoton.net
Summary of Operation: Website and internet marketing franchise. A unique proven product. One of the UK's fastest growing franchise companies.
More Information: theukfd.net/41248167

SSP International Sports Betting Ltd
Telephone: 020 7837 1810
Website: www.ssp.co.uk
Summary of Operation: International sports betting.
More Information: theukfd.net/16072714

Straight Business Solutions
Telephone: 0870 803 0821
Website: www.straightfinance.co.uk
Summary of Operation: One of the UK's fastest growing independent business consultancies dedicated to serving the needs of the business.
More Information: theukfd.net/51002808

Strategic Financials
Telephone: 0870 112 7320
Website: www.strategicfinancials.co.uk
Summary of Operation: Offer financial services to help businesses become more profitable with franchise locations.
More Information: theukfd.net/33769139

Success Dynamics
Telephone: 020 8686 8366
Website: www.successdynamics.co.uk
Summary of Operation: Success Dynamics provide Chief Executives, Managing Directors and HR Directors with the skills and solutions to understand their people and improve the way they work together. Success Dynamics has been operating in the field of psychometric evaluation for over 20 years and specialise in the design and supply of psychometric tools and other tests.
More Information: theukfd.net/51622267

SureCare Community Services Ltd
Telephone: 01244 321 199
Website: www.surecare.co.uk
Summary of Operation: Home care and nursing services. Office based recruitment of staff and organisation of office.
More Information: theukfd.net/54684753

TaxAssist Accountants
Telephone: 0800 0188297
Website: www.taxassist.net
Summary of Operation: Supply of accounting, taxation and associated services to small businesses with a turnover of under £1 million.
More Information: theukfd.net/67780351

Techclean Services Ltd
Telephone: 020 7724 4664
Website: www.techclean.co.uk
Summary of Operation: Specialise in cleaning computers and associated IT equipment.
More Information: theukfd.net/80182454

technilink iT Ltd
Telephone: 01962 600 101
Website: www.technilink.co.uk
Summary of Operation: Premier audio video and web conferencing suppliers in the UK.
More Information: theukfd.net/47237167

Technology Leasing
Telephone: 0800 027 2939
Website: www.technologyleasing.co.uk
Summary of Operation: Assists businesses and organisations who need to find a finance option for equipment they need.
More Information: theukfd.net/68457082

Telcoinabox
Telephone: 020 3326 5555
Website: www.telcoinabox.com
Summary of Operation: Telcoinabox has revolutionised the telecommunications industry as the only telecommunications franchise system for individuals or existing businesses.
More Information: theukfd.net/42867473

Tempsphere PLC
Telephone: 0870 803 4013
Website: www.tempsphere.com
Summary of Operation: Commercial services.
More Information: theukfd.net/44804271

The Academy For Chief Executives Ltd
Telephone: 0870 228 3369
Website: www.chiefexecutive.com
Summary of Operation: Mentoring and coaching Chief Executives.
More Information: theukfd.net/71216886

The Athena Network Franchise
Telephone: 0845 004 9262
Website: www.athenafranchise.com
Summary of Operation: Networking for women.
More Information: theukfd.net/13571145

The Business Club
Telephone: 01733 513 003
Website: www.the-businessclub.org
Summary of Operation: Business networking club.
More Information: theukfd.net/81818112

The Business Partnership (Management) Ltd
Telephone: 01509 856 111
Website: www.business-partnership.com
Summary of Operation: Franchise owners provide a full range of brokerage services across all market sectors.
More Information: theukfd.net/67029486

The Financial Management Centre UK Ltd
Telephone: 0845 862 7423
Website: www.tfmcentre.co.uk
Summary of Operation: Leading financial management consultancy that is committed and passionate in helping all sizes of organisation to achieve performance excellence through our innovative approach.
More Information: theukfd.net/47425070

The Interface Financial Group
Telephone: 0845 834 0332
Website: www.interfacefinancial.co.uk
Summary of Operation: Interface is the leading alternative funding source for small businesses.
More Information: theukfd.net/01003806

The Internet Marketing Company
Telephone: 0870 163 5121
Website: www.theinternetmarketingco.com
Summary of Operation: Offers websites, internet marketing services and training to small and start up businesses.
More Information: theukfd.net/50180243

The Jiff
Telephone: 01495 230 205
Website: www.thejiff.co.uk
Summary of Operation: Providing clients with a regular, environmentally approved bin washing.
More Information: theukfd.net/87358525

The Office Express Group Ltd
Website: www.oeg.co.uk
Summary of Operation: Supplies small and medium sized companies with office supplies including stationery and products products, uniforms, business gifts, commercial printing, packaging materials and safety wear.
More Information: theukfd.net/73377584

The Penn Group
Website: www.thepenngroup.co.uk
Summary of Operation: The Penn Group is a leading international management consulting business.
More Information: theukfd.net/60280226

The Quantum Organisation
Telephone: 01306 646 897
Website: www.quantumorganization.co.uk
Summary of Operation: Business development consultancy working with companies over extended time period.
More Information: theukfd.net/13238443

The Recruitment Network
Telephone: 01676 524 722
Website: www.networkbrandpartnerships.com
Summary of Operation: UK's largest independent recruitment business.
More Information: theukfd.net/75380317

The Revival Company
Telephone: 01865 891 694
Website: www.revivalco.co.uk
Summary of Operation: One-stop service to restore the contents or fabric of properties following damage from fire or floor.
More Information: theukfd.net/52642880

The Sales Recruitment Network (UK)
Telephone: 0118 971 2422
Website: www.tsrn.co.uk
Summary of Operation: A specialist sales recruitment agency.
More Information: theukfd.net/04132580

The Slice Ltd
Telephone: 0370 774 2014
Website: www.theslice.co.uk
Summary of Operation: Pay by results advertising agency.
More Information: theukfd.net/00809568

Thebestof.co.uk
Telephone: 0121 765 5556
Website: www.getthebestof.co.uk
Summary of Operation: The best of champions, the best business in each town in the UK, through a variety of innovative on and offline marketing initiatives, including networking.
More Information: theukfd.net/21844843

Travail Employment Group Ltd
Telephone: 01452 420 700
Website: www.travail.co.uk
Summary of Operation: Multi disciplined recruitment company, supplying both temporary and permanent staff within industry, commerce and public sector.
More Information: theukfd.net/74804274

VDI Telecom
Telephone: 0800 043 0126
Website: www.vditelecom.co.uk
Summary of Operation: Telecommunications franchise.
More Information: theukfd.net/51259431

Vehicle Consulting Ltd
Telephone: 08000 131 353
Website: www.vehicleconsultinglicense.com
Summary of Operation: Providing vehicle funding solutions to both business and personal customers.
More Information: theukfd.net/37823020

Wealth Watch
Website: www.wealthwatch.biz
Summary of Operation: Financial advisers franchise.
More Information: theukfd.net/02106352

Webmirer Ltd
Telephone: 0121 250 3850
Website: www.webmirer.co.uk
Summary of Operation: Web consultancy firm franchise.
More Information: theukfd.net/16790995

West End Training Ltd
Telephone: 0845 058 1375
Website: www.westendtraining.co.uk
Summary of Operation: Training and development including outplacement and profiling.
More Information: theukfd.net/25177600

Westaff
Telephone: 01452 304 090
Website: www.westaff.co.uk
Summary of Operation: Recruitment franchise.
More Information: theukfd.net/78830816

Whiterose Management
Telephone: 01258 818 188
Website: www.lifeafterdebt.co.uk
Summary of Operation: Insolvency rescue service.
More Information: theukfd.net/61671475

Wise Recycling Ltd
Telephone: 01507 463 100
Website: www.wiserecycling.co.uk
Summary of Operation: Cause related marketing.
More Information: theukfd.net/19299473

WPA
Telephone: 01823 625 120
Website: www.wpafranchise.co.uk
Summary of Operation: Leading health insurer.
More Information: theukfd.net/47477411

Wrinklies Direct
Telephone: 01372 740 484
Website: www.wrinklies.org
Summary of Operation: Recruitment agency specialising in placement of older people over 40.
More Information: theukfd.net/87315663

Xclusive Recruitment
Telephone: 01280 701 123
Website: www.xclusiverecruitment.com
Summary of Operation: Xclusive Recruitment provides national quality recruitment solutions to the logistics sector and has market leading retention rates. With a range of services and pricing to meet their clients various needs they do not just work with clients and candidates they 'partner' with them.
More Information: theukfd.net/70491251

Your Own Store
Telephone: 0845 619 8400
Website: www.yourownstore.co.uk
Summary of Operation: We provide top quality internet business websites that are fully ready to go providing you with a shortcut to making money online. We create top quality e-commerce stores loaded with products, search engine optimised and a fully operational online shop.
More Information: theukfd.net/17728001

Shortlist

Franchise Tips

Ensure your franchise is legally protected

All franchise owners sign a Franchise Agreement with the franchisor in order to secure their franchise, the main function of which is to clearly set out the extent of the rights to be granted, the territory in which those rights apply, the exclusivity of the rights in the territory and the term in which the rights exist. A typical agreement will outline the franchise owner's exclusive rights to market, build a business under, profit from and possibly sell sub-franchises under the brand within the territory for a reasonable term.

There are a number of specialist franchise lawyers operating in the UK and many are affiliated to the British Franchise Association (bfa). Because they are familiar with the nature of the franchising relationship, these practices will be able to judge a franchise contract that not only protects your business, but also keeps in mind commercial considerations.

SERVICES | Cleaning & Maintenance

Actively recruiting franchise owners

Opportunities exist from servicing the residential and commercial market. They range from job franchises to management franchise opportunities and many cleaning franchises can also be run from home or van-based delivery franchises. Franchise opportunities include **Betterclean Services, Dublcheck, FiltaFry Plus, Merry Maids, Minster Cleaning Services, Ovenclean** and **ServiceMaster Carpet & Upholstery Cleaning.**

SERVICES | Cleaning & Maintenance

Minster Cleaning Services

Summary of Operation: Minster is a management franchise providing an essential business-to-business service, the management of office cleaning and allied services under contract.

Ideal Franchise Owner Profile: You will need senior management experience.

Cost of Franchise: £28,225 + VAT plus working capital in the region of £40,000 - £60,000.

Franchise Owner Contact: Mike Parker

Year Company Established: 1982
Year of First Franchise Owner: 1992

Number of Company Outlets: 0
Number of Franchised Outlets: 39
Number of Franchise Owners Planned: 50

Overseas Operations Existing: None
Overseas Operations Planned: None
Management Service Fees: 7%

Breakdown of Package: Franchise fee £22,000, miscellaneous £6,225.

Financial Assistance Available: All major banks.

Training Provided: Initial and ongoing training provided.
Training Location: Birmingham head office.
Support Services: Minster's unique marketing system provides new contracts.

Areas of Priority Development: Aberdeen, Doncaster, London, Durham, Peterborough, Swansea, Guildford, Cambridge and Leicester.

Resales: A number of Minster franchise owners across the country are planning their retirement and offering their franchises for sale. Call Minster for full details of these resale opportunities.

More Information: theukfd.net/34827064

Minster Services Group UK
948-952 Kingsbury Road,
Erdington, Birmingham, B24 9PZ

t: 0121 386 1722
f: 0121 386 1191
e: minster@minstergroup.co.uk
w: www.minstergroup.co.uk

successecurity

With a Minster Management Franchise these two words are inextricably linked

" Before I took the plunge I needed to be absolutely sure that I was going to achieve success with security. I was able to discuss any concerns I had with existing Minster franchisees. Now I have a turnover of £1,250,000 p.a. and with the whole of Sheffield as my exclusive territory I have ongoing growth potential. I definitely have achieved success with security. "

James Lofthouse
Minster Franchisee, Sheffield

Commercial cleaning is an essential service and Minster are market leaders with over 6000 clients across the UK

James Lofthouse's investment had to be:

- A large exclusive territory
- A management business
- Recession resistant
- Capable of developing into a substantial operation
- A utility rather than a 'fashion' business
- A good return on investment
- Professionally marketed
- No selling

Looking for a franchise opportunity? Make sure the numbers add up!

28 years of proven success across the UK

£150K+ net profit potential

39 Branches

£30M sales/turnover

Some resale opportunities are now available in large established territories

bfa
FULL MEMBER

Minster is the biggest and the most successful Management Franchise in the UK

Ovenclean

Summary of Operation: Ovenclean is the UK's original oven cleaning specialist with a large network of established franchise owners. As an Ovenclean franchise owner, you can be assured of the highest standard of training and ongoing business support backed by a team with a long and successful track record in franchise development. With low overheads and high profitability, the rewards for hardworking franchise owners are unlimited.

Ideal Franchise Owner Profile: Suits active, practical, hard working individuals with good interpersonal skills who want to build a thriving franchise business. No previous experience required as extensive training and ongoing support is provided.

Cost of Franchise: £16,995 + VAT

Franchise Owner Contact: Alan Hope

Year Company Established: 1992
Year of First Franchise Owner: 1994

Number of Company Outlets: 0
Number of Franchised Outlets: 70

Management Service Fees:
Year 1 fixed fee of £150 per month.
Breakdown of Package: Full information provided within franchise brochure.

Projected Turnover:
1st Year: AOR   **2nd Year:** AOR   **3rd Year:** AOR

Projected Profit:
1st Year: AOR   **2nd Year:** AOR   **3rd Year:** AOR

Financial Assistance Available: All major high street banks.

Training Provided: Practical, sales and marketing training provided.
Training Location: Nationwide

Support Services: Ongoing technical, marketing and business support together with 24/7 UK based call centre.

Areas of Priority Development: Nationwide

More Information: theukfd.net/69041546

Ovenclean
5 Edwin Avenue, Hoo Farm,
Kidderminster, Worcestershire,
DY11 7RA

t: 0800 988 5434
f: 01562 864 969
e: info@ovenclean.com
w: www.ovenclean.com

bfa Associate Member

Dublcheck

Dublcheck House, Minerva Court, Minerva Avenue, Chester, CH1 4QT

Telephone: 01244 651 100
Fax: 01244 651 101
Email: franchise@dublcheck.co.uk
Website: www.dublcheck.co.uk

Summary of Operation: Dublcheck is a commercial cleaning franchise. As a Dublcheck franchise owner you can build a substantial commercial cleaning business supported by a company with many years' experience in supplying services to many high profile national groups and high street businesses.

Ideal Franchise Owner Profile: Committed people to people individuals from all backgrounds who, can deliver a service second-to-none, either hands-on or fully managed, supported by the Dublcheck brand.

Cost of Franchise: £9,950 to £190,950 + VAT depending on turnover level

Franchise Owner Contact: Carol Stewart-Gill

Year Company Established: 1993
Year of First Franchise Owner: 1994
Number of Company Outlets: 3
Number of Franchised Outlets: 100+
Number of Franchise Owners Planned: 4,000

Overseas Operations Existing: None
Overseas Operations Planned: Europe

Management Service Fees: 12.5%
Breakdown of Package: Contract business, training, admin package, etc.

Financial Assistance Available: All major banks.
Training Provided: All aspects of commercial cleaning and business operation.
Training Location: Head office
Support Services: Sales, invoicing, admin, credit control, operations, business development support are available. There is no need to be able to sell, as Dublcheck will get the business for you.
Areas of Priority Development: UK

More Information: theukfd.net/62447741

bfa Associate Member

FiltaFry Plus, The Filta Group Ltd

The Locks, Hillmorton, Rugby, CV21 4PP

Telephone: 01788 550 100
Fax: 01788 551 839
Email: enquiries@filtagroup.co.uk
Website: www.filtafryplus.co.uk

Summary of Operation: FiltaFry Plus is a mobile, onsite service for the microfiltration of cooking oils and vacuum cleaning of deep fat fryers and the supply of kitchen hygiene products and services.

Ideal Franchise Owner Profile: Franchise owner technicians do not need specific prior experience as full training is provided. However, a strong desire to succeed and provide excellent customer service is essential.

Cost of Franchise: From £14,950 + VAT

Franchise Owner Contact: Damian Slater

Year Company Established: 1995
Year of First Franchise Owner: 1996
Number of Company Outlets: 0
Number of Franchised Outlets: 65

Overseas Operations Existing: Australia, Portugal, USA, Italy, Indonesia, Poland, Kuwait, Hungary, South Africa, Malaysia, Jordan, Bulgaria and Greece.
Overseas Operations Planned: Worldwide

Management Service Fees: AOR

Training Provided: The company training programme covers every aspect of the business from the fryer management service through to the ongoing development of the business.
Training Location: Head office and field based.

Support Services: The support team is always available to give advice and guidance regarding the business through the various stages of its development and as part of the ongoing mentoring programme.

Areas of Priority Development: Various

More Information: theukfd.net/28043370

merry maids
Relax. It's Done.

bfa Full Member
Merry Maids
Servicemaster House, Tigers Road, Wigston,
Leicester, LE18 4WS

Telephone: 0116 275 9005
Fax: 0116 275 9002
Email: franchisesales@servicemaster.co.uk
Website: www.servicemaster.co.uk

Summary of Operation: Merry Maids is a
management franchise providing a professional
domestic cleaning service. We have a systematic
approach to training, cleaning, office management
and developing your customer base that will give
you the confidence to succeed in the management
of your home cleaning franchise.

Ideal Franchise Owner Profile: We are looking for
professional franchise owners to develop and
manage their own Merry Maids business. You must
have a willingness to serve your customers, treat
your employees with respect and have a
commitment to follow the Merry Maids system.

Cost of Franchise: £16,560 + VAT
Franchise Owner Contact: Marcelle Ingrouille
Year Company Established: 1959
Year of First Franchise Owner: 1989
Number of Company Outlets: 0
Number of Franchised Outlets: 100
Overseas Operations Existing: Europe, Middle East,
America and Canada.
Overseas Operations Planned: None
Management Service Fees: 7%
Breakdown of Package: License fee, training,
marketing material, stationery, software, products,
business launch and a full equipment pack for four
teams plus materials for the first year in business.
Training Provided: Intensive two weeks' training,
business launch with ongoing training, advice and
assistance where necessary.
Training Location: Leicester
Support Services: Franchise owners benefit from
name recognition, bespoke software, ongoing
training, technical support, management support,
sales, marketing assistance, IT, products and
equipment.
Areas of Priority Development: UK and Ireland.
More Information: theukfd.net/44065887

ServiceMASTER
Clean

bfa Full Member
ServiceMaster Carpet & Upholstery Cleaning
ServiceMaster House, Tigers Road, Wigston,
Leicester, LE18 4WS

Telephone: 0116 275 9005
Fax: 0116 275 9002
Email: franchisesales@servicemaster.co.uk
Website: www.servicemaster.co.uk

Summary of Operation: As a ServiceMaster
franchise owner you will provide a range of carpet
and upholstery cleaning services to residential and
commercial customers. This includes deep cleaning,
static control and soil treatment.

Ideal Franchise Owner Profile: You must have a
willingness to learn and the energy to work hard; a
self starter with good motivation to actively seek
new customers and an ability to follow a system. You
may be ambitious and have aspirations to grow the
business with your focus changing to a primarily
Management and Development role.

Cost of Franchise: £23,500 + VAT
Franchise Owner Contact: Marcelle Ingrouille
Year Company Established: 1959
Number of Company Outlets: 1
Number of Franchised Outlets: 180

Overseas Operations Existing: Europe, Middle East,
America and Canada.
Overseas Operations Planned: None

Management Service Fees: 10%
Breakdown of Package: Licence fee, training,
equipment, designated territory, marketing material,
stationery, software, products, set-up and business
launch.
Training Provided: Intensive two week training
course, business launch with ongoing training,
advice and assistance where necessary.
Financial Assistance Available: All major banks.
Support Services: We offer our franchise owners a
vast array of support functions: technical support,
sales, national accounts, marketing assistance,
business development, IT, management, products
and equipment.
Areas of Priority Development: All of UK and
Ireland.
More Information: theukfd.net/30016137

bfa Full Member

MOLLY MAID

MOLLY MAID House, 90 Moorbridge Road,
Maidenhead, SL6 8BW

Telephone: 01628 583 760
Fax: 01628 627 674
Email: ukso@mollymaid.co.uk
Website: www.mollymaid.co.uk

Summary of Operation: MOLLY MAID is a
management franchise which operates within a
secure business sector delivering high quality
reliable domestic cleaning to thousands of homes
across the UK. The role of a MOLLY MAID franchise
owner is to employ staff to provide our domestic
maid service to customers within an exclusive area.

Cost of Franchise: £16,975 + VAT plus £12,000
working capital.

Franchise Owner Contact: Andrew Parsons

Year Company Established: 1984
Number of Franchised Outlets: 72

More Information: theukfd.net/37274617

bfa Full Member

OvenU (Franchising) Ltd

Unit 3, Station Industrial Estate, Oxford Road,
Wokingham, RG41 2YQ

Telephone: 01325 251455
Email: info@ovenufranchise.co.uk
Website: www.ovenufranchise.co.uk

Summary of Operation: Premium standard oven
cleaning/valeting to the domestic and semi-
commercial market including guest houses, holiday
homes and rental properties. All cooking appliances
immaculately cleaned including, but not limited to,
hobs, extractor hoods, microwave ovens, Range
cookers and AGA. Only Eco-friendly biodegradable
OvenU branded products used.

Ideal Franchise Owner Profile: Practically minded
people seeking flexible hours with a willingness to
work with a clear market leader and being adaptable
to follow tried and tested systems and methodology.
Cost of Franchise: From £9,950 + VAT
Franchise Owner Contact: Ken Rostron
Financial Assistance Available: Yes (subject to
conditions).
More information: theukfd.net/11114761

bfa Full Member

Safeclean

Valspar Industries (UK) Ltd, 152 Milton Park,
Abingdon, OX14 4SD
Telephone: 01235 444 705
Fax: 01235 862 730
Email: safeclean@valspar.com
Website: www.safeclean.co.uk

Summary of Operation: Safeclean franchise owners
provide a wide range of services including the
cleaning, stain and spot removal of carpets,
upholstery, rugs, curtains and mattresses and
protection plans for home owners and
commercial outlets.

Ideal Franchise Owner Profile: Must have energy,
enthusiasm, self motivation, tenacity and desire to
build, and operate a successful and profitable
business.

Cost of Franchise: From £19,950 + VAT
Franchise Owner Contact: Steve Calvert
Financial Assistance Available: All major UK banks.

More Information: theukfd.net/65886001

Well Polished

Egerton House, 2 Tower Road,
Birkenhead, Wirral, CH41 1FN

Telephone: 0161 926 9882
Email: gill@fdsnorth.com

Summary of Operation: Management franchise in
the domestic cleaning sector. As a franchise owner
you will not be expected to do any cleaning yourself
– instead you will manage the cleaners.

Ideal Franchise Owner: This is a business concept
suitable for individuals with great people
management skills, aiming to build substantial
businesses following the path of the proven head
office operation.

Cost of Franchise: £9,500 + VAT

Franchise Owner Contact: Gill O'Brien

Financial Assistance Available: N/A

More information: theukfd.net/80245524

Adept Cleaning Services Ltd
Telephone: 01827 287 100
Website: www.adeptcleaninggroup.co.uk
Summary of Operation: Specialise in a number of areas, especially house and property clearances, carpet and upholstery cleaning, power jet washing, domestic and commercial cleaning for offices, communal areas and hotels etc.
More Information: theukfd.net/44062505

Aid to Freedom Ltd
Telephone: 08000 409 595
Website: www.aidtofreedomfranchise.com
Summary of Operation: Domestic cleaning introduction company offers introductions to domestic home cleaners. This is a home based management franchise, it's easy to run with low running costs and working capital.
More Information: theukfd.net/37006725

Autovaletdirect Franchising Ltd
Telephone: 0870 240 1628
Website: www.autovaletdirect.co.uk
Summary of Operation: Autovaletdirect franchise owners offer a wide range of products, which both protect the vehicle's paintwork and upholstery and keep it looking new and fresh. Franchise owners are also trained and equipped to correct minor paintwork problems such as scratches and colour fading etc.
More Information: theukfd.net/48112880

Autovalet-UK
Telephone: 0871 789 9001
Website: www.autovalet-uk.com
Summary of Operation: Car valeting.
More Information: theukfd.net/51722960

Belle Casa Ltd
Telephone: 0870 243 0197
Website: www.bellecasa.co.uk
Summary of Operation: Domestic cleaning with a difference. Management of staff and clients.
More Information: theukfd.net/48250560

Betterclean Services Ltd
Telephone: 08454 563536
Website: www.bettercleanservices.co.uk
Summary of Operation: Commercial contract cleaning company.
More Information: Turn to pages 36-37 or visit theukfd.net/76958733

Bin Boutique
Telephone: 07903 582 477
Website: www.binboutique.biz
Summary of Operation: Bin cleaning.
More Information: theukfd.net/18395058

Bone-Dry
Telephone: 01908 320 105
Website: www.timeforyoultd.co.uk
Summary of Operation: Carpet cleaning business using dry method.
More Information: theukfd.net/56850411

Bright & Beautiful UK Ltd
Telephone: 0845 241 0818
Website: www.brightandbeautifulhome.com
Summary of Operation: Award-winning concept in domestic homecare, providing eco-friendly cleaning, tidying, laundry and ironing; with the highest standards of security and service.
More Information: theukfd.net/10720310

Brilliant Window Cleaners
Telephone: 01252 837 436
Website: www.brilliantwindowcleaners.com
Summary of Operation: Brilliant Window Cleaners are your local specialists in window, gutter and conservatory cleaning for all types of property, whether residential or commercial.
More Information: theukfd.net/98340722

Brite Drives
Telephone: 0845 434 8656
Website: www.britedrives.com
Summary of Operation: Drive, patio and path cleaning services.
More Information: theukfd.net/25320426

Cannon Hygiene International Ltd
Telephone: 01524 60894
Website: www.cannonhygiene.com
Summary of Operation: Franchise package provides specially designed units: disposal of sanitary waste from ladies WCs together with exclusive sanitising fluid which treats waste and protects against HIV and Hepatitis B.
More Information: theukfd.net/08677602

Castle Angels Ltd
Telephone: 0871 716 7871
Website: www.castleangels.co.uk
Summary of Operation: Domestic cleaning.
More Information: theukfd.net/58038453

Franchise Listings

Clean Genie Ltd
Telephone: 01869 325 700
Website: www.clean-genie.co.uk
Summary of Operation: Clean Genie is a privately owned specialist cleaning company.
More Information: theukfd.net/00533226

Clean Like New
Telephone: 01279 626 450
Website: www.clean-like-new.com
Summary of Operation: Specialist deep cleaning and restoration of all hard surfaces including block paving, tiles and grout, swimming pools, specialist flooring, stone and brick etc.
More Information: theukfd.net/80949532

CleanMy Ltd
Telephone: 01432 279 612
Website: www.cleanmy.biz
Summary of Operation: Van-based supply of essential cleaning, hygiene and other products to all kinds of industrial and commercial clients.
More Information: theukfd.net/78849379

Clean2Gleam
Telephone: 0845 0521 222
Website: www.clean2gleam.com
Summary of Operation: Valeting services to both domestic customers as well as car dealerships and company fleets.
More Information: theukfd.net/63574492

Cleaning Doctor
Telephone: 028 6634 1288
Website: www.cleaningdoctor.net
Summary of Operation: Cleaning Doctor is an established brand with over 50 franchise branches throughout the UK and Ireland.
More Information: theukfd.net/88530142

Club-Clean
Telephone: 0800 043 7780
Website: www.club-clean.co.uk
Summary of Operation: Mobile golf club cleaning business, using ultrasonic cleaning technology.
More Information: theukfd.net/32326023

Cookerburra Oven Cleaning Services UK Ltd
Telephone: 0118 959 9922
Website: www.cookerburra.com
Summary of Operation: Domestic oven cleaning service.
More Information: theukfd.net/52335868

Daily Poppins
Telephone: 0800 0838535
Website: www.dailypoppins.co.uk
Summary of Operation: This is a management franchise in the domestic cleaning sector where you can either get involved in the day-to-day cleaning, or take a hands-on management approach and manage teams of cleaners in the area.
More Information: theukfd.net/02076161

Detail Clean (Franchising) Ltd
Telephone: 01582 529 429
Website: www.detailclean.co.uk
Summary of Operation: Domestic cleaning franchise.
More Information: theukfd.net/17752714

Dolly Char
Website: www.dollychar.com
Summary of Operation: Local domestic cleaning and ironing at an affordable price.
More Information: theukfd.net/16153155

Domestique
Telephone: 0808 1200 612
Website: www.domestique.co.uk
Summary of Operation: Domestique was born in July 2005. They realised that maybe there were a lot of people like themselves who weren't getting the more flexible service they wanted or deserved. So in Spring 2005 they decided to start their very own domestic cleaning service.
More Information: theukfd.net/77940973

Dustomatic
Telephone: 020 8567 5049
Summary of Operation: 90% of dirt goes into business premises through doors,the best way to prevent this is to trap it at the door with a dust control mat. The franchise owner changes the dirty mats for clean ones every month, up to 60 deliveries can be done in a day.
More Information: theukfd.net/84687113

Ecocleen Ltd
Telephone: 01284 703535
Website: www.ecocleen.com
Summary of Operation: Commercial cleaning franchise business, part of a large group, we offer a fantastic package for anyone wishing to earn serious money.
More Information: theukfd.net/33618224

Encore Car Cleaning
Telephone: 01603 661 601
Website: www.encorecarcleaning.co.uk
Summary of Operation: Car wash and valeting at work or whilst you shop, using fully trained accredited car cleaning operatives.
More Information: theukfd.net/77698314

FastKlean Franchise Ltd
Telephone: 020 8884 9149
Website: www.fastklean-franchise.co.uk
Summary of Operation: Domestic cleaning agency franchise which allows you to capitalise on this growing market, without having to get your hands dirty.
More Information: theukfd.net/00161672

Gleaming Cleaning
Telephone: 0116 241 2955
Website: www.gleamingcleaning.net
Summary of Operation: Carpet and upholstery cleaning and protection, patio and stonework cleaning, floor restoration and chimney sweeping.
More Information: theukfd.net/03416711

Hydro-Dynamix Ltd
Telephone: 01622 664 993
Website: www.hydro-dynamix.co.uk
Summary of Operation: Truck-mounted all surface cleaning system for eco-friendly cleaning of carpets, upholstery, driveways, patios, graffiti removal etc.
More Information: theukfd.net/42865232

Hygienics Ltd
Telephone: 0845 8335 052
Website: www.hygienicsfranchise.co.uk
Summary of Operation: Leader in the provision of disinfection and decontamination solutions.
More Information: theukfd.net/55944533

Jani-King (GB) Ltd
Telephone: 020 84814300
Website: www.janiking.co.uk
Summary of Operation: Management franchise in the commercial cleaning sector.
More Information: theukfd.net/58671083

Kingsmaid Ltd
Telephone: 0161 449 5843
Website: wwww.kingsmaid.co.uk
Summary of Operation: Cleaning services.
More Information: theukfd.net/23848881

Maid2Clean
Telephone: 0845 257 0677
Website: www.maid2clean.co.uk
Summary of Operation: A management franchise at the forefront of the domestic cleaning industry. Can create a substantial residual income. It is our aim that no-one can offer more in a franchise package than Maid2Clean.
More Information: theukfd.net/08482456

Maids in Waiting
Telephone: 0844 544 9961
Website: www.maidsinwaiting.co.uk
Summary of Operation: Cleaning franchise.
More Information: theukfd.net/61272485

My Clean Home
Telephone: 01244 379 309
Website: www.mycleanhomeuk.com
Summary of Operation: Domestic cleaning.
More Information: theukfd.net/65275865

Nationwide Cleaners
Telephone: 07986 600 316
Website: www.nationwidecleaners.co.uk
Summary of Operation: A management franchise operating at a very low initial and ongoing cost. You never undertake any cleaning.
More Information: theukfd.net/97674680

New City Franchising
Telephone: 0800 511 8815
Website: www.newcity.biz
Summary of Operation: Contract cleaning.
More Information: theukfd.net/22928806

NIC Services Group Ltd
Telephone: 0845 409 0910
Website: www.nicfranchise.co.uk
Summary of Operation: NIC Services Group offers an opportunity to invest in a virtually recession-proof industry with a company who has been involved in the cleaning industry for almost 50 years.
More Information: theukfd.net/05015662

NovoSail Ltd
Telephone: 01489 78 94 49
Website: www.novosail.com
Summary of Operation: The globally unique NovoSail system is a completely new concept for cleaning and finishing sails of all kinds.
More Information: theukfd.net/92573298

Oven Wizards Franchising Ltd
Telephone: 0845 300 9074
Website: www.ovenwizards.com
Summary of Operation: Oven cleaning services.
More Information: theukfd.net/06604274

Ovens 'R' Us
Website: www.ovensrus.co.uk
Summary of Operation: Mobile oven cleaning service.
More Information: theukfd.net/85434204

Pinnacle Cleaning Services
Telephone: 0121 863 636
Website: www.pinnaclecleaning.co.uk
Summary of Operation: Office cleaning contractors.
More Information: theukfd.net/94926253

Poppies (UK) Ltd
Website: www.poppies.co.uk
Summary of Operation: Provision of high quality domestic cleaning and related services.
More Information: theukfd.net/75441154

PVC Vendo
Telephone: 020 8908 1234
Website: www.pvcvendo.com
Summary of Operation: Commercial vehicle power washing.
More Information: theukfd.net/53734845

PW Needham Ltd
Telephone: 01127 831 317
Summary of Operation: Window cleaners.
More Information: theukfd.net/56825110

Rainbow International Ltd
Telephone: 01623 675 100
Website: www.rainbow-int.co.uk
Summary of Operation: Fire and flood restoration, carpet and upholstry cleaning, leather restoration, carpet and upholstery repair.
More Information: theukfd.net/30187532

SelClene Ltd
Website: www.selclene.co.uk
Summary of Operation: Domestic cleaning agency. All we aim to do is provide you with an honest, reliable and competent cleaner in your local area – irrespective of where you live.
More Information: theukfd.net/48434342

ServiceMaster Fire & Flood Restoration
Telephone: 0116 275 9050
Website: www.servicemaster.co.uk
Summary of Operation: Cleaning at fire and flood damaged premises, commercial and domestic for insurance companies from national accounts.
More Information: theukfd.net/20237302

Sonic Blind Cleaning Services SBCS
Telephone: 0800 019 9661
Summary of Operation: Blind cleaning services.
More Information: theukfd.net/52208766

Sonic Club Clean (UK) Ltd
Telephone: 020 8715 3443
Website: www.sonicclubclean.com
Summary of Operation: Golf club cleaning.
More Information: theukfd.net/79622874

Sonic Golf Ltd (UK)
Telephone: 0800 019 9661
Website: www.sonicgolf.co.uk
Summary of Operation: Ultrasonic golf cleaning services.
More Information: theukfd.net/74064463

Spic & Span Franchise Ltd
Website: www.spicandspanuk.com
Summary of Operation: Cleaning services.
More Information: theukfd.net/23728885

Supacleen
Telephone: 02920 232 525
Website: www.supacleenfranchise.co.uk
Summary of Operation: Management franchise of office cleaning and support services to professional organisations. A unique and essential commercial contract cleaning service.
More Information: theukfd.net/12544431

SuperGleam
Website: www.supergleam.com
Summary of Operation: Management franchise for wheelie bin cleaning.
More Information: theukfd.net/07271531

Swissmaid
Telephone: 08456 600 566
Website: www.swissmaid.co.uk
Summary of Operation: Reliable and competitive domestic and commercial cleaning services.
More Information: theukfd.net/42227147

The Dry Cleaning Development Partnership Ltd (DCDP)
Telephone: 0800 8223 440
Website: www.dcdpltd.co.uk
Summary of Operation: Suppliers of high quality dry cleaning machines and finishing equipment.
More Information: theukfd.net/41655462

The Mattress Doctor Ltd
Telephone: 0845 3306 607
Website: www.matdoc.co.uk
Summary of Operation: Mattress sanitisation.
More Information: theukfd.net/07547748

The Wheel Specialist
Telephone: 0845 017 6464
Website: www.thewheelspecialist-franchise.co.uk
Summary of Operation: The wheel specialist is operating in an ever increasing market worth £100,000's. With rapid start up and entry into a captive market this is the perfect franchise opportunity. Receive £1,000's worth in leads every month and enjoy the success you deserve.
More Information: theukfd.net/53362246

Time for You Ltd
Telephone: 0845 300 9074
Website: www.timeforyoultd.co.uk
Summary of Operation: Domestic cleaning.
More Information: theukfd.net/80426027

ToyGuard Ltd
Telephone: 0845 300 6181
Website: www.toyguard.co.uk
Summary of Operation: ToyGuard's free online resources are designed for childcare professionals. The tips and advice from our team of experts include downloadable hygiene procedure guides, wallcharts and posters to remind children about the importance of hygiene etc.
More Information: theukfd.net/93044395

Trash Express
Telephone: 0844 357 5681
Website: www.trashexpress.co.uk
Summary of Operation: Waste collection.
More Information: theukfd.net/43589906

U C Clear
Telephone: 01245 363 988
Website: www.ucclear.com
Summary of Operation: Window cleaning.
More Information: theukfd.net/93286515

UK Commercial Cleaning Services Ltd
Telephone: 0191 415 5610
Website: www.uk-cc.co.uk
Summary of Operation: UK Commercial Cleaning Services has grown significantly over the last five years and has successfully expanded its company-owned operation from its North East and Midlands depots to include national coverage.
More Information: theukfd.net/14807599

VIP Bin Cleaning Ltd
Telephone: 01953 857 830
Website: www.vipbincleaning.co.uk
Summary of Operation: VIP Bin Cleaning clean and deodorise all types of bins, from domestic wheeled bins to large commercial bins and compactors with their bespoke mobile cleaning unit.
More Information: theukfd.net/75700852

Vip-Valet Ltd
Telephone: 0870 8033 997
Website: www.vip-valet.co.uk
Summary of Operation: VIP Valet have developed an environmentally friendly and trusted method of car valeting.
More Information: theukfd.net/02064410

Washroom Resolutions (GB) Ltd
Telephone: 020 8827 0938
Website: www.washroomresolutions.com
Summary of Operation: Specialist hygiene programmes and treatments, which give washrooms an initial deep clean followed by a weekly maintenance care programme.
More Information: theukfd.net/92404813

Wellshine
Telephone: 0800 0462 912
Website: www.wellshine.co.uk
Summary of Operation: At Well shine we offer a localised service that cares for all your domestic requirements.
More Information: theukfd.net/4263674

White Knight Laundry Services Ltd
Telephone: 01189 462 233
Website: www.white-knight.co.uk
Summary of Operation: Personal laundry and dry cleaning services delivered and collected from home or work. Quality and convenience on your doorstep.
More Information: theukfd.net/72746155

Franchise Notes

Shortlist

Franchise Tips

Speak to franchise owners

When researching franchise opportunities, this part is crucial. Having met with the franchisor you will need to speak with as many of their existing franchise owners as possible. Obtain an up to date list when you meet with the franchisor and arrange a convenient time to contact them. Questions that you should consider asking them include:

- What attracted them to the franchise?
- How long have they been trading?
- How supportive has the franchisor been?
- Has the franchisor fulfilled their obligations?
- Have they achieved their business plan targets?
- How easy was the system to learn?
- What do you enjoy most about the business?

SERVICES | Health & Beauty

Actively recruiting franchise owners

Healthy living, beauty and fitness franchises are available in this sector. An ideal opportunity to enter the beauty and care industry. Franchise opportunities include **Blue Ribbon Community Care** and **Susan Hepburn Clinics**.

Susan Hepburn Clinics Ltd

Summary of Operation: Lose weight without dieting, quit smoking in one hour, moderate or quit alcohol and quit other addictions. The highly successful Susan Hepburn Clinics are looking for enthusiastic, dynamic, focused individuals to build their franchises with Founder Susan Hepburn and lead the brand in its UK franchise development.

Ideal Franchise Owner Profile:
Must be professional, able to relate to clients on a confidential basis, possess the drive and personal motivation needed to make the business a success and be a team player.

Cost of Franchise: from £25,750 + VAT

Franchise Owner Contact: Richard Langrick

Year Company Established: 1987

Number of Company Outlets: 1
Number of Franchise Owners Planned: UK 50

Overseas Operations Existing: None
Overseas Operations Planned: USA, Europe, China and Australia.

Management Service Fees: AOR

Breakdown of Package: Initial and ongoing training including everything required to set up your franchise business.

Projected Turnover: AOR
Projected Profit: AOR

Financial Assistance Available: Yes

Training Provided: How to operate and market new business, how to deliver weight loss to groups or individuals, reducing alcohol consumption techniques, quit smoking techniques, quit other addictions and any other new treatments that will be introduced

in the future. Ongoing business development training, marketing initiatives, and support will help keep your business moving in the right direction and assist with the growth of the business.

Training Location: London

Support Services: Ongoing support

Areas of Priority Development: Nationwide

More information: theukfd.net/38643435

Susan Hepburn Clinics (Franchising) Ltd.
136 Harley Street,
London,
W1G 7JZ

t: 01603 620301
e: franmatch@fdsltd.com

bfa Provisional Member
Blue Ribbon Community Care Ltd
118 London Road, Kingston upon Thames, KT2 6QJ

Telephone: 020 8546 3233
Fax: 0845 280 8400
Email: info@blueribboncare.org.uk
Website: www.blueribboncare.org.uk

Summary of Operation: Blue Ribbon Care is an independent health and social care provider specialising in a diverse personalised home care service throughout the UK.

Cost of Franchise: £22,500 + VAT plus working capital

Franchise Owner Contact: Noel Williams

Year Company Established: 2008
Year of First Franchise Owner: 2009

Number of Company Outlets: 3
Number of Franchised Outlets: 15
Number of Franchise Owners Planned: 35

Management Service Fees: 4.5% on a reducing scale.

Breakdown of Package: Comprehensive residential induction training course, Operations Manual, new PC with Microsoft, Sage and Staffplan Roster software, personalised and hosted email addresses and website with CMS, stationery pack, business forms and promotional materials, comprehensive staff training materials, initial membership of the Professional Care Association, assistance with compliance for the regulating authority, market research specific to your defined territory, licensing rights to a specific own defined territory, ongoing training for franchise owners and their staff and lots more.

Training Provided: Full training and support provided consisting of initial one week's residential and one week office based followed by on-going workshops and seminars.

Training Location: North Wales, Kingston upon Thames and own territory.

Support Services: 24/7 care and business support, including centralised recruitment and marketing.

More Information: theukfd.net/78308217

bfa Full Member
Caremark Ltd
Caremark Limited, C1 Yeoman Gate, Yeoman Way, Worthing, BN13 3QZ

Telephone: 01798 873 770
Email: franchise@caremark.co.uk
Website: www.caremark.co.uk

Summary of Operation: Caremark is a domiciliary care provider and offers a white-collar management franchise opportunity. The role of the franchise owner is to oversee the development of the business and manage a team of carers who provide quality home care in their designated territory.

Ideal Franchise Owner Profile: Franchise owners will need to be professional and passionate about the business, genuinely caring for other people, dedicated to working to the proven Caremark standards and committed to true business building.

Cost of Franchise: £29,500 + VAT plus working capital

Franchise Owner Contact: Patrick Thompson
More Information: theukfd.net/58746035

247 Professional Health (Franchising)
Telephone: 07739 701 702
Website: www.247phc.com
Summary of Operation: 247 Professional health supplies staff to residential homes, care homes, rest homes, nursing homes, EMI care homes, mental health centres and into the domiciliary care sector.
More Information: theukfd.net/87583271

A1 Nursing & Homecare Agency Ltd
Telephone: 01942 496 352
Website: www.a1nursing.co.uk
Summary of Operation: A1 Nursing & Homecare Agency is committed to providing you with a professional service of quality.
More Information: theukfd.net/48232118

Abacus Care (Homecare & Nursing Services) Ltd
Telephone: 01695 585 400
Website: www.abacuscare.com
Summary of Operation: Abacus Care is an employment business providing temporary staffing solutions to the nursing and health care industry.
More Information: theukfd.net/85804324

Dr SpaFish
Telephone: 01277 725 208
Website: www.drspafish.com
Summary of Operation: The Provision of a walk in pedicure treatment using the Garra Rufa Doctor Fish (Native species of Turkey) in a bright and friendly atmosphere located in high footfall shopping areas. Our USP is undoubtedly the unique 11 Stage Filtration and purification system we use, unique in it's quality of effectiveness and safety.
More Information: theukfd.net/59964844

Energie Fitness Clubs
Telephone: 0845 363 1020
Summary of Operation: Energie is one of the fastest growing fitness club brands in the UK. Clubs are built on commitment to high levels of service and a unique 'results guarantee'
More Information: theukfd.net/36421743

Energie Personal Fitness Ltd
Telephone: 0845 363 1020
Website: www.energiepf.com
Summary of Operation: Health and fitness clubs.
More Information: theukfd.net/56087028

ERA Healthcare
Telephone: 01243 605 111
Website: www.erahealthcare.com
Summary of Operation: Quality care service helping people requiring special needs assistance in their own homes.
More Information: theukfd.net/18245874

Essensuals
Telephone: 01753 612 040
Website: www.essensuals.co.uk
Summary of Operation: Hairdressing.
More Information: theukfd.net/14462555

Everycare (UK) Ltd
Telephone: 02920 455 300
Website: www.everycare.co.uk
Summary of Operation: Provision of domicillary care and nursing services.
More Information: theukfd.net/30867076

Excel Photonix Systems Ltd
Website: www.excelphotonix.com
Summary of Operation: Photo rejuvenation treatments for ageing or damaged skin.
More Information: theukfd.net/15537132

Fake Bake UK Ltd
Telephone: 08448 56 57 58
Website: www.fakebake.co.uk
Summary of Operation: The first superior self-tan to combine naturally derived tanning agents DHA and Erythulose – guaranteeing longer lasting, natural-looking results.
More Information: theukfd.net/91070823

Fight Fit Training & Development
Telephone: 020 7788 7825
Website: www.fightfit.co.uk
Summary of Operation: Fitness franchise.
More Information: theukfd.net/88225557

Fit 'N' Fun Kids Ltd
Telephone: 01326 379 428
Website: www.fitnfunkids.co.uk
Summary of Operation: Providers of day care, mobile creches, physical activity classes and children's entertainment.
More Information: theukfd.net/60168670

Fit4Less (Energie)
Telephone: 0845 363 1020
Website: www.fitless.net
Summary of Operation: No frills fitness clubs.
More Information: theukfd.net/74559627

Flexicare Home Services UK Ltd
Telephone: 01452 529 124
Website: www.flexicareuk.co.uk
Summary of Operation: Flexicare Home Services UK offers support and assistance to people aged 18 years and above that have health problems and disabilities. The Flexicare brand is synonymous with knowledge-based care practice and
More Information: theukfd.net/24920202

Foot Health Professionals
Telephone: 01634 863 851
Website: www.foothealthprofessionals.co.uk
Summary of Operation: As chiropodist and foot health professionals we treat all areas of foot health care.
More Information: theukfd.net/98174987

Forresters
Telephone: 0118 987 2860
Website: www.forresters4hair.com
Summary of Operation: Hairdressing salon.
More Information: theukfd.net/45479865

Francesco Group (Holdings) Ltd
Telephone: 01785 247 175
Website: www.francescogroup.co.uk
Summary of Operation: A nationwide chain of hairdressing salons.
More Information: theukfd.net/30003567

Graham Webb International
Telephone: 01869 277 884
Summary of Operation: Hairdressing salon.
More Information: theukfd.net/31403765

Gymophobics Ltd
Telephone: 01785 227 273
Website: www.gymophobics.co.uk
Summary of Operation: A new concept in ladies only gyms specifically designed for women.
More Information: theukfd.net/20352126

Headlines
Telephone: 01142 368 512
Summary of Operation: Hairdressing salon.
More Information: theukfd.net/17882614

Headmasters
Telephone: 0208 296 6493
Website: www.hmhair.co.uk
Summary of Operation: Hairdressing.
More Information: theukfd.net/70363457

HealthScreening Ltd
Telephone: 01823 325 023
Summary of Operation: Alternative and complementary medicines and therapies.
More Information: theukfd.net/34113385

Heart Tech
Telephone: 01323 468 856
Website: www.heart-tech.com
Summary of Operation: Heart testing machine
More Information: theukfd.net/31634735

Hedz International
Telephone: 01772 705 664
Website: www.hedzinternational.co.uk
Summary of Operation: Gents grooming salons.
More Information: theukfd.net/2752876

HOB Salons
Telephone: 01923 854 100
Website: www.hobsalons.com
Summary of Operation: Chain of hair salons.
More Information: theukfd.net/31546161

Home Instead Senior Care
Telephone: 01925 730 273
Website: www.homeinstead.co.uk
Summary of Operation: Home Instead Senior Care are unique in the care sector in that our sole focus is on the delivery of the highest standards of personal and companionship care to older people in their own homes.
More Information: theukfd.net/81810656

House Of Colour
Telephone: 01923 211 188
Website: www.houseofcolour.co.uk
Summary of Operation: Image consultants.
More Information: theukfd.net/15454806

I&K Hair
Telephone: 0191 491 1551
Website: www.iandkhair.com
Summary of Operation: As one of the top UK hair extensions manufacturer and distributor, we supply the finest 100% natural human hair extensions, synthetic hair extensions, clip in hair extensions, pre-bonded hair extensions, wigs, hair pieces and a wide range of quality hair extension accessories.
More Information: theukfd.net/63274907

Ideal Dental Care
Telephone: 01253 774 366
Website: www.idealdentalcare.co.uk
Summary of Operation: At Ideal Dental Care, we provide a full range of affordable dental treatments to help you and your family maintain a happy, healthy smile.
More Information: theukfd.net/92264124

Jacks Of London
Telephone: 020 8971 2038
Website: www.jacksoflondon.co.uk
Summary of Operation: Jacks Of London is the 'Original Modern Barber' offering men a high quality cut and style experience in stylish, male-only surroundings.
More Information: theukfd.net/65664407

Jason Shankey
Telephone: 028 9065 8000
Website: www.jasonshankey.com
Summary of Operation: Jason Shankey Male Grooming is a UK company that strives to improve the way men look, feel and think about themselves.
More Information: theukfd.net/80763586

Franchise Listings

Kare Plus Ltd
Telephone: 0845 094 9288
Website: www.kareplus.com
Summary of Operation: Nursing and domiciliary care, supplying nurses and carers to the NHS and to private placements.
More Information: theukfd.net/18316084

Keith Hall Hairdressing
Telephone: 0115 972 9914
Website: www.keithhallhairdressing.co.uk
Summary of Operation: Hairdressing salon.
More Information: theukfd.net/97048548

Ladies Workout Express Ltd
Telephone: 028 9024 5004
Website: www.ladiesworkoutexpress.co.uk
Summary of Operation: Ladies fitness centres.
More Information: theukfd.net/86568665

Laser-it Technologies
Telephone: 02392 479 112
Website: www.laser-ittech.co.uk
Summary of Operation: Non-invasive beauty treatments.
More Information: theukfd.net/94212304

LighterLife UK Ltd
Telephone: 01279 636 998
Website: www.lighterlifefranchise.com
Summary of Operation: Ambitious weight-loss and weight-management company.
More Information: theukfd.net/76832232

Likisma Presentations Ltd
Website: www.likismaaromatherapy.com
Summary of Operation: Sale of aromatherapy products.
More Information: theukfd.net/35871670

Lisa Shepherd Salons
Telephone: 01562 748 833
Website: www.lisashepherd.co.uk
Summary of Operation: Hairdressing salon franchise.
More Information: theukfd.net/95663833

Live Well at Home
Telephone: 0845 241 9799
Website: www.livewellathome.co.uk
Summary of Operation: Providing a range of dedicated care services.
More Information: theukfd.net/16988254

L'Occitane Ltd
Telephone: 020 7907 0300
Website: www.uk.loccitane.com
Summary of Operation: Cosmetic and beauty products.
More Information: theukfd.net/92399262

Look Fantastic
Telephone: 01273 425 264
Website: www.salons.lookfantastic.com
Summary of Operation: Hairdressing salon.
More Information: theukfd.net/40311654

Meditech Clinics
Telephone: 023 9241 5000
Website: www.meditechclinics.co.uk
Summary of Operation: Meditech Clinics provide the Beautytek service, a non-invasive body sculpting system combining state-of-the-art technology with a holistic approach, offering a cost effective alternative to surgical body shaping.
More Information: theukfd.net/02825610

Mirage Beauty Salon
Telephone: 0113 249 2509
Website: www.miragebeauty.co.uk
Summary of Operation: Beauty salon.
More Information: theukfd.net/53204930

Monkey Puzzle Day Nursery
Telephone: 01442 878 887
Website: www.monkeypuzzledaynurseries.com
Summary of Operation: Child care.
More Information: theukfd.net/58850782

Mortons Personal Fitness Clubs
Telephone: 01277 217 003
Website: www.mortonsfranchise.com
Summary of Operation: Personal fitness clubs.
More Information: theukfd.net/88670516

Motivation & Co.
Telephone: 01937 557 166
Website: www.motivation-and-co.com
Summary of Operation: Specialist recreation and motivation classes for residents and care homes.
More Information: theukfd.net/50407253

Motorcise Ltd
Website: www.motorcise.com
Summary of Operation: Exercise for women who are looking for a gentler way to fitness.
More Information: theukfd.net/46664113

Movers and Shapers
Telephone: 020 7372 4222
Website: www.moversandshapers.net
Summary of Operation: We promise to get you into the shape you want – quicker and with less effort than ever before.
More Information: theukfd.net/07755170

My Time Ltd
Telephone: 0121 766 6699
Website: www.mytime.org.uk
Summary of Operation: My Time CIC is an award winning counselling and self-esteem building service for all the community.
More Information: theukfd.net/46370823

Nailcraft Centre
Telephone: 029 207 66121
Website: www.nailcraftcentre.com
Summary of Operation: Beauty salons specialising in nailcare and ancillary products.
More Information: theukfd.net/26573238

Nailzone
Telephone: 0141 332 1999
Website: www.nailzone.co.uk
Summary of Operation: Nail beauty fashion and health service.
More Information: theukfd.net/39555853

Naturhouse (UK)
Telephone: 01784 255 065
Website: www.naturhouse.com
Summary of Operation: Naturhouse is the leading company in the dietetics and nutrition sector in Spain and it provides specialised services and exclusive products of the highest quality offering a five-star service at a three-star price in a constantly growing sector.
More Information: theukfd.net/26967027

Neal's Yard Remedies
Telephone: 01747 834 600
Website: www.nealsyardremedies.com
Summary of Operation: Neal's Yard Remedies is a pioneer of award-winning organic health and beauty. With the UK's largest range of certified organic products, over 170 - all made here in Britian, herbal remedies, aromatherapy and Therapy Rooms, Neal's Yard Remedies lead the way in ethical organic healthy beauty.
More Information: theukfd.net/48366206

Network Healthcare
Telephone: 0121 633 9045
Website: www.pertempshealthcare.co.uk
Summary of Operation: Established in 2001 as Pertemps Healthcare, Network Health and Social Care is part of the Network Group plc. The focus of our work is to provide specialist healthcare and recruitment services.
More Information: theukfd.net/87324505

New York City Nails
Telephone: 07791 333 968
Website: www.newyorkcitynails.com
Summary of Operation: New York City Nails is a chain of nail salons and nail bars in the UK and Ireland.
More Information: theukfd.net/00851845

No+Vello
Telephone: 020 8123 1466
Website: www.nomasvello.com
Summary of Operation: No+Vello is one of the undisputed worldwide leaders in IPL hair removal and skin rejuvenation.
More Information: theukfd.net/26899611

Nursing Solutions Ltd
Telephone: 01934 522 022
Website: www.nursingsolutions.co.uk
Summary of Operation: Provider of nursing and domiciliary care services.
More Information: theukfd.net/85452495

Oxford Skin Clinics
Telephone: 01245 349 589
Website: www.oxfordskinclinics.co.uk
Summary of Operation: Laser free tattoo removal clinics.
More Information: theukfd.net/18699548

Platinum Academy
Telephone: 0151 260 2705
Website: www.platinum-academy.co.uk
Summary of Operation: Training of beauty therapists.
More Information: theukfd.net/80565226

Pop-in Cosmetics
Telephone: 01279 860 250
Website: www.popincosmetics.co.uk
Summary of Operation: Distribution of high end cosmetics at discount prices on market stalls.
More Information: theukfd.net/16148581

Prestige Nursing (Franchise) Ltd
Telephone: 020 8254 7533
Website: www.prestige-franchise.co.uk
Summary of Operation: Management franchise in recruitment, specialising in the related fields of homecare services and healthcare staffing.
More Information: theukfd.net/34140810

Prevent PLC
Website: www.prevent.co.uk
Summary of Operation: Health screening service on location, schools and work etc.
More Information: theukfd.net/07063510

Purple Care Franchising Ltd
Telephone: 08456 187 121
Website: www.purple-care.com
Summary of Operation: Provide care in the community, otherwise known as home care or domicilary care, to those who wish to remain independent and to be cared for in their own home. A rewarding franchise at the heart of your local community.
More Information: theukfd.net/24533403

QED Clinical Services Ltd
Telephone: 01908 251 480
Website: www.qed-clinical.com
Summary of Operation: QED Clinical Services is the first contract research organisation using a franchise model as their operational structure.
More Information: theukfd.net/35725646

Quit Easy
Telephone: 0845 263 7151
Website: www.quiteasy.co.uk
Summary of Operation: The auricular reflexology technique used in Quit Easy treatments, known across the world as Reality 2000 and Elektromeriden Kobra, was pioneered in the 1980s by Italian Dr Enzo Lamberto, who took the sophisticated technology worldwide, opening centres and ridding customers across the globe of the urge to consume nicotine.
More Information: theukfd.net/78021526

Rapid Whites
Telephone: 0114 237 2232 Sunlodge
Summary of Operation: Rapid white tooth whitening system.
More Information: theukfd.net/03645127

RejuvaLife International Ltd
Telephone: 01372 842 211
Website: www.rejuvasliminternational.com
Summary of Operation: The ultimate health, weight and inch loss programme.
More Information: theukfd.net/12664153

RESULTS4U
Telephone: 0800 975 3075
Website: www.results4u.co.uk
Summary of Operation: RESULTS4U is a 30 minute express fitness club specifically designed for women who want fast results in a friendly atmosphere. If you want to rapidly lose inches and tone up then this is the club for you.
More Information: theukfd.net/25460142

Right at Home UK
Telephone: 01772 289 454
Website: www.rightathomeuk.com
Summary of Operation: Right at Home understands your concerns when it comes to making big decisions regarding your family. For many people, our in-home senior care is the best solution for maintaining a healthy lifestyle and loving relationships.
More Information: theukfd.net/54390335

Rosemary Conley Diet & Fitness Clubs
Telephone: 01509 620 222
Website: www.rosemaryconley.com
Summary of Operation: Operation of diet and fitness clubs.
More Information: theukfd.net/58686618

RUSH Hair
Telephone: 020 8241 2086
Website: www.rush.co.uk
Summary of Operation: RUSH have been running hairdressing salons since the formation of the brand in 1994 and have achieved international status as a hugely influential hairdressing group. RUSH take care of all the hassles of opening your own business from site location, design and shopfit, through to ongoing support and training.
More Information: theukfd.net/24002922

Safehands Network Ltd
Telephone: 0870 844 6688
Website: www.safehandsfranchise.com
Summary of Operation: Complete childcare and senior homecare service provisions.
More Information: theukfd.net/60222865

Saks Franchise Services Ltd
Telephone: 0845 678 0290
Website: www.saks.co.uk
Summary of Operation: UK's leading hair and beauty franchise group with salons on the high street and in health clubs. Services include hairdressing, advanced corrective skin treatments, permanent hair reduction, anti-ageing facials and injectables.
More Information: theukfd.net/52727132

Samedaydoctor
Telephone: 020 7631 0090
Website: www.samedaydoctor.co.uk
Summary of Operation: Samedaydoctor are a leading gum clinic, private doctors surgery, private clinic and STD clinic providing STD tests including HIV tests and Chlamydia tests.
More Information: theukfd.net/63638580

Sanguinum (UK) Ltd
Telephone: 020 7612 4771
Website: www.sanguinum.com
Summary of Operation: Alternative healthcare. The Sanguinum treatment is a medical metabolic weight loss programme which permits a healthy and lasting reduction in weight.
More Information: theukfd.net/95212148

Schapira Jackson Ltd (Virgin Vie)
Telephone: 0118 971 2025
Website: www.schapirajackson.com
Summary of Operation: The exclusive export licensee for Virgin Vie, a subsidiary of Richard Branson's Virgin Group.
More Information: theukfd.net/26085810

Seanhanna Salons
Telephone: 0208 944 0575
Website: www.seanhanna.com
Summary of Operation: Seanhanna is a highly pro-active and energetic hairdressing salon group with a difference. We aim to deliver quality hairdressing at all times with an extremely high level of service.
More Information: theukfd.net/88403089

Shapemaster
Telephone: 01484 666 674
Website: www.shapemaster.co.uk
Summary of Operation: Toning tables. One of the leaders in power assisted exercise.
More Information: theukfd.net/97146681

Shapeup & Go
Telephone: 0161 282 7317
Website: www.shapeupandgo.com
Summary of Operation: Ladies only fitness centre catering predominantly to an older clientele.
More Information: theukfd.net/87409629

Shokk Ltd
Telephone: 0161 877 7870
Website: www.shokk.co.uk
Summary of Operation: To bring professional fitness training to all young people aged between five and 18, to help them achieve an overall healthier lifestyle.
More Information: theukfd.net/75317572

Silky Soles Ltd
Telephone: 01142 684 470
Website: www.silkysoles.co.uk
Summary of Operation: Fish therapy retail opportunities within airports and shopping malls UK and Europe.
More Information: theukfd.net/20373011

SkinFirst
Telephone: 01925 267 475
Website: www.skinfirst.co.uk
Summary of Operation: SkinFirst offer non surgical skin treatments to help you regain your more youthful looks and eradicate those aspects of your appearance, such as unwanted hair, blemishes, wrinkles and sagging.
More Information: theukfd.net/6015407

SkinKind
Telephone: 01535 655 677
Website: www.skinkind.co.uk
Summary of Operation: Industrial skin care produces supply and service.
More Information: theukfd.net/12547204

Slim Holdings Ltd
Telephone: 01202 555 233
Summary of Operation: Medical slimming and cosmetic enhancement clinics.
More Information: theukfd.net/32042018

Smart Care Franchise Ltd
Telephone: 01932 855 353
Summary of Operation: Care franchise.
More Information: theukfd.net/89553374

Spice Isles
Telephone: 01244 651 100
Website: www.spiceisles.co.uk
Summary of Operation: Spice Isles is a beauty salon with a different approach.
More Information: theukfd.net/83286135

Sports Xtra (Franchising) Ltd
Telephone: 08453 716 121
Website: www.sports-xtra.com
Summary of Operation: Sports Xtra leads in providing the exercise program to help overcome childhood obesity.
More Information: theukfd.net/33252504

Stretch-n-Grow Ltd
Telephone: 0844 800 3398
Website: www.stretch-n-grow.co.uk
Summary of Operation: Holistic programme teaching the benefits of health, exercise and good nutrition to children.
More Information: theukfd.net/83203631

Strip Ltd
Telephone: 020 7590 0050
Website: www.2strip.com
Summary of Operation: Home of London's coolest wax bars and lingerie boutiques.
More Information: theukfd.net/21574571

Super Slim
Telephone: 0845 004 8593
Website: www.superslim.co.uk
Summary of Operation: Our way is simple, with easy to follow diets that suit everyone's lifestyle with very little food measuring.
More Information: theukfd.net/10994015

Supreme Home Care Ltd
Telephone: 01952 216 700
Website: www.supreme-homecare.com
Summary of Operation: Provide high quality and dependable home care for clients.
More Information: theukfd.net/88628299

SureSlim UK
Telephone: 0844 585 7560
Website: www.sureslimuk.com
Summary of Operation: Retail sale of wellness programmes for weight loss and general health. Ongoing client one to one support and motivation.
More Information: theukfd.net/25232057

The Best Of Health
Website: www.best-ofhealth.com
Summary of Operation: Reenergise yourself, reduce stress, improve health and performance.
More Information: theukfd.net/56636370

The Body Shop
Website: www.thebodyshop.co.uk
Summary of Operation: The Body Shop is a retailer and offers more than 900 natural beauty products.
More Information: theukfd.net/65162370

The Little Gym
Telephone: 020 3239 0080
Website: www.thelittlegym.co.uk
Summary of Operation: Physical fitness reacreational gymnastics for children with locations nationwide.
More Information: theukfd.net/71343205

The Local Care Company
Telephone: 01204 431 270
Website: www.thelocalcarecompany.co.uk
Summary of Operation: The Local Care Company provide effective and realistically priced care for the elderly in their own homes.
More Information: theukfd.net/85253014

The London Fitness Consultancy Ltd
Telephone: 020 7221 7799
Website: www.londonfitness.co.uk
Summary of Operation: A range of services, holistic approach to training and an unrivalled wealth of experience in the health and fitness industry.
More Information: theukfd.net/07056028

The Natural Way Weight Loss Centres Ltd
Telephone: 0808 1455 655
Website: www.thenaturalway-wlc-uk.co.uk
Summary of Operation: Prominent office-based weight loss business using professional counselling and motivational techniques.
More Information: theukfd.net/31350484

The Perfume Studio
Telephone: 01323 489 049
Website: www.theperfumestudio.com
Summary of Operation: Design your own fragrance at home.
More Information: theukfd.net/42803643

The Spinal Healthclinic
Telephone: 01277 205 746
Website: www.thespinalhealthclinic.com
Summary of Operation: Health clinics and chiropractors.
More Information: theukfd.net/63624223

The Tanning Shop
Telephone: 01325 360 900
Website: www.thetanningshop.co.uk
Summary of Operation: Specialist tanning provider within the UK and Ireland.
More Information: theukfd.net/61621641

The UK Health Partnership
Website: www.healthscreeningltd.co.uk
Summary of Operation: Preventative health screening, direct to the public via mobile units.
More Information: theukfd.net/25302058

TherapyWorks Ltd
Telephone: 01446 794 166
Website: www.therapyworks.co.uk
Summary of Operation: A physiotheraphy franchise.
More Information: theukfd.net/83896378

Tigerlily Childcare Ltd
Telephone: 01273 818 660
Website: www.tigerlilychildcare.co.uk
Summary of Operation: Nanny and maternity agencies.
More Information: theukfd.net/78251133

Tight Light
Telephone: 01702 346 828
Website: www.tightlight.co.uk
Summary of Operation: Beauty treatments, non surgical, for tightening loose skin.
More Information: theukfd.net/07056084

TONI&GUY
Telephone: 01753 612 040
Website: www.toniandguy.co.uk
Summary of Operation: Hair dressing salons.
More Information: theukfd.net/11127558

Turnstyle's The Football & Barber Shop Franchise
Telephone: 01883 717 414
Website: www.turnstyles.co.uk
Summary of Operation: A male barber shop.
More Information: theukfd.net/75475705

Ultim8 fitness Ltd t/as Hire Fitness
Telephone: 0845 226 1233
Website: www.hirefitness.co.uk
Summary of Operation: Hire Fitness is the UK and Irelands leading brand in home fitness equipment hire.
More Information: theukfd.net/26705056

Vision Express
Website: www.visionexpress.com
Summary of Operation: Opticians.
More Information: theukfd.net/84685266

Vision Plus Care Ltd (Specsavers)
Website: www.specsavers.co.uk
Summary of Operation: Optical retailing. Prospective partners must be qualified ophthalmic or dispensing opticians.
More Information: theukfd.net/50641410

Westrow
Telephone: 0113 245 6948
Website: www.westrow-hair.com
Summary of Operation: Hairdressing salon.
More Information: theukfd.net/67886730

Wise Choice Care
Telephone: 01928 569 233
Website: www.primrosecare.co.uk
Summary of Operation: Providers of homecare to people living independantly in thier own homes to people who have physical or learning disabilities.
More Information: theukfd.net/69646996

Workout Express Ltd
Website: www.ladiesworkoutexpress.co.uk
Summary of Operation: Ladies fitness centres.
More Information: theukfd.net/68646132

Zappas
Telephone: 01189 321 777
Website: www.zappas.co.uk
Summary of Operation: Hairdressing salon.
More Information: theukfd.net/85118867

Zooma
Telephone: 01202 483 918
Website: www.zoomakids.com
Summary of Operation: New salon concept where you can sit back and be pampered while the kids have fun.
More Information: theukfd.net/60278025

Franchise Notes

	Shortlist
_____	_____
_____	_____
_____	_____
_____	_____
_____	_____
_____	_____
_____	_____
_____	_____
_____	_____
_____	_____
_____	_____
_____	_____
_____	_____
_____	_____
_____	_____
_____	_____

Franchise Tips

Don't limit your search by sector

"No prior experience required", is one of the most common quotes you will read from a franchisor seeking franchise owners. The reason for this is the commitment within the franchise industry to franchise owner training – in fact all business format franchisors provide it. For the prospective franchise owner, what this means is that you can focus your search on a business that you feel will maximise your financial and lifestyle goals. Rather than looking at a narrow band of franchise opportunities, a full spectrum of potential avenues for business success are open to you.

SERVICES | Indoor & Outdoor Property Care

Actively recruiting franchise owners

Franchises in this sector are opportunities related to cars, vans and automobiles. Many of these franchises are van-based opportunities and can be home-based franchises. Investment levels are lower and many tend to be low cost franchise opportunities. Franchise opportunities include **All Trades Network, Granite Transformations, GreenThumb, NBC Bird and Pest Solutions** and **TruGreen.**

GreenThumb Ltd

Summary of Operation: Successful lawn care management franchise with proven track record in ethical and profitable franchising, with significant return on investment.

Ideal Franchise Owner Profile: Experience in business majoring in managerial and marketing.

Cost of Franchise: From £31,700 + VAT
Franchise Owner Contact: Mark Hallam

Year Company Established: 1986
Year of First Franchise Owner: 1998

Number of Company Outlets: 12
Number of Franchised Outlets: 191
Number of Franchise Owners Planned: 300

Overseas Operations Existing: None
Overseas Operations Planned: EU

Management Service Fees: 7% and 2% marketing.

Breakdown of Package: Exclusive licence, fully equipped liveried vehicle, machinery, materials, bespoke software, computer, uniforms, training, manuals and marketing campaign.

Projected Turnover: AOR
Projected Profit: AOR
Financial Assistance Available: NatWest, HSBC and Lloyds TSB.

Training Provided: Comprehensive initial two week training course.
Training Location: Head office and in territory.

Support Services: Sales and marketing assistance, software support, technical support etc.

Areas of Priority Development: Various. Limited remaining virgin territories but increasing resale opportunities nationally.

More Information: theukfd.net/46725587

GreenThumb Ltd
Integra, St Asaph Business Park,
St Asaph, Denbighshire, LL17 0DJ

t: 01745 586041
f: 01745 586063
e: franchise@greenthumb.co.uk
w: www.greenthumb.co.uk

A True Management Franchise

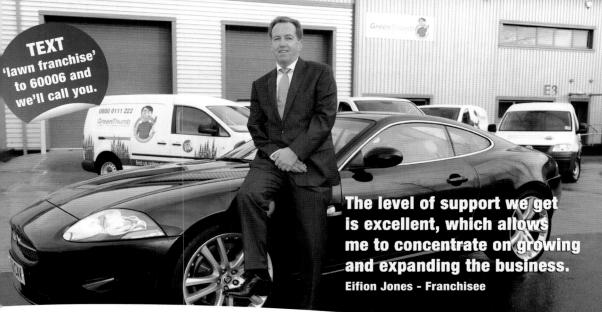

There are more than 20 Million homes in the U.K. and the vast majority have a lawn.

GreenThumb is by far the market leader in lawncare currently servicing over 450,000 lawns throughout the U.K. Our satisfied customers value our straight forward, professional and reliable service, which we have been delivering since 1986.

GreenThumb franchisees are experiencing the satisfaction, rewards and recognition that come from operating our successful and profitable business format franchise - our largest franchise services over 10,000 lawns and many of our others service over 3,000 lawns.

GreenThumb's goal is to service 1 million beautiful lawns within the next few years. We need the right people to help us achieve this.

This is NOT A JOB, but a Management Franchise Opportunity providing:

· Year-round business - not seasonal
· Repeat business year after year, after year
· Access to a huge, untapped market
· A proven successful and profitable method
· High customer satisfaction and referral rate
· Multiple van and crew structure
· Comprehensive training in our Method and systems
· Bespoke lawncare software
· Access to Nutragreen® feeds
· Total investment from £31,700 (+VAT)
· Resale Opportunities Available

For a full information pack on this ALL INCLUSIVE franchise, call us today on:

01745 58 60 41

or email us at:
franchise@greenthumb.co.uk

bfa
FULL MEMBER

www.greenthumb.co.uk

GreenThumb
LAWN TREATMENT SERVICE

GRANITE ®
transformations
The top that fits on top

bfa
ASSOCIATE

Granite Transformations

Summary of Operation: Combining the finest Italian granite, quartz or recycled glass, with state-of-the-art polymer technology, Granite Transformations produces unique agglomerate surfaces, which are either fitted directly over existing worktops or installed as new kitchen work surfaces. With the introduction of a door replacement programme, Granite Transformations now offers a complete kitchen makeover solution.

Ideal Franchise Owner Profile: Individuals, couples or families able to demonstrate 100% commitment and enthusiasm, preferably with a proven track record in sales, combined with strong people management skills. Granite Transformations will provide full product orientation, extensive in-house training and comprehensive operational support.

Cost of Franchise: £29,975 + VAT

Franchise Owner Contact: Katy Daws

Year Company Established: 1996, first UK franchise 2004

Year of First Franchise Owner: 2004

Training Provided: 4-week comprehensive induction course, consisting of on-the-job training and classroom tuition.

Support Services: National advertising, PR and online promotion, Franchise Advisory and Support Team (FAST) working in the field with franchise owners, and extensive marketing tools for targeting local new business opportunities.

More Information: theukfd.net/12874638

Granite Transformations
Unit 28, Decimus Park,
Kingstanding Way, Tunbridge Wells,
TN2 3GP

t: 01892 509 680
w: www.gtfranchise.co.uk
e: franchiseleads@granitetransforma-tions.co.uk

bfa Provisional Member

All Trades Network Ltd

Unit 4, Elder Court, Lions Drive, Blackburn,
Lancashire, BB1 2EQ

Telephone: 0161 926 9882
Email: gill@fdsnorth.com

Summary of Operation: Property repair specialists
servicing the insurance and property industries, and
private property owners. As an All Trades Network
franchise owner you will manage a complete
building repair and maintenance service, providing
one convenient and reliable point of contact for your
clients.

Ideal Franchise Owner Profile: We are looking for
hands-on individuals with management experience
who can provide a first class service to the insurance
and property industry, as well as private
householders. They must be committed to building
on the strength of the All Trades brand in their area.

Cost of Franchise: £20,000 + VAT
Franchise Owner Contact: Gill O'Brien
Year Company Established: 2002
Year of First Franchise Owner: 2005
Number of Company Outlets: 1
Number of Franchised Outlets: 33
Number of Franchise Owners Planned: 75
Overseas Operations Existing: None
Overseas Operations Planned: None
Management Service Fees: 10% of turnover

Breakdown of Package: Franchise Licence,
Operations Manual, initial and ongoing training, web
presence, yell.com (first year), HR and H&S cover
(first year), stationery and workwear starter pack,
software licences and packages.

Projected Turnover: AOR
Projected Profit: AOR
Financial Assistance Available: RBS and NatWest
Training Provided: Comprehensive training in
Blackburn and in your exclusive territory.
Training Location: Head office and on site.
Support Services: 24/7 call centre, ongoing training
and support, R&D, regular meetings and helpline.
Areas of Priority Development: Various UK.

More information: theukfd.net/67100677

bfa Full Member

NBC Bird & Pest Solutions

17A Maurice, Gaymer Road,
Attleborough, Norfolk, NR17 2QZ

Telephone: 01953 457 979
Fax: 01953 452 870
Email: enquiries@nbcbirdandpest.co.uk
Website: www.nbcbirdandpest.co.uk/franchise

Summary of Operation: NBC Bird & Pest Solutions is
the UK's largest and only national company to offer
falconry and proofing as methods of bird control in
addition to a complete range of pest control
services, all managed totally in-house. The franchise
offers outstanding commercial potential in a growing
industry worth in excess of £60million and whose
services are a necessity and not a luxury in any
economic climate.

Cost of Franchise: £18,500 + VAT

Franchise Owner Contact: John Dickson

Year Company Established: 1993
Year of First Franchise Owner: 2004

Number of Company Outlets: 2
Number of Franchised Outlets: 31

Management Service Fees: 14.5%
(inc.2.5% national marketing fee)

Breakdown of Package: The total investment of
£37,650 includes the franchise fee, our
comprehensive training and support programme
and everything you require to get up and running,
including £10,000 working capital.

Training Provided: An initial comprehensive four
week training plan covering all aspects of the
business and leading to industry recognised
qualifications, giving you the ability to provide a
professional service from day one. Continuous
improvement in industry and business related
developments are provided regularly at specialist
training events, as well as individual support to help
you establish your NBC Franchise.
Training Location: Nationwide

More Information: theukfd.net/35245457

Bespoke Garage Conversions
Telephone: 0800 280 0991
Website: www.bespokegarageconversions.com
Summary of Operation: Garage conversion company. Every job is completed to a pre-formed schedule that all tradesmen adhere to without compromise.
More Information: theukfd.net/65517574

Blue Moon Bathing
Telephone: 01202 666 654
Website: www.bluemoonbathing.com
Summary of Operation: Leading specialist in high quality easy access bathing products for the home. We understand your need for showers and baths that are easy to use, comfortable and safe.
More Information: theukfd.net/71137821

Bob Welfare Ltd
Telephone: 01803 606 651
Summary of Operation: Currency trading. Buying and selling of currencies online.
More Information: theukfd.net/75522475

Bradbury Security Ltd
Telephone: 01724 271999
Website: www.bradburyuk.com
Summary of Operation: Provision and fitting of security grilles, screens and doors.
More Information: theukfd.net/80211316

BTR Ltd
Telephone: 0151 355 2888
Website: www.dunweedin.co.uk
Summary of Operation: Dunweedin' is a new innovative rubber ground-cover product made from recycled tyres. It has been developed in the UK using 100% recycled materials.
More Information: theukfd.net/07767566

Canopies UK
Telephone: 01254 777 002
Website: www.canopiesuk.com
Summary of Operation: Provide a unique self-supporting range of canopies, offering a supply and installation service throughout the UK to both domestic and commercial customers. In addition, we undertake large supply only contracts in association with housing developers and the public sector to whom we offer our standard product range or a bespoke manufacturing service.
More Information: theukfd.net/51339429

Caravan Medic
Telephone: 01525 375 375
Website: www.thecaravanmedic.co.uk
Summary of Operation: Mobile cosmetic repair system for caravans and motor homes. Manufacturer and insurance company approved.
More Information: theukfd.net/54855028

Chem-Dry Franchising Ltd
Telephone: 01482 888 195
Website: www.chemdry.co.uk
Summary of Operation: Chem-Dry provides professional carpet and upholstery and fire and water restoration services.
More Information: theukfd.net/75682657

Cico Chimney Linings Ltd
Telephone: 01986 784 044
Website: www.chimney-problems.co.uk
Summary of Operation: The refining of domestic and non-domestic chimneys using Cicos cast in-situ refractory lining process. Non metallic thus no corrosion and no joints to leak.
More Information: theukfd.net/36207760

Climar Colourfence Ltd
Telephone: 01594 544 276
Website: www.colourfence.co.uk
Summary of Operation: Sales and installation of high quality fencing solutions.
More Information: theukfd.net/34544063

Collective Purchasing
Website: www.collectivepurchasing.co.uk
Summary of Operation: Creates supply savings, savings on food, savings on supplies.
More Information: theukfd.net/62455231

Colour Counsellors Ltd
Telephone: 020 7978 5023
Website: www.colourcounsellors.co.uk
Summary of Operation: Interior decorating colour catalogued samples of wall papers carpets and fabrics.
More Information: theukfd.net/02064001

Complete Weed Control Ltd
Telephone: 01451 820 746
Website: www.completeweedcontrol.co.uk
Summary of Operation: Specialist amenity and industrial weed control service to localauthority, public utility and amenity leisure clients.
More Information: theukfd.net/68461376

Countrywide Floorcare
Telephone: 020 8994 3170
Website: www.countrywidefloorcare.co.uk
Summary of Operation: Floor cleaning services.
More Information: theukfd.net/41826778

Countrywide Grounds Maintenance Ltd
Telephone: 0161 485 6666
Website: www.countrywidegrounds.com
Summary of Operation: Countrywide has years of experience with many leading companies. As the market for professional solutions expands we are able to deliver a quality cost-effective service whilst ensuring customer satisfaction.
More Information: theukfd.net/15506205

Countrywide Lawn Doctor
Telephone: 0161 485 6666
Website: www.countrywidelawndoctor.com
Summary of Operation: Year round domestic lawn treatment service which improves the quality and appearance of the lawn through a regular planned management programme according to the time of year.
More Information: theukfd.net/42037057

Creative Canvas Ltd
Summary of Operation: Manufacturer and distributer of canvases.
More Information: theukfd.net/04202387

Creative Ceilings Ltd
Telephone: 0871 222 2026
Website: www.creativeceilings.co.uk
Summary of Operation: Stretch ceiling systems are high quality, practical, safe and surprisingly economical suspended ceiling solutions for a wide range of applications.
More Information: theukfd.net/69822776

Cuisines Schmidt UK Ltd
Telephone: 07875 506 397
Website: www.cuisines-schmidt.com
Summary of Operation: Household retail.
More Information: theukfd.net/12666937

Cupboard Love UK Ltd
Telephone: 0121 711 4115
Website: www.cupboardlove.co.uk
Summary of Operation: Refurbishing existing kitchen and bedrooms with made to measurereplacement doors and worktops.
More Information: theukfd.net/22670783

DecorateLocal
Telephone: 0808 000 000 8
Website: www.localservicesnetwork.co.uk
Summary of Operation: Retrain and join our nationwide network of qualified decorators.
More Information: theukfd.net/08849868

Delcor Furniture
Telephone: 0191 237 1303
Website: www.delcor-furniture.co.uk
Summary of Operation: Hand craft sofas, chairs and footstools.
More Information: theukfd.net/08325197

Dial a Hubby UK
Telephone: 07921 374 329
Website: www.dialahubby.co.uk
Summary of Operation: Utilise your skills as a professional handyman including full certified locksmith training.
More Information: theukfd.net/64688878

Dinky Diggers
Telephone: 01443 806 151
Website: www.dinky-diggers.com
Summary of Operation: A service that offers building groundwork preparation where there is only a narrow access that traditional diggers cannot access.
More Information: theukfd.net/29631234

Drain Away
Telephone: 01202 779 797
Website: www.drainaway.co.uk
Summary of Operation: Drain Away carries out drain work for a variety of customers including, home owners, businesses, schools, local authorities and insurance companies.
More Information: theukfd.net/53103959

Drain Doctor Ltd
Telephone: 01733 753 939
Website: www.draindoctor.co.uk
Summary of Operation: National plumbing and drainage service company offering 24/7 service.
More Information: theukfd.net/25373022

Dreams and Wishes
Telephone: 07771 528 397
Website: www.dreams-and-wishes.co.uk
Summary of Operation: Helping busy parents design beautiful rooms for little ones.
More Information: theukfd.net/47719448

Dyno-Plumbing Ltd
Telephone: 020 8481 2200
Website: www.dyno.com
Summary of Operation: Professional plumbers offering a 24 hour emergency service.
More Information: theukfd.net/82683154

Dyno-Rod Ltd
Telephone: 020 8481 2200
Website: www.dyno.com
Summary of Operation: A business that provides a professional service for the cleaning and maintenance of drain and pipework systems on a 24 hour emergency and contract basis.
More Information: theukfd.net/21133065

Dyno-Secure Ltd
Telephone: 020 8481 2200
Website: www.dyno.com
Summary of Operation: A business that provides a mobile lock opening, fitting and security installation to homes and businesses.
More Information: theukfd.net/01761613

Eclipse Enterprises Ltd
Telephone: 0800 612 8846
Website: www.eclipsetinting.co.uk
Summary of Operation: Window tinting.
More Information: theukfd.net/55129729

Ed's Garden Maintenance
Telephone: 0845 108 0121
Website: www.edsgardenmaintenance.co.uk
Summary of Operation: Garden maintenance franchise providing a guarantee of work to get your business up and running followed by continuous support.
More Information: theukfd.net/1384678

ElecLocal
Telephone: 0808 000 000 8
Website: www.eleclocal.co.uk
Summary of Operation: Electrical installation and maintenance services.
More Information: theukfd.net/33155251

Energy My Way
Telephone: 01865 873880
Website: www.energymyway.co.uk
Summary of Operation: Our mission is to reduce the CO_2 emissions and energy costs associated with running any property.
More Information: theukfd.net/48260013

Envirocare Maintenance Solutions
Telephone: 0800 028 3329
Website: www.envirocarems.co.uk
Summary of Operation: Envirocare Maintenance Solutions are a nationwide landscape and playground maintenance company. We aim to provide a fully comprehensive service to all sectors of business, from industrial parks to housing associations to hospitals.
More Information: theukfd.net/63570033

Fastplumb
Website: www.fastplumbltd.com
Summary of Operation: Bathroom planners and furnishers.
More Information: theukfd.net/84753364

First4blinds Ltd
Website: www.first4blinds.com
Summary of Operation: Supply and fitting of domestic and commercial blinds.
More Information: theukfd.net/40726637

Fit-ex Ltd
Telephone: 01372 275 037
Website: www.fit-ex.com
Summary of Operation: Complete curtain and blind fitting service.
More Information: theukfd.net/22253853

Flying Colours
Telephone: 01675 471 150
Website: www.flycolours.co.uk
Summary of Operation: Flying Colours is the UK's leading expert in the removal of bumper scuffs, scratches, chipped paintwork and interior damage.
More Information: theukfd.net/09516331

FogX
Telephone: 0800 804 8804
Website: www.fogx.co.uk
Summary of Operation: Sealed unit repair specialists.
More Information: theukfd.net/23494784

Freedom Group of Companies
Telephone: 01924 887 766
Website: www.freedom-group.co.uk
Summary of Operation: Trade service by qualified tradesmen to buiness and domestic sector.
More Information: theukfd.net/50308537

Furniture Clinic
Telephone: 01207 279 960
Website: www.furnitureclinic.co.uk
Summary of Operation: Leather cleaners and conditioners, leather dye and restoration, leather repair, protection and aroma products.
More Information: theukfd.net/49615243

Furniture Medic
Telephone: 0116 275 9005
Website: www.servicemaster.co.uk
Summary of Operation: Furniture Medic are professionally-trained onsite restoration experts. Franchise owners repair wood, laminate, upholstery, leather and even marble.
More Information: theukfd.net/71273566

GarageTek
Telephone: 01491 579 975
Website: www.garagetek.com
Summary of Operation: In early 2000, a new home improvement market began and a new company was launched. That year, GarageTek became the first national firm to offer a custom, installed garage organisation and storage system.
More Information: theukfd.net/81050174

Garden Lodges
Telephone: 0800 043 4821
Website: www.gardenlodges.co.uk
Summary of Operation: Garden Lodges offer garden offices, lodges, studios, rooms and garden buildings with a complete planning and installation service nationwide.
More Information: theukfd.net/14668856

Gardeneer UK Ltd
Telephone: 0844 822 0777
Website: www.gardeneer.co.uk
Summary of Operation: Garden maintenance. The franchise can be run by a man and a van or more typically as a management franchise employing three or four gardeners.
More Information: theukfd.net/83774274

Gas-Elec Safety Systems
Telephone: 01895 420 777
Website: www.gas-elec.co.uk
Summary of Operation: Nationwide safety inspections of gas and electrical equipment and installations. Gas-Elec carries out impartial safety inspections and light remedial works.
More Information: theukfd.net/20447740

GasLocal
Telephone: 0808 000 000 8
Website: www.localservices.co.uk
Summary of Operation: Gas service.
More Information: theukfd.net/27331733

Gautier
Telephone: 01727 877 977
Website: www.gautier.co.uk
Summary of Operation: Premium French furniture brand.
More Information: theukfd.net/45441518

Glass Clean
Telephone: 01428 715500
Website: www.glassclean.co.uk
Summary of Operation: Shower screens collect a build up of lime scale and soap deposits, when used. By having a hydrophobic coating applied to your shower screen, it becomes easier to clean as the coating, which has bonded with the glass surface, prevents the build up of deposits.
More Information: theukfd.net/76272797

Glass Exchange
Telephone: 01425 273158
Website: www.glassexchangefranchise.co.uk
Summary of Operation: Double glazing repairs.
More Information: theukfd.net/64126772

Green Assess
Telephone: 0845 601 1361
Website: www.greenassess.co.uk
Summary of Operation: Green Assess is a specialist provider of Energy Performance Certificates (EPCs), personal search reports, renewable energy supplies and general home energy advice.
More Information: theukfd.net/62536212

Greensleeves Garden Care Ltd
Telephone: 01484 866 566
Website: www.greensleeves-uk.com
Summary of Operation: Involved in the treatment of lawns to a very high standard of customer service offering top quality support.
More Information: theukfd.net/63828474

Guard Home
Telephone: 01279 324 837
Website: www.guardhome.co.uk
Summary of Operation: Security systems.
More Information: theukfd.net/13462098

Handy Do

Telephone: 0845 226 33 20
Website: www.handydo.co.uk
Summary of Operation: Provision of plumbing, electrical and other property maintenance services.
More Information: theukfd.net/50386434

HandyMan 4 You

Telephone: 0192 632 0210
Website: www.handyman4you.co.uk
Summary of Operation: HandyMan 4 You is able to provide internal and external painting and decorating, as well as general maintenance services.
More Information: theukfd.net/78711675

Handywoman Franchise Ltd

Telephone: 0845 260 0692
Website: www.handywoman.co.uk
Summary of Operation: Handywoman professional property maintenace teams.
More Information: theukfd.net/01601673

High Tech Security

Telephone: 0800 321 30 10
Website: www.hightechsecurity.co.uk
Summary of Operation: Wide range of security services.
More Information: theukfd.net/15874879

Hillarys Blinds

Telephone: 0800 916 7760
Website: www.hillarys.co.uk
Summary of Operation: Shutters and blinds.
More Information: theukfd.net/99107567

Hire a Handyman

Telephone: 01757 630 999
Website: www.hire-a-handyman.co.uk
Summary of Operation: A professional handyman service.
More Information: theukfd.net/41464077

Hire a Hubby Franchise Ltd

Telephone: 0800 111 4664
Website: www.hireahubbygroup.com
Summary of Operation: Our mission is to provide customers from homes, offices, and factories with a complete property maintenance and handyman service for a multitude of jobs.
More Information: theukfd.net/85397509

Home Secure

Telephone: 020 8481 4300
Website: www.yourhomesecure.co.uk
Summary of Operation: Home security franchise in association with Yale.
More Information: theukfd.net/00846236

Housetwo Handyman

Telephone: 0845 095 6845
Website: www.housetwo.com
Summary of Operation: If you need to hire a trusted handyman in West Yorkshire just pick up the phone and contact us today for a fair and honest local handyman service.
More Information: theukfd.net/66379645

Humitech UK Ltd

Website: www.humitech.co.uk
Summary of Operation: Humitech is the manufacturer and exclusive distributor for the family of biosmart filters.
More Information: theukfd.net/18230206

Interiors by Decorating Den

Website: www.decoratingden.co.uk
Summary of Operation: Full service mobile interior design. soft furnishings floor coverings, wall covering, furniture, lighting and paints.
More Information: theukfd.net/81051838

IRT Surveys

Telephone: 01382 228 700
Website: www.irtsurveys.co.uk
Summary of Operation: Europe's largest infra-red building surveyor.
More Information: theukfd.net/97738612

Jim's Mowing Group

Telephone: 0845 500 1010
Website: www.jimsmowing.co.uk
Summary of Operation: Jims offer both the domestic and commercial market a full garden maintenance solution.
More Information: theukfd.net/53136414

Just Fitted Kitchens

Telephone: 01245 230 787
Website: www.justfittedkitchens.com
Summary of Operation: We specialise in the manufacture, design and installation of quality handmade kitchens to clients exact and specific requirements.
More Information: theukfd.net/86723237

Just Shutters

Telephone: 01202 240 769
Website: www.justshutters.co.uk
Summary of Operation: Just Shutters offers the complete range of plantation shutters including solid wood, we regularly install both solid and louvered shutters and specialise in all window shapes including round, angled, arched and the interesting shapes needed for conservatories and glass roofs.
More Information: theukfd.net/72586933

KerbAppeal

Telephone: 0118 949 7324
Website: www.kerbappealuk.com
Summary of Operation: Specialise in efficient and surprisingly affordable building and renovation work in the Reading and Henley-on-Thames areas. We offer a truly economical project managed service that will cost you less than any other form of construction.
More Information: theukfd.net/31089388

Kitchen George

Telephone: 020 8144 3755
Website: www.kitchen-george.com
Summary of Operation: Join the team of independent suppliers to the kitchen fitting trade, supplying high quality rigid kitchens, that have been made in Britain.
More Information: theukfd.net/58867120

Lakeside Security

Telephone: 01792 561 117
Website: www.lakesidesecurity.co.uk
Summary of Operation: Manufacture and installation of garage doors, security shutters and awnings.
More Information: theukfd.net/75373204

Lawn 3

Telephone: 0800 612 9465
Website: www.lawn3.co.uk
Summary of Operation: One of the fastest growing domestic lawn care companies in the UK.
More Information: theukfd.net/20363844

Lawnhopper Ltd

Telephone: 0151 353 0707
Website: www.lawnhopper.co.uk
Summary of Operation: Lawn treatment service including core aeration and machine scarification.
More Information: theukfd.net/18038518

Lawnscience

Telephone: 01908 504 664
Website: www.lawnscience.co.uk
Summary of Operation: One of the leading UK lawn care companies, providing customers with a programme of beneficial lawn treatments to improve the quality of their lawns. A profitable and rapidly growing business, offering a work/lifestyle balance that is right for you and your family.
More Information: theukfd.net/62052887

Lazy Lawn

Telephone: 01572 768 208
Website: www.lazylawn.co.uk
Summary of Operation: Suppliers of artificial grass ideal for any area. A range of artificial grass and artificial lawn.
More Information: theukfd.net/30022321

Lifecote

Telephone: 0800 043 2096
Website: www.dampproofingnationwide.com
Summary of Operation: Lifecote™ can treat damp and timber problems in all types of properties from a terraced house through to a listed building, school or commercial development.
More Information: theukfd.net/89955191

Lime Orchard

Telephone: 0845 539 1467
Website: www.limeorchard.co.uk
Summary of Operation: A unique chance to own and operate an innovative garden design and build a business capitalising on the strength of the brand.
More Information: theukfd.net/16872218

Lockfast

Telephone: 08701 454 441
Website: www.lockfast.org.uk
Summary of Operation: Lockfast has a country wide network of highly trained and experienced locksmiths who are able to respond rapidly to any emergency.
More Information: theukfd.net/11231651

Lockmasters Mobile Ltd

Telephone: 01525 718 895
Website: www.lockmastersmobile.co.uk
Summary of Operation: 24 hour moblie locksmith service including domestic and commercial work.
More Information: theukfd.net/40847478

LockRite Locksmiths Ltd
Telephone: 08000 787 275
Website: www.lockritesecurity.co.uk
Summary of Operation: Locksmiths.
More Information: theukfd.net/53812092

LocksXpress
Website: www.locksxpress.com
Summary of Operation: Our locksmiths are highly skilled and experienced and pride themselves on their professional and reliable approach.
More Information: theukfd.net/71321070

Loft Lagger
Telephone: 0845 601 1361
Website: www.loftlagger.co.uk
Summary of Operation: Loft insulation specialists.
More Information: theukfd.net/83722997

Loftman Industries
Telephone: 0121 441 3995
Website: www.loftmanindustries.co.uk
Summary of Operation: We specialise in fitting loft ladders, boarding, lights, windows and insulation for homes around the UK so that people can have easy access to another room in their house or an extra place to store their stuff.
More Information: theukfd.net/87514270

Marla Custom Blinds
Telephone: 01329 849 922
Website: www.marlacustomblinds.co.uk
Summary of Operation: Marla Custom Blinds invites you to become part of a network of highly trained, knowledgeable and motivated franchise operators. All Marla Custom Blinds franchise owners have the advantage of being able to offer a huge range of blinds and awnings, plus a comprehensive service that encompasses everything from survey to installation.
More Information: theukfd.net/96126577

Master Thatchers Ltd
Website: www.themasterthatchers.co.uk
Summary of Operation: Thatching franchise.
More Information: theukfd.net/16408328

Matts Mowing UK Ltd
Telephone: 01737 735 150
Website: www.mattsmowing.co.uk
Summary of Operation: Complete lawn care service.
More Information: theukfd.net/4668705

Metro Rod Ltd
Telephone: 0808 208 3098
Website: www.metrorod.co.uk
Summary of Operation: Drain care and repair.
More Information: theukfd.net/81147616

Mia Designer Surfaces
Telephone: 01273 413 314
Website: www.miadesignersurfaces.co.uk
Summary of Operation: Flooring specialists.
More Information: theukfd.net/91650036

Mixamate Holdings Ltd
Telephone: 0800 288 8001
Website: www.mixamate.com
Summary of Operation: Unique specialised service builders and home improvers for the provision of mixed concrete, the system is based upon a patented purpose built vehicle which carries all the materials.
More Information: theukfd.net/41678245

Mr Electric
Telephone: 01527 578 157
Website: www.mr-electric.co.uk
Summary of Operation: Commercial and residential electrical installation, maintenance and repair work.
More Information: theukfd.net/60485057

MyTiles
Summary of Operation: With a contemporary store design that is customer-friendly and incorporates bathroom and shower displays, an extensive range of tiles and high visibility advertising.
More Information: theukfd.net/78061041

New Image Tiles Ltd
Telephone: 01305 781 709
Website: www.new-image-tiles.co.uk
Summary of Operation: New Image Tiles is a family run company who take great pride in providing their customers with all of the help and guidance they require.
More Information: theukfd.net/77536766

nicenstripy
Telephone: 0845 230 7676
Website: www.nicenstripy.com
Summary of Operation: Residential lawn cutting, care service and gardening franchise.
More Information: theukfd.net/67567622

Nu Life Stone Care Ltd
Telephone: 0161 480 7284
Website: www.floorcarefranchise.co.uk
Summary of Operation: High income marble, stone and floor care franchise.
More Information: theukfd.net/2289357

Oakleaf Sales Ltd
Telephone: 01535 663 274
Website: www.oakleaf.co.uk
Summary of Operation: Oakleaf manufactures high quality decorative mouldings, offering a wide range including replica oak beams and antique oak wall panelling.
More Information: theukfd.net/88030642

Pat Test Pro
Telephone: 0800 1957 839
Website: www.pattestpro.co.uk
Summary of Operation: Commercial electrical safety testing.
More Information: theukfd.net/59368704

Paviour Doctor
Telephone: 0800 197 3440
Website: www.paviourdoctor.co.uk
Summary of Operation: Extensive knowledge of paving, combined with the most powerful advanced machinery and cleaning and sealing solutions.
More Information: theukfd.net/18821312

Plumblocal Ltd
Telephone: 0808 000 000 8
Website: www.plumblocal.co.uk
Summary of Operation: Re-train and qualify as a Plumber offering domestic and commercial plumbing services.
More Information: theukfd.net/71533624

Powerflush Ltd
Telephone: 0800 731 7939
Website: www.pflush.com
Summary of Operation: Make existing central heating systems work like new.
More Information: theukfd.net/31109563

Pro Lawncare Ltd
Telephone: 01480 812 393
Website: www.prolawncare.co.uk
Summary of Operation: Garden landscape services.
More Information: theukfd.net/85874761

Property Cashpoint
Telephone: 0191 250 4313
Website: www.propertycashpoint.co.uk
Summary of Operation: Property investment franchise.
More Information: theukfd.net/14916913

ReactFast Solutions Ltd
Telephone: 0121 666 5680
Website: www.reactfastfranchises.co.uk
Summary of Operation: Emergency and contract plumbing, heating, drainage and locksmith services.
More Information: theukfd.net/71512017

Red Hot Camera
Telephone: 0787 327 2078
Website: www.redhotcamera.com
Summary of Operation: We provide a comprehensive 'one stop shop' range of services to ensure you will be fully prepared when marketing your home.
More Information: theukfd.net/59982557

Re-Nu Kitchens
Telephone: 01202 687 642
Website: www.re-nukitchens.co.uk
Summary of Operation: Replacement kitchen and bedrooms made to measure doors.
More Information: theukfd.net/09856678

Renubath Services Ltd
Telephone: 0800 138 2202
Website: www.renubath.co.uk
Summary of Operation: Bath renovations and invisible chip repairs to enamel, plastics,worktops and windows etc.
More Information: theukfd.net/56764812

RG Maintenance Services Ltd
Telephone: 01362 858 190
Website: www.rgmaintenance.co.uk
Summary of Operation: Commercial ground, building and environmental maintenance services.
More Information: theukfd.net/66580142

Ripples Ltd
Telephone: 01225 335 111
Website: www.ripples.ltd.uk
Summary of Operation: Ripples has become famed for designing and creating bespoke, luxury bathroom spaces.
More Information: theukfd.net/41121741

Rooferman
Telephone: 08000 341 799
Website: www.rooferman.co.uk
Summary of Operation: Man in a van franchise offering roof maintenance services.
More Information: theukfd.net/75982170

Royle Security Ltd
Telephone: 0500 1 0500 2
Website: www.roylesecurity.com
Summary of Operation: Supply and installation of alarms, CCTV, door entry and security lighting.
More Information: theukfd.net/75741247

Sash-Glaze
Telephone: 01794 518 808
Website: www.sashglaze.com
Summary of Operation: Sash-Glaze is a new franchise opportunity offering inexpensive safe secondary glazing for cold sash windows.
More Information: theukfd.net/45301673

Security I
Telephone: 08455 191 668
Website: www.securityi.co.uk
Summary of Operation: Securit, intruder alarms etc.
More Information: theukfd.net/21733489

SkidProof International Ltd
Telephone: 0870 7478 051
Website: www.skidproof.co.uk
Summary of Operation: Anti-slip coating franchise operation.
More Information: theukfd.net/83195865

Skillfix
Website: www.skillfix.com
Summary of Operation: Domestic plumbing emergencies, commercial plumbing emergencies, central heating annual service and central heating system breakdown etc.
More Information: theukfd.net/82302043

Sliding Sash Solutions Ltd
Telephone: 01293 410 177
Website: www.slidingsashsolutions.co.uk
Summary of Operation: Specialising in sash window replacement, restoration and repair. Sliding Sash Solutions offer sash windows services and window franchise owner opportunities.
More Information: theukfd.net/49539174

Spectacular Driveways UK Ltd
Telephone: 08450 455 567
Website: www.spectaculardriveways.co.uk
Summary of Operation: Decorative paving and floors. Pattern imprinted concrete.
More Information: theukfd.net/76202288

Speedheat UK Ltd
Telephone: 01908 562 211
Website: www.speedheat.co.uk
Summary of Operation: As well as clean, efficient, responsive and completely invisible, Speedheat is the only electric underfloor heating in the UK that is designed and installed to meet your individual needs. Fitted by a nationwide franchise of skilled professional engineers with a full back-up service.
More Information: theukfd.net/97963926

Stay Clean Window Cleaning
Telephone: 0117 982 1857
Website: www.staycleanwindows.co.uk
Summary of Operation: Stayclean Window Cleaning provides a high quality commercial and residential window cleaner service.
More Information: theukfd.net/82300483

Stonebond
Telephone: 01603 74 11 93
Website: www.stonebond.co.uk
Summary of Operation: The Stonebond system is a unique combination of natural stone chippings and specialised resins, bonded together to create a solid surface which is highly decorative as well as being extremely tough and durable. Designed for driveways, patios and paths and can also be installed in conservatories, entrance lobbies and on steps.
More Information: theukfd.net/86124130

Stumpbusters UK
Telephone: 01844 342 851
Website: www.stumpbusters.co.uk
Summary of Operation: Removal of tree stumps using advanced machinery.
More Information: theukfd.net/81880602

Sumo Services Ltd
Telephone: 0845 456 1104
Website: www.sumoservices.com
Summary of Operation: Underground utility detection and survey services.
More Information: theukfd.net/53705107

Supagrass Ltd
Telephone: 020 8808 0242
Website: www.supagrass.co.uk
Summary of Operation: Lawn treatment service specialaising in domestic lawns. We ferilise and weedkill in spring and summer. Moss kill, scarify, hollow tine aerate and top dress in the Autumn and Winter.
More Information: theukfd.net/73428558

Surface Doctor (GB) Ltd
Telephone: 0800 9 800 900
Website: www.surfacedoctor.co.uk
Summary of Operation: Resurfacing anything from baths and tiles to kitchen units and appliances, onsite. Our services are equally suited to domestic and commercial premises.
More Information: theukfd.net/87007274

Survair
Telephone: 0845 458 5364
Website: www.survair.co.uk
Summary of Operation: Providing total approach to industrial and commercial property maintenance. Apply protective coatings to walls, floors and roofs to protect buildings from water ingress to U.V.
More Information: theukfd.net/83155176

Sutton's Contracts Maintenance Ltd
Telephone: 01920 444 388
Website: www.suttonfranchises.com
Summary of Operation: Building facility support company based in London which was originally formed to provide fast response building maintenance.
More Information: theukfd.net/91276680

The 50plus Organisation Ltd
Telephone: 0845 225 0495
Website: www.the50plus.co.uk
Summary of Operation: Provides electrical, plumbing and general maintenance services. The service is provided by the mature workforce of people of all ages.
More Information: theukfd.net/35600725

The Christmas Decorators
Telephone: 0870 890 3633
Website: www.thechristmasdecorators.com
Summary of Operation: Christmas decorations and installation.
More Information: theukfd.net/37634524

The Curtain Exchange
Telephone: 01787 319 099
Website: www.thecurtainexchange.co.uk
Summary of Operation: The Curtain Exchange offers a full range of new bespoke and ready made curtains and accessories with branches around the UK.
More Information: theukfd.net/55251780

The Dulux Design Service
Telephone: 0845 880 6888
Website: www.duluxdesignservice.co.uk
Summary of Operation: Our interior designers can help you get your home looking exactly the way you've always wanted, simply and affordably. We will bring you the latest and very best in interior design at competitive prices, to suit your own individual style and taste.
More Information: theukfd.net/46399526

The Flat Roof Company
Telephone: 01937 530 788
Website: www.flatroof.co.uk
Summary of Operation: A marriage of innovative product and professional service, to bring to the flat roof owning public, the service and satisfaction they have needed.
More Information: theukfd.net/88477336

The Garage Conversion Company (UK) Ltd
Telephone: 01234 834 797
Website: www.garageconversion.com
Summary of Operation: Convert domestic garages into habitable rooms such as play rooms, offices, gyms and cinema rooms.
More Information: theukfd.net/12682482

The Garage Door Company (Scotland) Ltd
Telephone: 0131 337 3332
Website: www.garage-door.co.uk
Summary of Operation: Supply Installation and repair of all types of garage doors and gates both manual and automatic.
More Information: theukfd.net/46086705

The Garage Door Team
Telephone: 0800 915 0001
Website: www.thegaragedoorteam.com
Summary of Operation: Garage door franchise opportunity.
More Information: theukfd.net/55606440

The Grassman Ltd
Telephone: 01295 271 712
Website: www.thegrassman.co.uk
Summary of Operation: We specialise in the preparation and maintenance of grass, and currently mow and care for many small lawns at very affordable rates.
More Information: theukfd.net/91256430

The Kitchen & Bedroom Transformation Co Ltd
Telephone: 01689 831 400
Website: www.kabtfranchise.co.uk
Summary of Operation: Transforming existing kitchens and bedrooms at a fraction of the cost of fitting a new one and designing and fitting new kitchens and bedrooms at direct from factory prices. Showroom based after initial period.
More Information: theukfd.net/17620428

The Lawn Company Ltd
Website: www.lawn.co.uk
Summary of Operation: The lawn company. TLC for your lawn. Interactive lawn forums and lawn shop for your lawn care products. Bespoke lawn care services, weed and moss control etc.
More Information: theukfd.net/58544842

The Plastic Surgeon
Summary of Operation: Surface repairs for wood, metal and plastic.
More Information: theukfd.net/77614838

The Premier Door Company
Telephone: 01724 842 187
Website: www.thepremierdoorcompany.co.uk
Summary of Operation: The first impression of your property is your entrance and here at the Premier Door Company we have one of the largest ranges of doors in the UK.
More Information: theukfd.net/35650952

The Tile Doctor
Telephone: 0845 652 4652
Website: www.tiledoctor.biz
Summary of Operation: Tile Doctor is a UK based business for tile cleaning, stone cleaning, grout cleaning and tile, stone and grout sealing. The specialised nature of the services Tile Doctor provides are beyond the abilities of regular cleaning companies and are of little interest to the typical tiling contractor.
More Information: theukfd.net/89833212

Thermocrete Chimney Lining Systems Ltd
Telephone: 01274 544 442
Website: www thermocrete.com
Summary of Operation: Lining and repairing chimneys, CCTV surveys and reaming chimneys.
More Information: theukfd.net/21062232

TileLocal
Telephone: 0808 000 0000
Website: www.localservices.co.uk
Summary of Operation: Local tiling services franchise with locations nationwide.
More Information: theukfd.net/75761969

Total Paving Solutions
Telephone: 0131 338 7207
Website: www.totalpavingsolutions.co.uk
Summary of Operation: Restoration of paved surfaces, landscaping and construction. With over 25 years experience and 1000's of satisfied customers, Total Paving Solutions is bursting with inspirational ideas and imaginative materials to help turn your vision into reality.
More Information: theukfd.net/3321802

Trade Man's World
Telephone: 0800 183 0482
Website: www.trademansworld.com
Summary of Operation: The firm provides labourers and skilled tradespeople for domestic maintenance and home improvement projects.
More Information: theukfd.net/21440212

TVSAS
Telephone: 01189 582 299
Website: www.tvsas.com
Summary of Operation: TVSAS was established in 2001 to provide a more professional TV and satellite installation service. We understand that our customers television programming needs vary. For that, we have partnered with the nation's premiere one-off and subscription providers.
More Information: theukfd.net/32061818

UK Blinds Direct
Telephone: 01706 341 170
Website: www.ukblindsdirect.com
Summary of Operation: Offering an extensive range of attractive, practical, custom-made and ready-to-fit products.
More Information: theukfd.net/50224736

Urban Planters Franchise Ltd

Telephone: 01562 881 025
Website: www.urbanplanters.co.uk
Summary of Operation: Supply, installation and maintenance of tropical plant displays to commercial premises. We supply and maintain plants to small local businesses, multinationals, bars, restaurants, shopping centres, health clubs and everything in-between. We are professionally trained to design schemes which use the right type of plant for the space to create instant and lasting impact.
More Information: theukfd.net/78370623

Uticolor (Great Britain) Ltd

Telephone: 020 8803 9256
Website: www.uticolor.co.uk
Summary of Operation: Leather furniture repair and restoration services.
More Information: theukfd.net/72734407

Ventrolla Ltd

Telephone: 01423 859 323
Website: www.ventrolla.co.uk
Summary of Operation: Through our national network of craftsmen we have established ourselves as the market leader in sash window and casement window renovation, offering a guaranteed and unique service that avoids the need for unnecessary and costly replacement.
More Information: theukfd.net/02112860

Weed Man

Telephone: 08458 382 387
Website: www.weed-man.co.uk
Summary of Operation: Provides responsible and professional lawn care services to customers needing help maintain healthy surroundings for themselves and their families including elderly, the time-pressed, and those living in areas where horticultural challenges require specialist expertise.
More Information: theukfd.net/15530853

Yourplumber

Telephone: 0800 988 8899
Website: www.yourplumber-uk.com
Summary of Operation: Fast, friendly service and fair prices all delivered by a fully trained and qualified expert.
More Information: theukfd.net/73498339

Did you know...

• Despite the ongoing recession, franchisors in general achieved their turnover targets, with the number of franchise owners as a commonly cited factor in realising turnover expectations.

They likewise expect improved turnover levels and increased uptake of franchised outlets, reflecting higher optimism for the next two years.

• Franchisors recognise that the number of franchise owners within the franchise system will continue to have considerable impact on turnover in the coming years. In view of efforts to increase their franchise owner base, franchisors need to achieve improved financing capabilities, develop their own information resources and acquire human resource competence to effectively train new franchise recruits and pursue internal expansion.

• The inability of franchisors to source capital for expansion is seen as a key barrier to growth, and franchisors hurdle this obstacle by looking at various funding sources. As one important funding source is the licence (initial investment) fees from new franchise owners, franchisors benefit from having a suitable selection of franchise owners with sound credentials and financing capabilities.

However, franchise decisions are not solely confined to the said criteria, as chemistry between franchisor and franchise owner also impacts on the former's decision in awarding franchises.

Industry-specific experience, perceived inclination toward business, attitudes and personality may also come into play in franchise owner selection. It is recognised, however, that the extent to which industry-specific experience impacts selection is contingent on the nature of the franchise business, as surveyed franchise owners typically did not need specialised skills in setting up their respective franchises.

Franchise Notes

Shortlist

_____   _____
_____   _____
_____   _____
_____   _____
_____   _____
_____   _____
_____   _____
_____   _____
_____   _____
_____   _____

Franchise Tips

Draw upon the support of your franchisor

The somewhat clichéd claim 'in business for yourself, but not by yourself' has become a classic marketing line for franchisors marketing their franchise opportunities, justified by the support services supplied to the franchise owner network by the franchisor. By making available a franchise to individuals with no previous business experience, many franchisors recognise the need to assist new franchise owners in getting their business off the ground. This support is funded by the ongoing management service fee paid by franchise owners.

Basic pre-launch support will cover putting together the business plan, right the way up to pre-agreeing funding packages with lenders. Site selection is another area in which franchisors can provide assistance, while telephone support is practically a given when it comes to franchise owner support. Dedicated IT and operational support is usually offered for franchise owners in more complicated sectors, while technical advice is essential for specialist areas.

As franchise owners gain more experience they will require less constant advice and guidance from the franchisor, leading many franchisors to promise an intensive initial support system followed up by a more general programme for the more experienced network.

SERVICES | Leisure & Travel

Actively recruiting franchise owners

From sports and leisure franchises to international travel agents, these are popular franchise opportunities in the UK. Franchise opportunities include **Global Cruising, The Camping and Caravanning Club** and **Travel Center Worldwide**.

Global Cruising

Summary of Operation: The Global Cruising Cruise Travel Professional Franchise opportunity is unique in the Travel industry providing unrivalled access to exclusive products, unique opportunities and a foothold in the UK's fastest growing holiday sector. Supported and working as part of the Freedom Travel Group itself part of the Co-Operative Travel Group.

The Global Cruising opportunity can be operated on a full or part time basis giving valuable supplementary incomes as well as concessionary cruise travel. To truly maximise this opportunity we would recommend that you have a minimum of 30 hours a week to commit although you can work up to this over a period of time.

Ideal Franchise Owner Profile: Good at selling, working with people and creative marketers with a passion for cruise and travel.

Cost of Franchise: £10,999 + VAT
Franchise Owner Contact: Richard Langrick
Number of Company Outlets: 27
Number of Franchised Outlets: Launching retail stores in 2011
Number of Franchise Owners Planned: No limit
Overseas Operations Existing: 0
Overseas Operations Planned: Launching in Europe late 2011 / 2012

Management Service Fees: Monthly & Annual fees only payable if minimum targets not achieved.
Breakdown of Package:
3 day induction at the Global Cruising Training Centre, ongoing online training through our Captain's Academy, ship visit for familiarisation, Introductory membership into ACE (Association of Cruise Experts), the Cruise Clinic Equipment, managed local website and e-marketing system, the RSVP Cruise Club Pack, access to business support website, access to The Bridge intranet for 24 hour business support and access to the Global Cruising UK direct mail local profile and delivery service.

Financial Assistance Available: Barclays

Training Provided: You will be fully trained at our new Global Cruising Cruise Specialist Training Centre starting with an induction course and an introduction to the Global Cruising Captain's Academy.
Training Location: Portsmouth
Support Services: Full support by the Global Cruising (UK) management team, which has a vast scope of experience covering all aspects of the cruise industry and the business and franchise sector.

Areas of Priority Development: London and the North East although UK wide opportunities exist.

More information: theukfd.net/45786904

Global Cruising
Adcroft House,
15 Roath Road, Portishead,
Bristol, Avon, BS20 6AW

t: 01603 620301
e: franmatch@fdsltd.com

Travel Center Worldwide

Travel Center Worldwide

Summary of Operation: Travel Center Worldwide offer a sales, marketing and facilitation business, specialising in 'off the beaten track' long trips.

Ideal Franchise Owner Profile: Highly intelligent, fast thinking and with the ability to get things done efficiently.

Cost of Franchise: £60,000 + VAT

Franchise Owner Contact: Boris Prince

Year Company Established: 1999
Year of First Franchise Owner: 1999

Number of Company Outlets: 1
Number of Franchised Outlets: 8
Number of Franchise Owners Planned: 55

Overseas Operations Existing: None
Overseas Operations Planned: Europe in 2011

Management Service Fees: 8%

Projected Turnover:
1st Year: £250,000   **2nd Year:** £400,000
3rd Year: £350,000

Projected Profit:
1st Year: Breakeven **2nd Year:** AOR
3rd Year: AOR

Financial Assistance Available: No

Training Provided: Initial training four weeks.
Training Location: London

Support Services: Building the business and developing to full potential.

Areas of Priority Development: UK nationwide

More Information: theukfd.net/81622454

**Travel Center Worldwide
Cedar Holdings, Ipswich Road,
Tasburgh, Norwich, NR15 1NS**

t: 01508 470 686
e: borisp@tcw.co.uk

Franchise Listings

The Camping and Caravanning Club (Franchising) Ltd
Greenfields House, Westwood Way, Westwood Business Park, Coventry, CV4 8JH

Telephone: 08701 287 240
Email: franchiseinfo@thefriendlyclub.co.uk
Website: www.friendlyfranchise.co.uk

Summary of Operation: The Camping and Caravanning Club is the oldest organisation for campers, however they choose to camp. This means that you have the benefit of over 100 years experience of knowing what campers want and how to create a profitable campsite. With access to our ever growing member network, any new site will immediately have hundreds of thousands of eager campers looking for a new adventure at a beautiful site.

Ideal Franchise Owner Profile: We are looking for enthusiastic and passionate franchise owners who want to purchase a campsite to run as a Camping and Caravanning Club Site.

Cost of Franchise: £35,000 + VAT

Franchise Owner Contact: Jane Walton

Year Company Established: 1901

Number of Company Outlets: 92
Number of Franchised Outlets: 15
Number of Franchise Owners Planned: 50
Management Service Fees: 10% of pitch fee.
Financial Assistance Available: No

Training Provided: The Club offers an extensive training and development programme for franchise owners on the network.

Training Location: Some of the training modules will take place at Greenfields house and some can be conducted on site.

Support Services: Ongoing support is provided to all franchise owners.

Areas of Priority Development: UK

More Information: theukfd.net/84551825

Absolute Fun Casino
Telephone: 01202 600 699
Website: www.absolutefuncasino.co.uk
Summary of Operation: Fun casinos for weddings and corporate events.
More Information: theukfd.net/42518648

Accessible Travel & Leisure
Telephone: 01452 729 739
Website: www.accessibletravel.co.uk
Summary of Operation: Holidays and travel.
More Information: theukfd.net/83154068

Accor Hospitality
Telephone: 020 8237 7474
Website: www.accorhotels.com
Summary of Operation: From budget to luxury, online booking, business travel, weekend getaways and vacations.
More Information: theukfd.net/33780575

Barrhead Travel Service Ltd
Telephone: 01268 786 999
Website: www.barrheadtravel.co.uk
Summary of Operation: Barrhead Travel Service is an Appointed Representative of ITC Compliance Limited which is authorised and regulated by the Financial Services Authority (FSA).
More Information: theukfd.net/75153530

Ceroc Enterprises Ltd
Telephone: 020 8969 4401
Website: www.ceroc.com
Summary of Operation: A Ceroc franchise owner operates the Ceroc business which incorporates management promotion of dance classes as part of a complete night out. Ceroc is a fusion of jive and Salsa and is the largest, most established and most professional organisation in the field of modern partner dance.
More Information: theukfd.net/83034323

Chocolate Delight
Telephone: 0870 770 2919
Website: www.chocolatedelight.co.uk
Summary of Operation: Chocolate Delight is an innovative and unique company offering mobile chocolate experiences and to date has entertained thousands of people globally using everyone's favourite food - chocolate!
More Information: theukfd.net/51361135

Choice Hotels Europe
Telephone: 020 7061 9600
Website: www.choicehotelseurope.com
Summary of Operation: Choice Hotels Europe provide accommodation under the hotel brands of Comfort Inns, Quality Hotels, Sleep Inns and Clarion Hotels & Suites.
More Information: theukfd.net/23280414

Country Lanes
Website: www.countrylanes.co.uk
Summary of Operation: Britain's bicycle holidays specialist that operates cycle tours, bicycling vacations, bike hire, cycling breaks and luxury cycle tours in England.
More Information: theukfd.net/78182273

Creation Dance Ltd
Telephone: 0870 140 3234
Website: www.creationdance.co.uk
Summary of Operation: Creation runs fun and informal adult dance classes.
More Information: theukfd.net/18959025

Days Inn UK
Telephone: 020 8762 6600
Website: www.hotelfranchise.com
Summary of Operation: Hotels operating throughout the UK.
More Information: theukfd.net/88091513

Dinner Dates UK Ltd
Telephone: 020 8741 1252
Website: www.dinnerdates.com
Summary of Operation: Dining and social events company.
More Information: theukfd.net/44740662

easyHotel Ltd
Telephone: 020 7241 9000
Website: www.easyhote.com
Summary of Operation: easyHotel offers cheap hotel bookings in the UK and worldwide. Find the latest deals and specials about cheap hotels.
More Information: theukfd.net/87538713

Emporium Parties
Telephone: 01303 298 377
Website: www.emporiumpartiesfranchise.co.uk
Summary of Operation: Emporium Parties entertain and organise children and teenage parties and have gone from strength to strength.
More Information: theukfd.net/20357442

Explorer Travel
Telephone: 01908 31 55 55
Website: www.explorertravel.co.uk
Summary of Operation: Web based travel company offering clients internet prices with a personal service and fully protected travel.
More Information: theukfd.net/32106363

Freedom Travel Gateway
Telephone: 0800 050 1022
Website: www.freedomtravelgateway.co.uk
Summary of Operation: The Freedom Travel Group is owned by the Co-operative Travel Group, the UK's largest independently owned travel distribution group.
More Information: theukfd.net/69478373

FunkyDiva Music
Telephone: 02083 201 246
Website: www.funkydivamusic.com
Summary of Operation: FunkyDiva is a cutting edge multi-purpose jukebox system.
More Information: theukfd.net/54718670

Go Cruise
Telephone: 0800 954 0067
Website: www.cruisefranchise.co.uk
Summary of Operation: Cruise specialists, part of a growing, exciting industry selling cruises to the public, tailoring products to suit their needs.
More Information: theukfd.net/31571268

Group20
Telephone: 0808 2020 828
Website: www.grp20.com
Summary of Operation: Super car club.
More Information: theukfd.net/54482662

Hilton Hotels PLC
Telephone: 020 7856 8000
Website: www.hilton.co.uk
Summary of Operation: Owns, manages or franchises a hotel portfolio of some of the world's best known and highly regarded brands.
More Information: theukfd.net/88568146

IHG (InterContinental Hotels Group)
Telephone: 01895 512 000
Website: www.ihgplc.com
Summary of Operation: IHG owns, manages, leases or franchises nearly 4,400 hotels and over 640,000 guest rooms globally.
More Information: theukfd.net/76235084

Franchise Listings

Last Man Stands Ltd

Telephone: 07815 313 686
Website: www.lastmanstands.com
Summary of Operation: Last Man Stands is the widest reaching amateur cricket league in the world. Spread over five countries and 30 different cities, with 20,000 registered players all competing.
More Information: theukfd.net/15334558

Lets Stay UK Ltd

Telephone: 0845 409 4510
Website: www.letsstay.co.uk
Summary of Operation: Holiday accommodation franchise. We provide holidays in the UK, holiday cottages, short breaks, weekend breaks, Britain's best getaways, last minute offers and accommodation bargains.
More Information: theukfd.net/21315651

MBM Corporate Ltd

Telephone: 0845 017 0707
Website: www.mbmcorporate.co.uk
Summary of Operation: MBM started life as Music Business Management way back in early 1993. The company now has over 30,000 artists on their national database, covering over 60 different types of entertainment for the young and older generations.
More Information: theukfd.net/22263202

Music for Health

Telephone: 01243 783 212
Website: www.musicforhealthheadoff.co.uk
Summary of Operation: Music for people in residential homes. Music for Health provides unique, interactive, holistic, music-based workshops, working with people between the ages of 16 and 109 years in care homes of all types, day centres and hospices.
More Information: theukfd.net/65825095

Pacer Leisure Vehicles International Ltd

Telephone: 01494 484 664
Website: www.pacerleisure.co.uk
Summary of Operation: Designed with the benefit of over 30 years experience in competitive sport, each of our leisure vehicles have been evolved to achieve one specific goal - to be the best in it's market sector.
More Information: theukfd.net/65472377

Popstars Academy - Parties & Dance Classes

Telephone: 0870 850 6018
Website: www.popstarsacademy.com
Summary of Operation: The UK specialists for popstar parties and dance classes.
More Information: theukfd.net/63148321

Quintessentially

Telephone: 020 7758 3340
Website: www.quintessentially.com
Summary of Operation: Quintessentially is a club created to make life that much easier, that much richer and that much more fun for its members. They have an irresistible package of offers, privileges, bespoke services and access to inside track information, which will make your annual fee seem like the best deal you've ever done.
More Information: theukfd.net/58846098

Racing Challenge Ltd

Telephone: 01993 867 703
Website: www.racing-challenge.com
Summary of Operation: A unique racing car simulator experience. Choose a four or eight seater simulators for your event or party.
More Information: theukfd.net/17532181

Searchmate UK Ltd

Telephone: 01189 657 521
Website: www.searchmate.co.uk
Summary of Operation: Searchmate - a premier introduction agency.
More Information: theukfd.net/12544085

Simply Out Of School Ltd

Telephone: 0800 129 460
Website: www.simplyoutofschool.co.uk
Summary of Operation: After school and holiday clubs.
More Information: theukfd.net/67146584

Sing Live Ltd

Telephone: 01609 780 315
Website: www.singliveuk.com
Summary of Operation: Bringing the joy of singing to everyone and providing extraordinary opportunities to perform in the UK and around the globe in large and amazing venues. With eleven companies around the country - train and perform with professional vocal coaches and musicians and meet many new friends.
More Information: theukfd.net/75550908

The Business Growth Show
Telephone: 0121 237 6097
Website: www.thebusinessgrowthshow.co.uk
Summary of Operation: Organise events.
More Information: theukfd.net/99632634

The Ceramic Experience Ltd
Telephone: 0131 554 4455
Website: www.theceramicexperience.com
Summary of Operation: Ceramic painting studios with café and soft play centres.
More Information: theukfd.net/44253720

The Global Travel Group Ltd
Telephone: 0844 826 4567
Website: www.membership.globaltravelgroup.com
Summary of Operation: Opportunity to join exciting world of travel at fraction of normal cost operate from home, retail or office.
More Information: theukfd.net/71405803

The Movie Booth
Telephone: 0870 143 6769
Website: www.themoviebooth.com
Summary of Operation: Invest in a DVD rental kiosk – revolutionising the way in which people rent DVD's in the UK and Ireland, there are several models available from The Movie Booth.
More Information: theukfd.net/15708272

The Wheelie Good Party Company
Telephone: 020 8386 2894
Website: www.wheeliegoodparty.co.uk
Summary of Operation: Childrens driving parties, jeeps.
More Information: theukfd.net/35890364

Travel Counsellors
Telephone: 01204 536 191
Website: www.tctravelacademy.co.uk
Summary of Operation: Bespoke travel advisory service.
More Information: theukfd.net/47672523

Treasure Trails Ltd
Telephone: 01872 263 692
Website: www.treasuretrails.co.uk
Summary of Operation: Treasure Trails is the award winning company, specialising in providing fun, healthy and informative leisure activities.
More Information: theukfd.net/74018373

Uniglobe Travel (British Isles) Ltd
Telephone: 0845 2570 332
Website: www.travelfranchise.com
Summary of Operation: Full service travel agency mainly serving business travel.
More Information: theukfd.net/37045265

Visitjourneys.com Ltd
Telephone: 020 7231 4672
Website: www.visitjourneys.com
Summary of Operation: Journeys Hostels is a budget accomodation company with hostels in London and Brighton.
More Information: theukfd.net/87881206

Visitor UK Ltd
Telephone: 01205 311 858
Website: www.visitoruk.com
Summary of Operation: Town information websites; entertainment, eating out, where to go etc.
More Information: theukfd.net/50413585

W H Brakspear & Son PLC
Website: www.brakspear.co.uk
Summary of Operation: Hotels chain.
More Information: theukfd.net/32125317

Whizz Bang Pop
Telephone: 08450 17 10 77
Website: www.whizzbangpop.co.uk
Summary of Operation: At Whizz Bang Pop we specialise in providing high quality, fun filled entertainers for children's birthday parties and also events with children including weddings, christenings, store openings and fun days.
More Information: theukfd.net/42794960

Wildchilds
Telephone: 01325 365 292
Website: www.wildchilds.co.uk
Summary of Operation: Party and event company, specialists in conceptual ideas, event planning and delivery. Wildchilds provide a full service for all sorts of parties and special events.
More Information: theukfd.net/75509951

XTC Discos Franchising Ltd
Telephone: 0115 933 5577
Website: www.xtcdiscos.com
Summary of Operation: Supply of disco and other entertainment services to the licensed trade, hotels, corporate and private clients.
More Information: theukfd.net/87533415

Tap Into a *WORLD* of **Opportunity**

European Franchising

EuropeanFranchising.net offers listings of
European and International franchise profiles.
Originally a print publication, European Franchising
now profiles famous and emerging International franchise
opportunities seeking investors to expand in European markets via
National or Regional Master franchising. European Franchising is easy
to navigate, as visitors are able to browse by franchise category or by
franchise name. The website contains information about genuine
European franchise opportunities, latest franchise news, guidance
for franchise owners and franchisors as well as the European
Franchise Showcase.

www.EuropeanFranchising.net

€UROPEAN
FRANCHISING

Franchise International

Like European Franchising, Franchise-International.net was formerly a
print publication and is available as a website providing information on the
latest International franchise opportunities. Visitors are able to browse
through International franchise opportunities by category or name. The
website contains the latest franchise news, advice and guidance for
franchise owners and franchisors, as well as the International Franchise
Showcase. Franchise International is a valuable source of information for
people looking to invest in a franchise that has serious international
growth potential.

www.Franchise-International.net

FRANCHISE
INTERNATIONAL

SERVICES | Print, Signs & Design

Actively recruiting franchise owners

Sign franchises can involve creating, maintaining and installing signs as part of brand development for a number of businesses. This sector also includes a number of print franchises and design franchises. Franchise opportunities include **Agency Express, Freebie's, Primesigns, Recognition Express** and **The Wedding Guide**.

For sale boards nationwide

bfa
FULL MEMBER

Agency Express

Summary of Operation: The UK's largest specialist estate agency 'For Sale' board company. A low investment/low overhead van based franchise, providing a daily service to over 25% of all UK estate agency offices.

Ideal Franchise Owner Profile: Franchise owners come from a wide range of backgrounds, although good DIY skills and an enjoyment of driving are essential. Full training covers all other aspects of the business and many franchise owners have expanded their businesses by putting additional vehicles on the road.

Cost of Franchise: £18,500 or €26,000 + VAT

Franchise Owner Contact: Ben Brookes

Year Company Established: 1998
Year of First Franchise Owner: 1998

Number of Company Outlets: 3
Number of Franchised Outlets: 97
Number of Franchise Owners Planned: 120

Overseas Operations Existing: Ireland
Overseas Operations Planned: Yes

Management Service Fees: 15%

Breakdown of Package: 10 year renewable agreement, fully protected territory, deposit on van, eight days training and all tools and equipment.

Projected Turnover:
1st Year: AOR   **2nd Year:** AOR   **3rd Year:** AOR

Projected Profit:
1st Year: AOR   **2nd Year:** AOR   **3rd Year:** AOR

Financial Assistance Available: All major banks

Training Provided: Full eight days including theory, hands-on and marketing.
Training Location: Norwich plus within franchise owner's own territory.

Support Services: Full ongoing support via large dedicated support staff.

Areas of Priority Development: All

More Information: theukfd.net/75246003

Agency Express
Rectory Road, East Carleton,
Norwich, Norfolk, NR14 8HT

t: 01508 579 800
f: 01508 570 891
e: enquiries@agencyexpress.co.uk
w: www.agencyexpress.co.uk

Freebie's UK

Summary of Operation: Production of local 'Freebie' magazine for dining out and what's on.

Ideal Franchise Owner Profile: Looking for outgoing business minded entrepreneur, willing to build on our existing business format franchise. A background in design and sales is essential with the ability to direct a team.

Cost of Franchise: £27,500 + VAT

Franchise Owner Contact: Richard Campbell

Year Company Established: 1994
Year of First Franchise Owner: 1994

Number of Company Outlets: 2
Number of Franchised Outlets: 17
Number of Franchise Owners Planned: 52

Overseas Operations Existing: None
Overseas Operations Planned: Europe

Management Service Fees: 10%

Breakdown of Package: Training, in-house publication, production, support advice and franchise owner fee.

Projected Turnover:
1st Year: AOR   **2nd Year:** AOR   **3rd Year:** AOR

Projected Profit:
1st Year: AOR   **2nd Year:** AOR   **3rd Year:** AOR

Training Provided: 15 days
Training Location: Head office and on-site.
Support Services: Ongoing specifically in production.

Areas of Priority Development: National

More Information: theukfd.net/41317550

Freebie's UK
Cedar Lodge, Ipswich Road,
Tasburgh, Norwich, Norfolk,
NR15 1NS

t: 01508 470 686
e: rcampbell@freebies.co.uk

Primesigns

Summary of Operation: Primesigns offer design and print solutions coupled with excellent customer service at extremely competitive prices. Our franchise proposition has been developed over a number of years and we are now ready to work with like-minded individuals to expand the Primesigns brand across the UK.

Ideal Franchise Owner Profile: No previous print experience is required, Primesigns are looking for potential franchise owners who have a love of hard work and have a hands-on approach to building a successful and profitable, customer-orientated sales business. Ideally our franchise owner's would have sales experience as well as experience managing people.

Cost of Franchise: £23,995 + VAT

Franchise Owner Contact: Steve Taylor

Year Company Established: 1997

Number of Company Outlets: 2

Number of Franchise Owners Planned: 100 in 5 years

Management Service Fees: 9%

Breakdown of Package: Exclusive territory, use of Primesigns trade marks, methodology and systems, Operations Manual, comprehensive training course, store launch programme, IT infrastructure, business stationery and marketing materials and corporate workwear.

Training Provided: Four weeks covering all aspects of the business for example, time keeping to bookkeeping, artwork to manufacture and introduction to closing sales.

Training Location: Two weeks are held in one of our premises and two weeks on location at your shop.

More information: theukfd.net/64308507

Primesigns
248 Terminus Road,
Eastbourne,
East Sussex,
BN21 3DE

t: 01323 639 000/07792 401 533
e: info@primesignsfranchise.co.uk
w: www.primesignsfranchise.co.uk

Unique Solutions in Promoting Your Image

Recognition Express

Summary of Operation: Supplier and manufacturer of corporate and personalised products to businesses. Recognition Express has eight defined income streams from personalised name badges and promotional products, to branded clothing and business gifts.

Ideal Franchise Owner Profile: People who will build relationships, communicate well and work hard, who have real ambition to successfully run a business-to-business operation.

Cost of Franchise: £30,000 + VAT

Franchise Owner Contact: Sue Toplis

Year Company Established: 1979

Number of Company Outlets: 1
Number of Franchised Outlets: 45
Number of Franchise Owners Planned: 85

Overseas Operations Existing: Ireland, Spain, Portugal and Germany.
Overseas Operations Planned: South Africa.

Management Service Fees: 10%

Recognition Express
Unit 2 Cartwright Way, Forest
Business Park, Bardon, Coalville,
Leicestershire, LE67 1UB

t: 01530 513 300
f: 01530 513 309
e: stoplis@recognition-express.com
w: www.franchisoftheyear.com

Breakdown of Package: Licence to trade, three weeks training, twenty month marketing launch programme, centralised appointment generation, extensive marketing collateral, personalised web site, access to Recognition Express Extranet, production equipment and samples, finance package, Contact Management System, manuals and ongoing business support.

Financial Assistance Available: All major banks.

Projected Turnover:
1st Year: £60,000   **2nd Year:** £120,000
3rd Year: £180,000
Projected Profit:
1st Year: AOR   **2nd Year:** AOR   **3rd Year:** AOR

Training Provided: Three weeks training to cover territory management, production and procurement, finance and extensive sales and marketing initiatives.

Training Location: One week on territory, one week Bardon, five days production on-site.

Support Services: Full business support including - but not limited to - business planning, sales, marketing, procurement and finance plus in-house technical support. Franchise owners receive comprehensive marketing systems including appointment generating, marketing collateral and a range of marketing tools and samples. Additionally, franchise owners have their own website plus access to Recognition Express Extranet and a full range of business management support.

Areas of Priority Development: UK

More Information: theukfd.net/23223020

Wedding Guide Ltd
213 Beauchamps Drive, Wickford, SS11 8NS

Telephone: 01268 769 999
Fax: 01268 769 888
Email: info@theweddingguide.co.uk
Website: www.theweddingguide.co.uk

Summary of Operation: Form and run your own local recommended wedding source supplies club. Members participate in your local directory for brides and on the national website which is the biggest and busiest of its type in Europe. Established franchise owners earn between £50,000 and £96,000 per year.

Ideal Franchise Owner Profile: Self-motivated communicator who likes meeting people.

Cost of Franchise: £17,500 + VAT

Franchise Owner Contact: Terry Steel

Year Company Established: 1983
Year of First Franchise Owner: 1984

Number of Company Outlets: 2
Number of Franchised Outlets: 13
Number of Franchise Owners Planned: 22

Overseas Operations Existing: USA and Canada
Overseas Operations Planned: N/A

Management Service Fees: 10%
Breakdown of Package: AOR

Financial Assistance Available: HSBC

Training Provided: Full

Training Location: Wickford, Essex and in-field.

Support Services: Artwork, printing and internet.

Areas of Priority Development: West Midlands, Hampshire, Dorset, SW London, Surrey, West Country, South Wales, Oxford, Buckinghamshire, Hertfordshire and Scotland.

More Information: theukfd.net/73446342

ABC Photography
Telephone: 0800 043 1612
Website: www.abcphotography.co.uk
Summary of Operation: Professional mobile photographers specialising in child and family portrait photography, within nursery schools, playgroups and todler groups. Specialising in photographing the under fives.
More Information: theukfd.net/09655949

Adbikes
Telephone: 020 7720 3222
Website: www.adbikes.com
Summary of Operation: Adbikes specialises in providing a range of innovative, high impact outdoor advertising solutions for businesses or agencies nationwide.
More Information: theukfd.net/70173193

Ads On Wheels
Telephone: 0870 742 9999
Website: www.adsonwheels.co.uk
Summary of Operation: With a unique advertising vehicle, customers can be targeted in relevant areas.
More Information: theukfd.net/37114602

AlphaGraphics UK Ltd
Telephone: 01904 751 080
Website: www.alphagraphics.co.uk
Summary of Operation: AlphaGraphics is one of the leading worldwide provider of rapid responseprint and related business services.
More Information: theukfd.net/82462212

AngloINFO
Telephone: 01491 836 394
Website: www.angloinfo.com
Summary of Operation: AngloINFO is an online media company providing local business directory, classified advertising and information services in the English language.
More Information: theukfd.net/88733708

Barrett & Coe
Telephone: 01603 629 739
Website: www.barrettandcoe.co.uk
Summary of Operation: A leading contemporary portrait and wedding photography franchise in the UK offering a flexible range of full-time and part-time options.
More Information: theukfd.net/20636243

Big Image Photography Ltd
Telephone: 01621 840 167
Website: www.bigimagephotos.co.uk
Summary of Operation: Big Image offer an efficient, professional event photography service covering every type of social, sporting and corporate event. We print studio quality photographs at the event using state of the art portable studio equipment. All photos can be purchased on the day or from our secure website after the event on a range of photo gift items.
More Information: theukfd.net/94411101

Bond-a-Frame
Telephone: 01243 789 343
Summary of Operation: Independently operated picture framing studio and gallery, which specialises in creative picture framing.
More Information: theukfd.net/31686824

Book-Builder
Telephone: 01420 479 995
Website: www.book-builder.co.uk
Summary of Operation: Offering easy to compile highly professional yearbook and eventbooks for schools, clubs, associations and companies. Yearbooks are mainly bought by schools whereas eventbooks cater for specific events and activities, including local sports competitions, swimming galas, gymkhanas and golf clubs etc.
More Information: theukfd.net/86432313

Bound Biographies
Telephone: 01869 232 911
Website: www.boundbiographies.com
Summary of Operation: Bound Biographies is the premier life story writing company in the UK.
More Information: theukfd.net/50481065

Call My Local
Telephone: 0844 372 9424
Website: www.callmylocal.com
Summary of Operation: National business finder directory.
More Information: theukfd.net/76781043

Class Photography
Website: www.class-photography.com
Summary of Operation: Professional schools and events photography.
More Information: theukfd.net/63713181

Countrywide Signs Ltd
Telephone: 01638 508 077
Website: www.countrywide-signs.com
Summary of Operation: Countrywide Signs provides estate agents with a very valuable professional service – supplying, erecting and maintaining their 'For Sale' signs. A straightforward concept, but a task which properly carried out is of exceptional importance.
More Information: theukfd.net/73414636

DE Photo
Telephone: 01342 894 519
Website: www.dephoto.biz
Summary of Operation: Sports event photographers. Photos taken and printed on site in less than one minute. Travelling around your exclusive territory capturing the highlights from sports, social and corporate events.
More Information: theukfd.net/37687008

Dor-2-Dor (UK)
Telephone: 0844 357 1152
Website: www.dor2dor.com
Summary of Operation: Leaflet printing and distribution. Door drop marketing.
More Information: theukfd.net/15333132

Eco Art Cards
Telephone: 0845 450 0843
Website: www.ecoartcards.com
Summary of Operation: Eco Art Cards are now offering franchises to individuals and couples to work with us and own their own exclusive area of the country, managing existing clients and dealing with new ones.
More Information: theukfd.net/23026044

eprintglobal
Website: www.eprintglobal.co.uk
Summary of Operation: eprintglobal is a unique online franchise opportunity offering a convenient print on demand solution for every size of business.
More Information: theukfd.net/13224428

Families Magazines Ltd
Telephone: 020 8696 9680
Website: www.familiesonline.co.uk
Summary of Operation: Publishing local families magazines.
More Information: theukfd.net/51838341

FastSigns International, Inc.
Telephone: 01246 456 512
Website: www.franchise.fastsigns.com
Summary of Operation: Business-to-business signs and digital printing management franchise, widely recognised as the sign industry's leading franchise with over 550 locations worldwide including 24 in the UK.
More Information: theukfd.net/65164811

FYEO Portraits
Telephone: 0871 218 0343
Website: www.foryoureyesonly.me.uk
Summary of Operation: FYEO Portraits is a specialist female team of photographers and make-up artists. We are experts at creating flattering portraits of brides, regardless of age or body shape, as a personal gift for both you and your groom to treasure forever.
More Information: theukfd.net/42887274

Grippit UK Ltd
Telephone: 01629 55309
Website: www.grippit.co.uk
Summary of Operation: Manufacturer of notice boards and poster cases.
More Information: theukfd.net/18844474

Ink Shop
Telephone: 01634 566 144
Website: www.inkshop.co.uk
Summary of Operation: Print shop franchise.
More Information: theukfd.net/15314120

Ink Shop Printing
Telephone: 01236 611 907
Website: www.theinkshop.co.uk
Summary of Operation: Graphic design and quick printing, providing a complete range of full colour products printed to a very high standard at a very competitive price. A complete package of quality, value and service brought together in a simple easy to use package.
More Information: theukfd.net/59503165

Ink Xpress Franchising Management Ltd
Telephone: 01473 242 720
Website: www.inkxpress.com
Summary of Operation: Specialised while-u-wait inkjet cartridge refilling service for Hewlett Packard, Lexmark and printhead-style Canon, Olivetti and Xerox cartridges.
More Information: theukfd.net/23273622

IQ Media Ltd
Telephone: 01625 418 666
Website: www.iqmedia-uk.com
Summary of Operation: IQ Media is an opportunity which harnesses advances in technology to deliver successful ways to provide media services, to include video, new media, live event production and marketing.
More Information: theukfd.net/87323728

Ivory Tower Cards Ltd
Telephone: 01628 626 866
Website: www.ivorytowercards.com
Summary of Operation: Greetings cards.
More Information: theukfd.net/67320637

Kall Kwik (UK) Ltd
Telephone: 01895 872 000
Website: www.kallkwik.co.uk
Summary of Operation: The provision of business-to-business communications by the use of ourskills in print copy and design.
More Information: theukfd.net/28753341

Ladies First
Telephone: 029 2039 6600
Website: www.ladiesfirst.co.uk
Summary of Operation: A free glossy lifestyle magazine for women.
More Information: theukfd.net/12531356

Little Angels UK Ltd
Telephone: 01242 216 816
Website: www.littleangelsportraits.com
Summary of Operation: Photography services for school children.
More Information: theukfd.net/85250258

Look Local Ltd
Telephone: 0845 519 1374
Website: www.looklocal.com
Summary of Operation: Local business directory. Working from home, franchise owners sell advertising space to local businesses in order to create a local business directory.
More Information: theukfd.net/86713188

Minuteman Press International
Telephone: 01925 757 794
Website: www.minutemanpress.com
Summary of Operation: Full service printing and graphics centres in retail format.
More Information: theukfd.net/74824425

My Little Wrapper

Telephone: 0121 765 5552
Website: www.getmylittlewrapper.co.uk
Summary of Operation: A 'business in a box' that you can run, part-time, from your own kitchen table.
More Information: theukfd.net/78960579

National Signs Ltd

Telephone: 0845 222 5005
Website: www.nationalsigns.co.uk
Summary of Operation: Manufacture and supply of all types of signs, banners and vehicle graphics using mobile sign vehicle units.
More Information: theukfd.net/10780634

NXO PLC

Telephone: 0870 757 7885
Website: www.nxofranchise.net
Summary of Operation: Offering strategic consultancy and full service marketing capability to SME's private and public sector clients.
More Information: theukfd.net/67620501

Original Poster Company Ltd

Telephone: 01932 267 300
Website: www.originalposter.com
Summary of Operation: Distribution of high quality greeting cards to established retail outlets.
More Information: theukfd.net/26650048

Parents News (UK)

Website: www.parents-news.co.uk
Summary of Operation: Monthly tabloid free publication with focused distribution to parents.
More Information: theukfd.net/66427272

Petal Portraits

Telephone: 0845 838 2134
Website: www.petalportraits.co.uk
Summary of Operation: Petal Portraits are baby and child portrait specialists capturing the everyday moments of your child's life.
More Information: theukfd.net/05043177

Photography For Little People

Telephone: 01207 299 500
Website: www.photographyforlittlepeople.com
Summary of Operation: Fun, unique concept that combines photographing little ones and/or their families and/or taking impressions of their hands and feet.
More Information: theukfd.net/35965068

Pinksheep Printing

Telephone: 0208 619 0451
Website: www.pinksheep.co.uk
Summary of Operation: Quality printing.
More Information: theukfd.net/62864857

Plan-it-Cards

Telephone: 01428 714 700
Website: www.plan-itcards.co.uk
Summary of Operation: Franchise owners sell and market Plan-it Cards exclusive greetings cards to retail customers within a clearly defined territory. They visit their customers on a monthly basis and service the displays.
More Information: theukfd.net/76731634

Printing.com

Telephone: 0845 078 7177
Website: www.printing.com
Summary of Operation: Print, design and supply for SME's.
More Information: theukfd.net/74211881

Prontaprint Ltd

Telephone: 01895 872 075
Website: www.prontaprint.com
Summary of Operation: Digital design, print and copy franchise. Using the latest technology and with the backing of the Adare Group.
More Information: theukfd.net/67066217

Sign-A-Rama

Telephone: 024 7665 9933
Website: www.signarama.co.uk
Summary of Operation: Full range of sign-making, graphics and digital printing services that businesses need.
More Information: theukfd.net/18125386

Signs Express Ltd (UK)

Telephone: 01603 625 925
Website: www.signsexpress.co.uk
Summary of Operation: Long established management franchise opportunity within the lucrative sign industry. Premises based with full training and ongoing support.
More Information: theukfd.net/33610435

Signs Now

Website: www.signsnow.co.uk
Summary of Operation: The design, fabrication and installation of all kinds of signs for business.
More Information: theukfd.net/62232183

Snappy Snaps Franchises Ltd
Telephone: 020 8741 7474
Website: www.snappysnaps.com
Summary of Operation: Retail photo and imaging processing.
More Information: theukfd.net/75322328

The Entertainment Guide Franchising Ltd
Telephone: 0870 850 7859
Website: www.theentertainmentguide.co.uk
Summary of Operation: Entertainment publication, reviewing and featuring top restaurants, bars, nightclubs, shopping centres, fitness outlets, health and beauty.
More Information: theukfd.net/67397704

The Family Grapevine
Telephone: 01793 849 928
Website: www.thefamilygrapevine.co.uk
Summary of Operation: The Family Grapevine is a magazine for families, supporting parents from the day they get the first twinkle in the eye, to the day when their teenager finally leaves home.
More Information: theukfd.net/19880594

The Flyer (Franchising) Ltd
Telephone: 01394 211 461
Website: www.flyerfranchising.co.uk
Summary of Operation: Create, publish and distribute a quality monthly magazine.
More Information: theukfd.net/71462035

The Giant Card Company
Website: www.giantpartyshop.com
Summary of Operation: Hiring giant cards 6ft high and balloon decorating for all events.
More Information: theukfd.net/20401216

The Personalised Book Company
Telephone: 01379 641 444
Website: www.bestbook.co.uk
Summary of Operation: Personalised childrens books, first name analysis, surname history, personalised products created from software.
More Information: theukfd.net/73384578

The Print Partner
Telephone: 01274 460 006
Website: www.theprintpartner.net
Summary of Operation: Printing services.
More Information: theukfd.net/48646025

The Snippet Ltd
Telephone: 07989 320 893
Website: www.thesnippet.net
Summary of Operation: Free weekly five minute upbeat read with 'No bad news' offering exclusive and affordable advertising to local businesses.
More Information: theukfd.net/2687548

Totally Dynamic
Telephone: 01603 742 482
Website: www.totally-dynamic.co.uk
Summary of Operation: Printing and vehicle wrapping service.
More Information: theukfd.net/56858044

Venture UK Ltd
Telephone: 01606 558 854
Website: www.thisisventure.co.uk
Summary of Operation: Venture offers bespoke photographic experiences in its 55 studios across the UK.
More Information: theukfd.net/12805651

Wellbeing Magazine Ltd
Telephone: 01892 541 621
Website: www.wellbeingmagazine.com
Summary of Operation: Local online and published community magazine available in towns around the UK.
More Information: theukfd.net/61818308

Xpress
Telephone: 01895 274 646
Website: www.xpress.co.uk
Summary of Operation: Commercial printing franchise.
More Information: theukfd.net/79900672

Xpress Art Ltd
Telephone: 01628 509 029
Website: www.xpress-art.co.uk
Summary of Operation: Xpress Art is an established company specialising in consumer canvas and wide format printing for the retail and corporate markets.
More Information: theukfd.net/63095737

Yellow Tom UK Ltd
Telephone: 01977 514 300
Website: www.yellowtom.ie
Summary of Operation: Yellowtom is much more than an online local business directory.
More Information: theukfd.net/12842928

SERVICES | Real Estate & Lettings

Actively recruiting franchise owners

There are a range of white collar franchise opportunities in both the estate agency and letting agency franchise sector. These include property management, letting agents and estate franchises for sale. Franchise opportunities include **Countrywide Franchising (Bairstow Eves), Century 21 Estate Agents, House-Hut, Martin & Co** and **Platinum Property Partners**.

Countrywide Franchising Ltd (Bairstow Eves)

Summary of Operation: Lettings and estate agency franchise opportunity using the very well established Bairstow Eves Countrywide brand, part of the Countrywide Group plc. Franchise owners develop and operate their own lettings and estate agency business using the brand, knowledge, training and systems of the franchisor.

Ideal Franchise Owner Profile: Individuals from all backgrounds who have the drive and ambition to develop a substantial service business. Franchise owners will demonstrate general management skills, team leadership qualities and the ability to contribute to brand growth.

Cost of Franchise: From £35,000 + VAT plus working capital.

Franchise Owner Contact: Jamie McMullan and Chris Tinney

Year Company Established: 1999
Year of First Franchise Owner: 2000

Number of Company Outlets: 1,300
Number of Franchised Outlets: 122
Number of Franchise Owners Planned: 300

Management Service Fees: 8% of turnover

Breakdown of Package: Use of the Bairstow Eves brand, franchise systems, marketing material, training programmes, IT software and branded property website. Additional income generation from property related services via other divisions within the Countrywide Group.

Financial Assistance Available: Leading UK banks.

Training Provided: A 30-day training programme is provided to all new Bairstow Eves franchise owners and staff, equipping newcomers to the estate agency and lettings franchise with the knowledge they require to run a successful property service business.

Training Location: Sales and lettings training courses are delivered at the national training centre in Buckinghamshire. Additional training courses are held in regional locations around the UK throughout the year.

Support Services: Franchise owners receive ongoing support and advice from the franchising team based at Milton Keynes and from dedicated field based Franchise Support Managers. The franchise system includes a range of procurement, marketing and operational tools.

Areas of Priority Development: England and Wales.

More Information: theukfd.net/05665663

Countrywide Franchising Ltd (Bairstow Eves)
Countrywide House,
88-103 Caldecotte Lake Drive,
Caldecotte, Milton Keynes,
Buckinghamshire, MK7 8JT

t: 01908 961 200
e: enquiries@bairstowevesfranchising.co.uk
w: www.bairstowevesfranchising.co.uk

Platinum Property Partners LLP

Summary of Operation: Property investment franchise supported by a world-class team of experts. This is an opportunity for high net worth individuals using proven systems and strategies to build a highly profitable property portfolio that delivers market-beating returns and provides excellent pension provision and financial security.

Ideal Franchise Owner Profile: High net worth entrepreneurs, business owners and senior managers or board directors in employed positions.

Cost of Franchise: £52,970 + VAT
Franchise Owner Contact: Steve Bolton
Year Company Established: 2007
Year of First Franchise Owner: 2007

Number of Company Outlets: 2
Number of Franchised Outlets: 84
Number of Franchise Owners Planned: 500
Overseas Operations Existing: No
Overseas Operations Planned: 2012 potentially USA, Canada and Australia.

Management Service Fees: 5%
Breakdown of Package: Comprises: pre-mentoring pack, comprehensive start up mentoring programme, stationery package, promotional materials, Operations Manual and licence fee.

Projected Turnover:
Year 1: £78,878 **Year 2:** £157,755 **Year 3:** £315,510

Projected Profit:
Year 1: £31,608 **Year 2:** £63,216 **Year 3:** £126,431
Financial Assistance Available: N/A

Training Provided: Intensive start-up mentoring on a one to one basis, then monthly training workshops for the lifetime of the business.

Training Location: In territory.

Support Services: Post-mentoring support from mentor and head office; access to the PPP 'Power Team' of financial, legal, property and business experts; access to advice from Franchise Property Manager; access to internal forum; KPI reporting; conference calls, newsletters and bulletins; access to a Business Development Manager and Marketing Director to assist with promotion and development of franchise owner's business; PR and brand awareness; ongoing research and development into sector; stationery and advertising materials; passive investment opportunities; workshops and exclusive social networking events.

More information: theukfd.net/83087008

Platinum Property Partners LLP
Suite 5 & 6, 5 Lansdowne Place,
17 Holdenhurst Road,
Bournemouth, BH8 8EW

t: 01202 652100
e: b.bradley@platinumpartners.co.uk

House-Hut
First Floor Offices, The Welsh Mill, Parkhill Drive, Frome, BA11 2BW

Telephone: 01373 473 782
Fax: 05603 155 334
Email: franchise@house-hut.com
Website: www.house-hut.com

Summary of Operation: House-Hut is an award winning estate agent with an operating model combining seductive low fees with an unbeatable high level of service making us the first choice for house selling in the areas we operate. Our innovative operations offer an affordable franchise with the lowest possible start up costs. We also offer low cost individual franchises with start up costs 50% less than a full franchise.

Ideal Franchise Owner Profile: Good communication and interpersonal skills are essential. An interest in property is desirable as are good English and numeracy skills. No experience in estate agency is required.

Cost of Franchise: £17,950 + VAT
Franchise Owner Contact: Paul Collier
Year Company Established: 2005
Year of First Franchise Owner: 2010
Number of Company Outlets: 1
Number of Franchised Outlets: 2
Number of Franchise Owners Planned: 200
Management Service Fees: 10.5% pcm
Breakdown of Package: We offer the back up and support of a successful estate agency complete with distinctive fully branded marketing and advertising materials, dedicated website and estate agency software systems, comprehensive training manual and ongoing training and development.

Training Provided: One month intensive training package which includes accommodation, full training from scratch in all aspects of running an estate agency. First month's intensive advertising campaign, branch set up on website and email systems. Initial supply of stationery, sale boards and marketing material.
Training Location: Somerset head office.
Support Services: Full ongoing support, regular advertising material, website maintenance and upgrades, software support.

More information: theukfd.net/61654062

MARTIN&CO
the UK's Nº1 letting agent

bfa Full Member
Martin & Co (UK) Ltd
8 Trinity, 161 Old Christchurch Road, Bournemouth, BH1 1JU

Telephone: 01202 292829
Fax: 01202 405540
Email: propertyfranchise@martinco.com
Website: www.propertyfranchise.co.uk

Summary of Operation: An award winning residential letting specialist with the largest and fastest growing office network in the UK, and strong online presence. Our industry leading franchise package allows you to build a secure, long-term repeating income and an asset for the future.

Ideal Franchise Owner Profile: High calibre, self-motivated and ambitious individuals with good people skills. No property background required.
Cost of Franchise: £18,500 + VAT
Franchise Owner Contact: Scott Burgess
Year Company Established: 1986
Year of First Franchise Owner: 1995
Number of Company Outlets: 0
Number of Franchised Outlets: Over 170
Number of Franchise Owners Planned: 200+
Management Service Fees: 9% of fee income.
Breakdown of Package: Exclusive territory, start up stationery, boards, office homepage, marketing material, comprehensive modular training programme and ongoing field support from industry professionals. We also provide assistance with obtaining bank funding, finding premises and recruiting staff.
Financial Assistance Available: High street banks to 70%.
Training Provided: Four week induction training and hand-held launch. Mentoring by an experienced franchise owner. Our Training Academy organises a heavily subsidised regional training programme for continuing professional development of franchise owners and their staff.
Training Location: At head office, mentor franchise offices and own office.
Support Services: Unlimited support from an experienced Operations Director and head office team. Dedicated internal recruitment department to assist in finding staff. Legal and IT helpdesks.
Areas of Priority Development: Nationwide

More Information: theukfd.net/48113385

bfa Full Member

Northwood (GB) Ltd

Main Barn, Cams Hall Estate,
Fareham, PO16 8UT

Telephone: 01329 829 904
Email: sales@northwoodfranchises.co.uk
Website: www.northwoodfranchises.co.uk

Summary of Operation: A lettings and estate agency franchise with over 70 offices across the UK. We are known for our 'unique' Guaranteed Rental Income Scheme which sets us apart from our competitors and gives our franchise owners an edge.

Ideal Franchise Owner Profile: High calibre individuals interested in growing a significant business that have passion and drive. No prior industry experience is required.

Cost of Franchise: £39,950 + VAT
Franchise Owner Contact: Nicholas Cooper
Financial Assistance Available: NatWest and HSBC Bank subject to status.

More Information: theukfd.net/56718473

A Quick Sale Ltd

Telephone: 01904 771995
Website: www.aquicksale.co.uk
Summary of Operation: A Quick Sale is the number one property buyer in the UK.
More Information: theukfd.net/10623287

Anderson Croft Ltd

Telephone: 01865 370 161
Website: www.andersoncroft.com
Summary of Operation: Anderson Croft provide a modern, professional, transparent and low cost solution to buying or selling your home.
More Information: theukfd.net/01886136

Belvoir Property Management

Telephone: 01476 570 000
Website: www.belvoirfranchise.com
Summary of Operation: Belvoir is firmly established as one of the largest independent specialist lettings agencies in the UK, with strong branding, an excellent reputation within the industry and strong emphasis on quality customer service.
More Information: theukfd.net/66350407

Besley Hill

Telephone: 01454 415 610
Website: www.besleyhill.co.uk
Summary of Operation: Quick verbal free market valuation of your home over the phone.
More Information: theukfd.net/51100015

Big Pub Guide

Telephone: 01237 451 525
Website: www.bigpubguide.co.uk
Summary of Operation: UK pub guide directory where our aim is 'bringing people and pubs together' using the Pub Guide.
More Information: theukfd.net/25585816

Castle Estates Franchising Ltd

Telephone: 0870 839 2747
Website: www.franchise.castle-estates.co.uk
Summary of Operation: Property management is the bringing together of landlords and tenants.
More Information: theukfd.net/47616028

Century 21

Telephone: 0870 21 11 399
Website: www.century21uk.com
Summary of Operation: Global estate agency brand in operation since 1971 offering the opportunity to become a residential sales, lettings and commercial agent.
More Information: Turn to page 61 or visit theukfd.net/22895551

Charestate

Telephone: 01392 360 600
Website: www.charestate.co.uk
Summary of Operation: Charestate is an online estate agent that provides property, lettings and mortgages. We give 10% of our charges to charity.
More Information: theukfd.net/77364336

Clearsky Franchise Ltd

Website: www.clearsky.co.uk
Summary of Operation: To support clients by helping them to acquire a home of distinction overseas and to offer support to establish rental income.
More Information: theukfd.net/88246728

Concentric Lettings Ltd

Telephone: 0844 414 2010
Website: www.concentriclettings.co.uk
Summary of Operation: Letting agency.
More Information: theukfd.net/30407843

Enfields
Telephone: 01489 865 889
Website: www.enfields.co.uk
Summary of Operation: Offering high calibre individuals the opportunity to run a management franchise providing residential sales and lettings services. Additional revenue streams can be generated from financial services, new homes, foreign properties and more.
More Information: theukfd.net/65177425

Engel & Voelkers
Telephone: 01562 881 010
Website: www.engelvoelkers.co.uk
Summary of Operation: Specialists in the sale of prestigious properties.
More Information: theukfd.net/22892871

Gateway Homes UK Ltd
Telephone: 0113 380 1970
Website: www.gateway-homes.co.uk
Summary of Operation: Gateway Homes has established itself as a market leader in a highly competitive house buying industry. Gateway buys and sells property below market value.
More Information: theukfd.net/40989714

Goodchilds Estate Agency
Telephone: 0845 674 3951
Website: www.goodchilds-uk.com
Summary of Operation: Estate agents and lettings.
More Information: theukfd.net/32586008

Greenrose Network (Franchise) Ltd
Telephone: 01462 896 148
Website: www.country-properties.com
Summary of Operation: Residential estate agency, sales and lettings. Respected and highly regarded brand that is recognised as a symbol of reassured professionalism and quality.
More Information: theukfd.net/42678313

Habitus
Telephone: 0870 0106 667
Website: www.habitus.co.uk
Summary of Operation: Since our establishment over fifty years ago, Habitus have been at the forefront of the residential property industry and no more so than now as we confidently pioneer a revolution in home buying and selling.
More Information: theukfd.net/27322645

HaveNoAgent.com Ltd
Telephone: 0208 421 4195
Website: www.havenoagent.com
Summary of Operation: Our approach is quite simple, we think the time is right to connect the seller or landlord with those interested in their properties.
More Information: theukfd.net/19468306

Home Inventories Ltd
Telephone: 01372 745 745
Website: www.homeinventories.co.uk
Summary of Operation: Inventories for landlords and tenants.
More Information: theukfd.net/89247093

Hunters Franchising Ltd
Telephone: 01904 756 128
Website: www.huntersfranchising.co.uk
Summary of Operation: Hunters Franchising is part of a thriving, award winning estate agency and lettings group.
More Information: theukfd.net/52707704

I-Agent
Telephone: 0845 257 3155
Website: www.i-agents.co.uk
Summary of Operation: I-Agent can offer everything from a simple property listing right through to full estate agency service.
More Information: theukfd.net/17375727

Just Lets Residential Property Management
Telephone: 01733 346 255
Website: www.justlets.com
Summary of Operation: Residential property management.
More Information: theukfd.net/81832871

Legal & General Franchising Ltd
Website: www.legalandgeneral.com
Summary of Operation: Estate agents services, lettings, sales and financial services.
More Information: theukfd.net/42872748

Legal 4 Landlords
Telephone: 0845 567 4001
Website: www.legal4landlordsfranchise.com
Summary of Operation: A chance to be involved with the fastest growing private rented sector business in the UK.
More Information: theukfd.net/34546225

LetsXL Ltd
Telephone: 08453 660 660
Website: www.letsxl.co.uk
Summary of Operation: Insurance for the household letting market, landlords and tenants.
More Information: theukfd.net/35157456

Link Up Properties
Telephone: 01444 257 222
Website: www.linkprop.co.uk
Summary of Operation: Estate agency franchise.
More Information: theukfd.net/13400134

Medics On The Move
Telephone: 0844 335 6955
Website: www.medicsonthemove.co.uk
Summary of Operation: A dedicate personal service that makes it easy for you to find a home.
More Information: theukfd.net/27116644

Move In Move Out
Telephone: 0114 304 9050
Website: www.moveinmoveout.co.uk
Summary of Operation: One of the UK's lowest priced fixed fee online estate agent.
More Information: theukfd.net/52528372

MovingWorks
Telephone: 01772 611 631
Website: www.movingworks.co.uk
Summary of Operation: Estate agency.
More Information: theukfd.net/30341481

No Letting Go
Telephone: 0845 659 9980
Website: www.nolettinggo.co.uk
Summary of Operation: Inventory management for rental properties.
More Information: theukfd.net/36181063

PALI Ltd
Telephone: 0151 691 1170
Website: www.paliltd.co.uk
Summary of Operation: Home information pack (HIP) and conveyancing search providers to estate agents and solicitors.
More Information: theukfd.net/44638108

Phoenix Business Transfer Agents
Telephone: 0844 567 5016
Website: www.phoenixbusinesssales.co.uk
Summary of Operation: Estate agents.
More Information: theukfd.net/37550891

Princegate Estates PLC
Telephone: 01189 773 200
Website: www.princegate.com
Summary of Operation: Property re-development.
More Information: theukfd.net/78103246

PSG Franchising Ltd
Telephone: 01484 773277
Website: www.propertysearchgroup.co.uk
Summary of Operation: The Property Search Group provide all your conveyancing needs under one roof through a national network.
More Information: theukfd.net/76175630

RE/MAX Scotland
Telephone: 01698 464 200
Website: www.remax-scotland.com
Summary of Operation: Flats and houses for sale across Scotland.
More Information: theukfd.net/69676276

Reeds Rains
Telephone: 0800 977 8700
Website: www.reedsrains.co.uk
Summary of Operation: Profitable estate agency.
More Information: theukfd.net/30020642

Rentin Group
Telephone: 01949 829 109
Website: www.rentin-group.com
Summary of Operation: A holiday property rentals business.
More Information: theukfd.net/75038257

Scottish & Newcastle Pub Enterprises
Telephone: 0131 528 2694
Website: www.pub-enterprises.co.uk
Summary of Operation: Leased and tenanted pub business.
More Information: theukfd.net/15320445

Seekers Residential Lettings
Telephone: 01622 671878
Website: www.seekersmaidstone.co.uk
Summary of Operation: Estate agency franchise.
More Information: theukfd.net/16733504

Select Properties (UK) Ltd
Telephone: 01793 855 117
Website: www.selectpropertiesfranchise.com
Summary of Operation: Letting agency and sales.
More Information: theukfd.net/1120213

Smart House
Telephone: 0845 053 3680
Website: www.smarthouse.co.uk
Summary of Operation: Whole house audio, automatic curtains and blinds and digital CCTV.
More Information: theukfd.net/34463777

Surelet Franchising Ltd
Telephone: 01452 313 315
Website: www.surelet-franchise.co.uk
Summary of Operation: A specialist residential property mananagement company.
More Information: theukfd.net/07057476

TeamAbroad
Telephone: 01458 834 195
Website: www.teamabroad-avon.com
Summary of Operation: TeamAbroad giving you the choice of over 50,000 properties worldwide.
More Information: theukfd.net/22453407

The Buying Agents
Telephone: 0843 289 8475
Website: www.thebuyingagents.com
Summary of Operation: The Buying Agents is the UK's first national home buyer's agent service.
More Information: theukfd.net/89489348

The Property Search Group
Telephone: 01484 773 266
Website: www.thehipalliance.co.uk
Summary of Operation: Personal searches of residential properties for the legal sector.
More Information: theukfd.net/44210935

Townends Group
Telephone: 01932 736 500
Website: www.townends.co.uk
Summary of Operation: Estate agents.
More Information: theukfd.net/16712042

UKpropertyshop
Telephone: 0845 313 1051
Website: www.ukpropertyshop.tv
Summary of Operation: Offering unique solutions proposition to the home seller and buyer.
More Information: theukfd.net/98863081

Velo Real Estate Ltd
Telephone: 01706 344 224
Website: www.veloestates.co.uk
Summary of Operation: Estate agents.
More Information: theukfd.net/58478127

Waterside Properties
Telephone: 023 9277 7073
Website: www.watersideproperties.co.uk
Summary of Operation: Waterside are not your average estate agents. We are a market leader in the sale and letting of waterside homes.
More Information: theukfd.net/17272954

We're Moving Ltd
Telephone: 020 7924 1566
Summary of Operation: Estate agency.
More Information: theukfd.net/50104274

Winkworth Franchising Ltd
Telephone: 020 8576 5580
Website: www.winkworth.co.uk
Summary of Operation: Sales and rental estate agency franchise.
More Information: theukfd.net/86708587

World Property Centre Group (UK)
Telephone: 01633 852 212
Summary of Operation: Holiday homes.
More Information: theukfd.net/88527148

Xperience
Telephone: 0845 337 0220
Website: www.xperience.co.uk
Summary of Operation: Estate agency, lettings, sales and management.
More Information: theukfd.net/12727260

X-Press Legal Services
Telephone: 01925 577 377
Website: www.xpresslegal.co.uk
Summary of Operation: Land and property search agents.
More Information: theukfd.net/99148836

Your Hip Search
Telephone: 01925 633 233
Website: www.yourhipsearch.co.uk
Summary of Operation: Fees payable on referred sales leads only. No commissions charged on self-generated work and clients.
More Information: theukfd.net/7649449

Your Move
Telephone: 01904 715 304
Website: www.your-move.co.uk
Summary of Operation: The fastest growing estate agency franchise in the UK today.
More Information: theukfd.net/80601578

SERVICES | Sales, Delivery & Distribution

Actively recruiting franchise owners

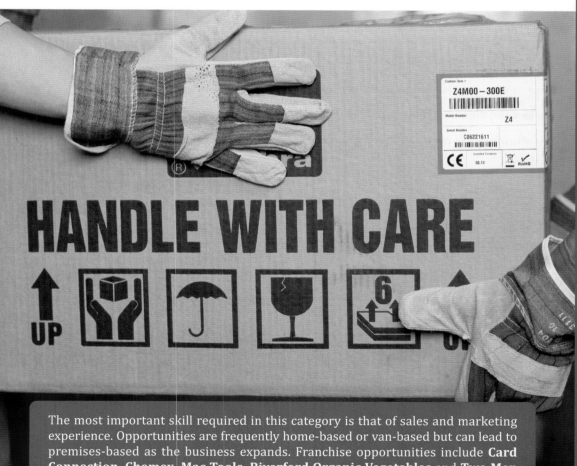

The most important skill required in this category is that of sales and marketing experience. Opportunities are frequently home-based or van-based but can lead to premises-based as the business expands. Franchise opportunities include **Card Connection, Chemex, Mac Tools, Riverford Organic Vegetables** and **Two Men And A Truck**.

Card Connection

Summary of Operation: Card Connection is the UK's leading greeting card franchise.

Ideal Franchise Owner Profile: Successful candidates would ideally have some management experience as once established, they would be expected to employ a small team, operate a warehouse and have several liveried vans on the road.

Cost of Franchise: £35,000 + VAT

Franchise Owner Contact: Andrew Cutler

Year Company Established: 1992

Year of First Franchise Owner: 1992

Number of Company Outlets: 1
Number of Franchised Outlets: 80
Number of Franchise Owners Planned: 50

Overseas Operations Existing: N/A
Overseas Operations Planned: N/A

Management Service Fees: £1,250 per annum

Breakdown of Package: All territory sales within the UK are established businesses.

Projected Turnover: AOR
Projected Profit: AOR

Financial Assistance Available: LloydsTSB, NatWest and RBS.

Training Provided: Eight days initially plus substantial ongoing support.

Training Location: Head office and in field.

Support Services: Business development.

Areas of Priority Development: Larger management franchises.

More Information: theukfd.net/03867056

Card Connection
Park House, South Street,
Farnham, Surrey, GU9 7QQ

t: 01252 892 300
f: 01252 892 339
e: enquiries@card-connection.co.uk
w: www.card-connection.co.uk

Chemex International (UK)

Summary of Operation: Mobile sale and distribution of cleaning and hygiene products to business clients in the hospitality & catering, leisure and healthcare industries. Franchise owners provide consultancy, training and support to all sectors of industry.

Ideal Franchise Owner Profile: People with drive, determination and tenacity with a desire to become successful business builders are needed across the UK. Your ability to develop excellent relationships with long-term, repeat order customers is where your premium service differentiates you from the competition.

Chemex International (UK)
Hawthorns House, Halfords Lane,
Smethwick, Birmingham, B66 1BB

t: 0121 565 6315
m: 07967 059209
f: 0121 565 6303
e: michael.wilson@chemexuk.com
w: www.chemexuk.com

Cost of Franchise: £25,000 + VAT

Franchise Owner Contact: Mike Wilson

Year Company Established: 1984
Year of First Franchise Owner: 1985

Number of Company Outlets: 0
Number of Franchised Outlets: 67
Number of Franchise Owners Planned: 80

Overseas Operations Existing: Canada, Cyprus, Malta, Denmark, Ireland and France.

Overseas Operations Planned: Turkey, Spain, Romania, France, Australia, South Africa and Brazil.

Management Service Fees: 6% of gross sales

Breakdown of Package: Licence, full training, computer hardware and software, marketing pack and product start up package. National accounts and full sales back-up.

Financial Assistance Available: All major banks.

Training Provided: Full initial training includes two weeks induction at head office plus 12 weeks 'Rapid Establishment' in field training schedule.

Training Location: Company head office and on territory.

Support Services: Franchise owners operate from fully-equipped mobile showrooms and are provided with everything they need to start their business, together with a comprehensive support package, launch campaign, field and head office support.

More Information: theukfd.net/91634899

Mac Tools Europe

Summary of Operation: Automotive tool distribution.

Ideal Franchise Owner Profile: Business, engineering or sales background; must be highly motivated, enthusiastic and self-disciplined.

Cost of Franchise: £50,000 + VAT

Franchise Owner Contact: Paul Clegg

Year Company Established: 1938 (USA) - 1980 (UK)
Year of First Franchise Owner: 1990

Number of Franchised Outlets: 100
Number of Franchise Owners Planned:
120 by June 2011

Overseas Operations Existing: 16
Overseas Operations Planned: Europe

Management Service Fees: None

Breakdown of Package: Fully merchandised van, exclusive territory, 350 customers, training and an administration system.

Projected Turnover:
1st Year: £110,000   **2nd Year:** £125,000
3rd Year: £150,000

Projected Profit:
1st Year: £35,000   **2nd Year:** £40,000
3rd Year: £47,000

Financial Assistance Available: Business Plan, cash flow forecasting tools.

Training Provided: 30 days
Training Location: USA and the UK
Support Services: Yes

Areas of Priority Development: UK

More Information: theukfd.net/61678433

Mac Tools Europe
c/o Stanley UK, Europa View,
Sheffield Business Park,
Sheffield, S9 1XH

t: 08450 600 060
e: franchise@mactools.co.uk
w: www.mactools.co.uk

Two Men And A Truck

Summary of Operation: TWO MEN AND A TRUCK® is the largest franchised moving company in North America because of our high referral rate, strong market identity, dedication to customer service, and moving expertise. A TWO MEN AND A TRUCK® franchise opportunity is best described as "A franchise moving business for the business professional."

Ideal Franchise Owner Profile: Franchises are locally owned and operated by business people who typically have strong sales, marketing and management backgrounds, and who believe in delivering the highest standards in customer service and satisfaction. Franchise owners are also very active in their communities and promote themselves as local business owners in the markets they service.

Cost of Franchise: Initial franchise fee is £29,950 + VAT

Franchise Owner Contact: Mike Harrison
Year Company Established: 1985
Year of First Franchise Owner: 1989
Number of Company Outlets: 2
Number of Franchised Outlets: 215
Number of Franchise Owners Planned: 70

Breakdown of Package: Turnkey programme including training, shopfit and launch.

Two Men And A Truck
One Victoria Square,
Birmingham,
B1 1BD

t: 0121 632 2643
e: info@twomenandatruck.co.uk
w: www.twomenandatruck.co.uk

Financial Assistance Available: No

Training Provided: Training elements covered include; how to market a TWO MEN AND A TRUCK® franchise, computer and accounting systems, recruitment and operational management.

Training Location: A new franchise owner will go to Lansing, Michigan in the United States and be trained for two weeks by the management and Home Office staff through STICK MEN UNIVERSITY®. The Dublin Learning Centre also hosts management and frontline training courses throughout the year.

Support Services: Franchise owners enjoy the benefits of: registered trademarks, powerful brand name, exclusive franchise marketing areas, two weeks of training, pre-opening assistance on site, ongoing field support, proprietary operating software, annual meetings and conventions, marketing material and financial benchmarking.

Areas of Priority Development:
East and West Midlands.

More Information: theukfd.net/58862658

bfa Provisional Member

Cargocall Franchising

Hellmann House, Lakeside Industrial Estate,
Colnbrook, Slough, Berkshire, SL3 0EL

Telephone: 0800 0787 747
Email: info@cargocall.com
Website: www.cargocall.com

Summary of Operation: Worldwide freight forwarding - arranging and managing the movement of goods for companies that import and export goods and raw materials. Brokerage type business system with low overheads and start-up costs. White-collar business to business franchise with full training and ongoing support.

Ideal Franchise Owner Profile: Professional-minded individuals who are well organised with sales experience. Also possessing good communication and negotiation skills.

Cost of Franchise: £26,300 + VAT

Franchise Owner Contact: Gary Clere

More Information: theukfd.net/18549403

bfa Full Member

Snack-in-the-Box

Belvedere Point, Penner Road,
Havant, Hampshire, PO9 1QY

Telephone: 023 9241 5000
Fax: 023 9247 5005
Email: info@sitb.co.uk
Website: www.sitb.co.uk

Summary of Operation: Snack-in-the-Box (SITB) delivers snacks and drinks to the work place in association with MARS via a self service box and vending machines. Franchise owners deliver snacks and drinks to small and medium sized workplaces with 2-100 employees. The system is well established and has a proven record of success.

Cost of Franchise: £25,000 - £60,000 + VAT

Franchise Owner Contact: Sean Cleveland

Support Services: SITB are renowned for their excellent support and the franchise is easy to learn.

More Information: theukfd.net/71261175

021 Network

Website: www.021network.com
Summary of Operation: Nationwide express parcels company.
More Information: theukfd.net/56775487

An Advert To Offer

Telephone: 01455 284 709
Website: www.advert2offer.co.uk
Summary of Operation: An Advert To Offer specialise in full colour print at unbeatable prices with delivery times that are as quick as a couple of hours on some orders.
More Information: theukfd.net/70644837

ANC Group Ltd

Website: www.anc.co.uk
Summary of Operation: Nationwide express parcels collection and delivery service.
More Information: theukfd.net/67045315

Aquaid (Franchising) Ltd

Telephone: 01223 508 109
Website: www.aquaid.co.uk
Summary of Operation: Supplying water cooler machines and water to businesses and organisations in the UK and Europe
More Information: theukfd.net/33760206

Bishops Move Group

Telephone: 020 8391 8200
Website: www.bishopsmove.com
Summary of Operation: International and national relocation specialists to include business relocations, storage, self storage, domestic relocations UK and international relocations.
More Information: theukfd.net/36642872

Bluestar Vending

Telephone: 01380 738 338
Summary of Operation: Our Salysol and Pringles bar snack vending machines offer a brilliant solution to the problem of providing eye-catching and original bar snacks.
More Information: theukfd.net/56127413

Buy-local.net

Telephone: 0845 880 7055
Website: www.buy-local.net
Summary of Operation: Retailing of local food via home delivery to residential and catering customers.
More Information: theukfd.net/78920210

Card Line Greetings Ltd

Telephone: 0121 522 4457
Website: www.cardline.co.uk
Summary of Operation: Greetings card distribution to retailers on a consignment basis.
More Information: theukfd.net/64538681

Colneis Greeting Cards

Telephone: 01394 271 668
Website: www.colneisgreetingcards.com
Summary of Operation: A distributor of high quality exclusive design greetings cards.
More Information: theukfd.net/73176015

DU Franchise Ltd t/as Distribution Unlimited

Telephone: 0845 466 4656
Website: www.dufranchise.co.uk
Summary of Operation: Professional, reliable and targeted leaflet distribution.
More Information: theukfd.net/03776168

Epost2day Ltd

Telephone: 01202 576 356
Website: www.epost2day.com
Summary of Operation: Mail services.
More Information: theukfd.net/11317406

Factory First

Telephone: 0845 6036 385
Website: www.factoryfirst.co.uk
Summary of Operation: Commercial catering equipment for independent catering outlets.
More Information: theukfd.net/06364152

Fastway Couriers

Telephone: 01908 633 700
Website: www.fastwaycouriers.co.uk
Summary of Operation: Van based franchise which offers the franchise owner the opportunity to build a thriving courier business with the back-up support of a global brand.
More Information: theukfd.net/32125453

FiltaCool

Telephone: 01788 513 088
Website: www.filtacool.co.uk
Summary of Operation: FiltaCool provides a 100% natural humidity control solution to all refrigerated and cold storage within thousands of establishments throughout the UK.
More Information: theukfd.net/41866746

Happy Days Greetings Ltd

Telephone: 0113 273 3633
Summary of Operation: Greeting cards.
More Information: theukfd.net/70655183

Hymix Ltd

Telephone: 01952 200 900
Website: www.hymix.com
Summary of Operation: Concrete mixer and pump manufacturers.
More Information: theukfd.net/13116951

Interlink Express Parcels Ltd

Telephone: 01562 881 030
Website: www.interlinkexpress.com
Summary of Operation: A management franchise operating a depot collecting and delivering parcels.
More Information: theukfd.net/85232061

Jaguar Couriers Ltd

Telephone: 01952 588 690
Website: wwwjaguarcouriers.co.uk
Summary of Operation: Nationwide courier delivery service.
More Information: theukfd.net/56865010

Moviebank

Telephone: 020 8458 8585
Website: www.mb24.co.uk
Summary of Operation: Vending Machines.
More Information: theukfd.net/46033782

My Mag

Website: www.mymaguk.com
Summary of Operation: A magazine, distributed free to homes in your local community and in which local businesses advertise.
More Information: theukfd.net/51805748

Pack & Send

Telephone: 01189 584 628
Website: www.packsend.co.uk
Summary of Operation: Pack & Send operates from conveniently situated shops on the high street and is the UK's leading packaging and delivery company – our specialist range of packaging materials and techniques and our comprehensive delivery services allow us to pack and send anything.
More Information: theukfd.net/89648433

Primary Times

Telephone: 01491 845 800
Website: www.primarytimes.net
Summary of Operation: Primary Times is a what's on, where to go, what to do guide for parents and teachers of primary school children.
More Information: theukfd.net/46783780

Royal Mail Group Ltd

Telephone: 020 7250 2888
Website: www.royalmail.com
Summary of Operation: Mail delivering
More Information: theukfd.net/19355302

Sameday UK Ltd

Telephone: 01925 221 122
Website: www.samedayuk.com
Summary of Operation: Sameday UK is an established company with a strong corporate image providing a professional and comprehensive same day delivery service throughout the UK and Europe utilising modern technology to ensure the highest standards of quality.
More Information: theukfd.net/82440852

SMA Worldwide

Telephone: 0118 965 7503
Website: www.smaworldwidefranchise.com
Summary of Operation: Courier and freight services.
More Information: theukfd.net/46867640

Snack Machine Ltd

Telephone: 020 8481 3705
Website: www.snackmachine.co.uk
Summary of Operation: Vending machines.
More Information: theukfd.net/56085250

Snap-on Tools Ltd

Telephone: 01536 413 800
Website: www.snap-on.com
Summary of Operation: Distribution of automotive hand tools.
More Information: theukfd.net/67147748

Southwest Greens UK

Telephone: 08452 304 794
Website: www.southwestgreens.co.uk
Summary of Operation: Southwest Greens UK is one of the worldwide family of independent distributors of Southwest Putting Greens Inc.
More Information: theukfd.net/28510644

Sweets For Life Ltd

Telephone: 01254 676 760
Website: www.sweetsforlife.co.uk
Summary of Operation: Sales and distribution of confectionery, ideally suited for two people.
More Information: theukfd.net/54775270

Taxi Truck

Telephone: 0800 731 1479
Website: www.taxitruck.com
Summary of Operation: Taxi truck is a specialist transport company. We will move or deliver anything from homes and offices to the smallest household goods.
More Information: theukfd.net/07001529

The Filta Group Ltd

Telephone: 01788 550 100
Website: www.filtagroup.com
Summary of Operation: Specialist cleaning services.
More Information: theukfd.net/65035211

The Real Bean Coffee Company

Telephone: 0800 652 8144
Website: www.realbean.co.uk
Summary of Operation: Sales and distribution of coffee machines and consumables.
More Information: theukfd.net/77423359

The Sweet Partnership

Telephone: 01293 551 599
Website: www.tspf.co.uk
Summary of Operation: Confectionery distribution and delivery to businesses.
More Information: theukfd.net/58118250

Voucher Packs

Telephone: 01253 892 814
Website: www.voucherpacks.co.uk
Summary of Operation: Voucher Packs is the UK's premier local co-operative direct mail service with a proven track record of delivering for advertisers.
More Information: theukfd.net/42677774

XDP Express

Telephone: 01675 475 754
Website: www.xdp.co.uk
Summary of Operation: Courier and express parcels delivery.
More Information: theukfd.net/06351837

SERVICES | Specialised

 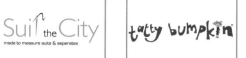  

Actively recruiting franchise owners

Children & Education
Children and educational franchise opportunities represent many low-cost investment levels required and are amongst the most popular.

Pet & Animal Services
Pet franchises are very enjoyable opportunities including home dog training, pet care franchises, animal franchises, and pet sitting franchises.

Other Specialised Services
There are a wide variety of other specialist franchise opportunities which can cover niche business sectors.

Specialised franchise opportunities include **ComputerXplorers, Suit the City, Tatty Bumpkin** and **The Video Inventory Agency.**

ComputerXplorers

bfa
PROVISIONAL

ComputerXplorers Ltd

Summary of Operation: ComputerXplorers teaches computer skills to children aged three to 13. ComputerXplorers' goal is to help children discover their own technology and computer skills through exploration in younger children building skills in maths, literacy, science, art etc. and in older students improving learning, productivity and performance through the adoption of ICT skills and knowledge.

Ideal Franchise Owner Profile: ComputerXplorers is looking for franchise owners who consider themselves to be 'people people' with strong communication skills who are well organised and have a high work ethic – most importantly, however, we want people with passion!

Cost of Franchise: £29,500 + VAT

Franchise Owner Contact: Janet Matthews

Year Company Established: 2005
Year of First Franchise Owner: 2005

Number of Company Outlets: 0
Number of Franchised Outlets: 15
Number of Franchise Owners Planned: 60

Overseas Operations Existing: Ireland
Overseas Operations Planned: Yes

Management Service Fees: 10%

Breakdown of Package: Licence to trade, comprehensive training in both UK and UK, twelve month marketing launch programme, extensive marketing collateral, personalised web site, access to ComputerXplorers Extranet, finance package, detailed Contact Management System, manuals and ongoing business support.

Financial Assistance Available: Major banks.

Training Provided: ComputerXplorers provides three weeks of initial training, two of which are in Houston, USA. Training includes sales, marketing, curriculum management, finance and business development.
Training Location: UK and USA

Support Services: Full business support is provided including but not limited to business planning, sales development, marketing planning and financial management. The company provides comprehensive marketing tools and appointment-generating system, full collateral and your own website and support.

Areas of Priority Development: Throughout the UK and Ireland.

More Information: theukfd.net/33864357

ComputerXplorers Ltd
Unit 2, Cartwright Way, Forest Business Park, Bardon, Coalville, LE67 1UB

t: 01530 513 308
w: www.computerxplorers.co.uk
f: 01530 513 309
e: jmatthews@computerxplorers.co.uk

SERVICES | Specialised
Children & Education

Leaps and Bounds by Tumble Tots
Bluebird Park, Bromsgrove Road,
Hunnington, Halesowen, B62 0TT

Telephone: 0121 585 7003
Email: info@leaps-and-bounds.co.uk
Website: www.leaps-and-bounds.co.uk

Summary of Operation: Leaps and Bounds was conceived to fulfil a demand from pre-school settings for a movement and physical development programme.

Breakdown of Package: Territory, equipment, technical development, lesson plans, fees and insurances, training (including business and technical management) plus ongoing support.

Cost of Franchise: £11,000 + VAT

Franchise Owner Contact: Anne Griffin

More Information: theukfd.net/08510706

Liverpool Institute For Performing Arts (LIPA *4:19*)
Mount Street, Liverpool, L1 9HF

Telephone: 0161 926 9882
Email: gill@fdsnorth.com

Summary of Operation: The Liverpool Institute for Performing Arts (LIPA) has set up a part-time performing arts academy franchise aimed at children aged four to 19. Franchise owners take a managerial role and oversee the running of the academy and can also teach some classes themselves (providing they have an appropriate qualification).

Ideal Franchise Owner: Teaching experience not essential.
Cost of Franchise: £13,500 + VAT
Franchise Owner Contact: Gill O'Brien
Financial Assistance Available: N/A

More information: theukfd.net/94046560

Tatty Bumpkin Ltd
The Oak Barn, Allens Farm, Allens Lane, Plaxtol, Sevenoaks, TN15 0QZ

Telephone: 0845 6800480
Email: franchise@tattybumpkin.com
Website: www.tattybumpkin.com

Summary of Operation: A Tatty Bumpkin franchise generates income through fun yoga inspired music and movement activity classes for children aged six weeks – seven years and through sales of Tatty Bumpkin's organic carbon neutral fair trade clothing and accessories. The unique multi-income franchise gives you the flexibility to work to your own schedule while being part of an award winning ethical business.

Ideal Franchise Owner: Hard working and ambitious but with the desire to create a better work/life balance. A minimum of 20-30 hours a week is required and they must enjoy challenges, are sociable and want to enjoy their career. Self-motivated, well organised and can manage their time effectively.

Cost of Franchise: £10,000 + VAT
Franchise Owner Contact: Sam Morgan
Year Company Established: 2004
Year of First Franchise Owner: 2008
Number of Company Outlets: 1
Number of Franchised Outlets: 24
Number of Franchise Owners Planned:
9-16 per year
Management Service Fees: 12.5%

Breakdown of Package: Full training, website, email, 0845 number, merchandise and accessories to run classes as well as a uniform, ongoing support and free advertising design etc.

Training Provided: Four days teacher training for franchise owner and one teacher plus two days business training for franchise owner.
Training Location: Kent
Support Services: Management support, ongoing training, sales and marketing advice, advertising graphic design, merchandise and accessories.

Areas of Priority Development: North England, Scotland and Wales.

More information: theukfd.net/68948073

EuroTalk Ltd
Telephone: 020 7371 7711
Website: www.eurotalk.com
Summary of Operation: Distribution of Eurotalk, which is the world's largest selling language course on CD.
More Information: theukfd.net/50412874

Family Martial Arts
Telephone: 01896 750 818
Website: www.familymartialartsuk.com
Summary of Operation: Taekwon-Do based Martial Art School, using Korean kicking techniques, traditional boxing, kick-boxing and Ju-Jitsu.
More Information: theukfd.net/30027728

Film Steps
Telephone: 0844 324 5414
Website: www.filmsteps.com
Summary of Operation: Part-time film making Schools after school hours and weekends for children.
More Information: theukfd.net/19286917

Fire Training International Ltd
Telephone: 0800 158 4428
Website: www.fire-training-uk.com
Summary of Operation: Fire training UK offer training courses in fire safety training, fire marshal and warden training, portable appliance testing and fire risk assessment.
More Information: theukfd.net/42228529

First Class Learning
Telephone: 0800 458 3797
Website: www.firstclasslearning.co.uk
Summary of Operation: First Class Learning has been designed by a team of maths and English specialists with a wealth of experience in primary, secondary and special needs education and a commitment to enhancing children's learning.
More Information: theukfd.net/85979626

FitKids Ltd
Telephone: 08700 85 1000
Website: www.fitkids.co.uk
Summary of Operation: UK national organisation offering premium training in children's health related fitness and FitKids.
More Information: theukfd.net/51882264

Funky Monkeys Franchising Ltd (UK)
Telephone: 0870 803 2763
Website: www.funkymonkeys.co.uk
Summary of Operation: Funky Monkeys is a new approach to indoor childrens play areas. Your child can play, learn and have fun while you relax and enjoy the best coffee and refreshments around, in our healthy cafe.
More Information: theukfd.net/42056858

Go-Kart Party UK Ltd
Telephone: 0870 116 2000
Website: www.go-kartparty.co.uk
Summary of Operation: Go-Kart Party provide a fun filled business, entertaining children using specially designed electric go karts working inside or outside, all year round. Ideal for a part time or full time start, can be run from home with low overheads.
More Information: theukfd.net/74843503

Gol Munidal
Telephone: 01256 332 218
Website: www.gol-mundial.com
Summary of Operation: Sports coaching for children, Saturday events.
More Information: theukfd.net/00548614

Gymboree (UK)
Telephone: 020 8288 9727
Website: www.Gymboree-UK.com
Summary of Operation: Play music and arts classes for children under five focussing on learning skills development and sensory stimulation.
More Information: theukfd.net/72601404

Helen Doron Ltd
Telephone: 020 8311 8057
Website: www.helendoron.com
Summary of Operation: Maths and English enrichment programs for children.
More Information: theukfd.net/57539215

Helen O'Grady Drama Academy
Telephone: 01481 200 250
Website: www.helenogrady.co.uk
Summary of Operation: Self-development classes as an after-school activity for children between the ages of five to 17 years – using drama in a fun way.
More Information: theukfd.net/33451280

Home Study Courses Ltd
Telephone: 01934 713 563
Website: www.inst.org
Summary of Operation: Distance learning courses, distance education, home-study courses, garden design courses, interior design, writing.
More Information: theukfd.net/36426661

Hooray Hooray
Telephone: 07730 609 220
Website: www.hoorayhooray.co.uk
Summary of Operation: The early years music and movement programme.
More Information: theukfd.net/36379577

Images School Art Exhibitions
Telephone: 01472 360 300
Website: www.imagesart.co.uk
Summary of Operation: Art exhibitions of children's work in their own schools.
More Information: theukfd.net/53224671

Interactive Music Club
Telephone: 07764 367 397
Website: www.interactivemusicclub.co.uk
Summary of Operation: After-school music clubs.
More Information: theukfd.net/41148230

Jabberjacks Franchising Ltd
Telephone: 01509 413 873
Website: www.jabberjacks.co.uk
Summary of Operation: Jabberjacks provides educational activity through pre-school classes in local venues and private nurseries, together with party entertainment for children aged between two and seven years.
More Information: theukfd.net/88423229

Jo Jingles Ltd
Telephone: 01494 778 989
Website: www.jojingles.com
Summary of Operation: Pre-school music, singing and movement classes in the UK, Ireland and Western Australia. Available in over 600 centres, classes are fun and interactive.
More Information: theukfd.net/57083028

Jumping Clay UK & Ireland
Telephone: 028 9020 4180
Website: www.jumpingclay.co.uk
Summary of Operation: Offers an exciting way for children to learn through play.
More Information: theukfd.net/86423646

KindaRoo
Telephone: 01243 377 431
Website: www.kindaroo.co.uk
Summary of Operation: Specialised fun fitness creative educational movement programme for two to five year olds.
More Information: theukfd.net/01470758

Kip McGrath Education Centres
Telephone: 01452 382 282
Website: www.kipmcgrath.co.uk
Summary of Operation: Kip McGrath Education Centres (KMEC) is an internationally established success.
More Information: theukfd.net/53870831

Kumon Educational (UK)
Telephone: 0800 854 714
Website: www.kumon.co.uk
Summary of Operation: Maths and English after school study centres. Develops mastery of basic skills and builds lasting confidence with excellent concentration skills and study habits.
More Information: theukfd.net/47733523

La Jolie Ronde Ltd
Telephone: 01949 839 715
Website: www.lajolieronde.co.uk
Summary of Operation: La Jolie Ronde offers French and Spanish language learning for children aged three to 11 years.
More Information: theukfd.net/11832110

Laptop Learning
Telephone: 01803 50 60 70
Website: www.laptoplearning.co.uk
Summary of Operation: Laptop Learning helps people to improve their computer skills.
More Information: theukfd.net/91622102

LCF (UK) Ltd
Telephone: 01489 786 473
Website: www.lcfclubs.com
Summary of Operation: Fun activities and learning for pre-schoolers.
More Information: theukfd.net/85680179

Little Kickers
Telephone: 01235 859 250
Website: www.littlekickers.co.uk
Summary of Operation: Children and play education.
More Information: theukfd.net/36616357

Little Superstars Sports Club
Telephone: 07904 311 552
Website: www.littlesuperstars.co.uk
Summary of Operation: Little Superstars offer a range of unique, fun and active multi sports sessions for children from the age of walking to 11 years.
More Information: theukfd.net/56029165

Local Wine School.com
Telephone: 0191 281 8045
Website: www.localwineschool.com
Summary of Operation: Independently owned wine schools providing fun wine education.
More Information: theukfd.net/11362111

Mad Academy
Telephone: 0118 926 1384.
Website: www.madacademy.co.uk
Summary of Operation: The Music and Dance Academy provides free-spirited classes for pre-school children which combine high energy music and dance with carefully structured learning. We aim to help children develop confidence, co-ordination and social skills, whilst learning to express themselves creatively and encouraging a life long love of music.
More Information: theukfd.net/44825075

MagiKats Tuition Centres
Telephone: 0844 870 9896
Website: www.magikats.co.uk
Summary of Operation: Offers out of school English and maths tuition for mainly five to 16 year olds.
More Information: theukfd.net/70517431

Mars Venus Coaching
Telephone: 07917 121 940
Website: www.marsvenuscoaching.com
Summary of Operation: At Mars Venus Coaching, we provide training programs, workshops, life coaching, and executive coaching services that dramatically enhance personal and organisational performance.
More Information: theukfd.net/24614825

Matt Fiddes Martial Arts Schools
Telephone: 0800 0354 660
Website: www.mattfiddes.com
Summary of Operation: Martial arts training.
More Information: theukfd.net/07824767

Messy Monsters
Telephone: 0161 798 4518
Website: www.messymonsters.co.uk
Summary of Operation: Art and craft club for babies and young children.
More Information: theukfd.net/50257344

MindLab Europe PLC
Telephone: 01628 509 021
Website: www.mindlabeurope.com
Summary of Operation: MindLab's after school programme uses board games from around the world to develop children's thinking.
More Information: theukfd.net/26154873

Monkey Music
Telephone: 01582 766 464
Website: www.monkeymusic.co.uk
Summary of Operation: To introduce music to very young children in a way they can easily understand and enjoy.
More Information: theukfd.net/55178238

Mucky Pups
Telephone: 01625 537219
Website: www.mucky-pups.com
Summary of Operation: Mucky pups art and craft clubs are the original and best art and craft club for children.
More Information: theukfd.net/28885316

Music Bugs
Telephone: 0844 578 1010
Website: www.musicbugs.co.uk
Summary of Operation: Fun music classes for babies, toddlers and pre-schoolers.
More Information: theukfd.net/32253852

Musical Bumps
Telephone: 01732 321 217
Website: www.musicalbumps.com
Summary of Operation: Top quality, relaxed and fun music classes for babies and children to share and enjoy with their parents or carers.
More Information: theukfd.net/16260208

Musical Minis
Telephone: 020 8868 0001
Website: www.musicalminis.co.uk
Summary of Operation: A structured programme to operate musical classes for pre-school children to assist them with their early development.
More Information: theukfd.net/41152507

New Youth Theatre
Telephone: 01522 787 601
Website: www.newyouththeatre.co.uk
Summary of Operation: At New Youth Theatre, we bring musical theatre to local communities and have given thousands of young people across the region a unique experience of being onstage.
More Information: theukfd.net/57310566

Nobleprog Ltd
Telephone: 020 7558 8274
Website: www.nobleprog.co.uk
Summary of Operation: Training courses.
More Information: theukfd.net/43554151

OCFM
Telephone: 01626 360 999
Website: www.ocfm.co.uk
Summary of Operation: The OCFM specialise in furthering your education in the Martial Arts.
More Information: theukfd.net/33704221

Party Crew
Telephone: 0845 838 1314
Website: www.partycrew.co.uk
Summary of Operation: Children's parties.
More Information: theukfd.net/30843033

Pattacakes Cookery School
Telephone: 01582 762 986
Website: www.pattacakes.com
Summary of Operation: Teaching children, adults, parties and organisations to cook.
More Information: theukfd.net/87355270

Pauline Quirke Academy
Telephone: 08456 732 022
Website: www.pqacademy.com
Summary of Operation: This opportunity offers you the chance to run a Pauline Quirke Academy – a new generation of week-end drama schools – teaching children from ages four to 18 and inspiring a passion for performing arts.
More Information: theukfd.net/69121095

Pingu's English
Telephone: 020 8687 6104
Website: www.pingusenglish.com
Summary of Operation: An educational, fun and entertaining children's English language course based on the enormously popular animated television character, Pingu.
More Information: theukfd.net/97861831

Pitman Training Group PLC
Telephone: 01937 548 562
Website: www.pitman-training.com
Summary of Operation: Premium provider of IT and business skills training. White collar management premises based franchise with the largest independent training network within the UK.
More Information: theukfd.net/71266428

Playtime Activity & Party Centre
Telephone: 01932 246 747
Website: www.playtimecentre.com
Summary of Operation: The ultimate children's franchise opportunity. We combine an indoor activity and party centre with a high quality coffee shop where parents can relax whilst the children are at play.
More Information: theukfd.net/29814827

Popstar Parties
Telephone: 01530 513 305
Website: www.popstarparties.org
Summary of Operation: A 'work from home' franchise targeted at the huge celebrations market place. Great fun and full back up from experienced and successful franchisors.
More Information: theukfd.net/51883248

Premier Sport
Telephone: 01953 499 049
Website: www.makesportyourbusiness.com
Summary of Operation: Children's coaching company which specialises in sports teaching and instruction in curriculum time, as well as after school, breakfast, lunch and holiday clubs.
More Information: theukfd.net/10454552

Primary Books
Website: www.primarybooks.co.uk
Summary of Operation: Organising and managing book fairs and clubs in primary schools.Offering accomprehensive book supply service to schools including full day book fair events and library audit and supply.
More Information: theukfd.net/45746142

Progressive Sports Ltd
Telephone: 0845 094 1827
Website: www.progressive-sports.co.uk
Summary of Operation: Providing schools and communities with a range of services in physical education and sport.
More Information: theukfd.net/15884527

Franchise Listings

Puddle Ducks
Telephone: 01477 535 527
Website: www.puddleducks.com
Summary of Operation: Teaching babies and children to swim.
More Information: theukfd.net/63830017

Pyjama Drama
Telephone: 07938 555 775
Website: www.pyjamadrama.com
Summary of Operation: Here at Pyjama Drama we love to pretend, dance, explore and play. Classes are full of fun and games that encourage young children to use their imaginations, and to develop social skills such as concentration, co-operation and confidence.
More Information: theukfd.net/70412279

Razzamataz Theatre Schools Ltd
Telephone: 01228 550 129
Website: www.razzamataz.co.uk
Summary of Operation: Opportunity to join the UKs fastest growing children's theatre schools, as seen on Dragon's Den! Drama, singing and dance lessons for children aged four to 18 years, unique curriculum, full training given.
More Information: theukfd.net/70778223

Really Green Driving
Telephone: 07501 495 879
Website: www.reallygreendriving.com
Summary of Operation: Really Green Driving is an environmentally friendly driving school which is now being franchised across the UK.
More Information: theukfd.net/15228753

Rhythm Time
Telephone: 0121 711 4224
Website: www.rhythmtime.net
Summary of Operation: Introducing babies and pre-school children to the basics of music.
More Information: theukfd.net/10084425

Sinclair Training
Telephone: 0845 434 7797
Website: www.sinclairtraining.com
Summary of Operation: Sinclair Training bring a highly effective and distinctive, non-traditional selling system and sales training methodology to a wide range of salespeople, business owners and management giving them control of the sales process.
More Information: theukfd.net/23422985

Skip2BFit Ltd
Telephone: 01843 603 020
Website: www.skip2bfit.co.uk
Summary of Operation: Skipping classes.
More Information: theukfd.net/87510863

SlimDance (UK) Ltd
Telephone: 0844 774 3972
Website: www.slimdance.co.uk
Summary of Operation: The SlimDance Team are dedicated to providing the perfect platform for their franchise owners to receive the highest returns possible in income, freedom, and recognition in the field of dance and lifestyle education. Teaching dance should be about fun passion and laughter.
More Information: theukfd.net/91925922

Smallprint (Franchising) Ltd
Telephone: 0117 944 4888
Website: www.smallp.com
Summary of Operation: Children's silver fingerprint jewellery. Beautiful pieces of handcrafted jewellery that capture your child's fingerprint in polished silver.
More Information: theukfd.net/35683161

Smart Talkers
Telephone: 0844 704 5888
Website: www.smarttalkers.org.uk
Summary of Operation: Pre-school communication groups.
More Information: theukfd.net/92097113

Smileys Childcare Agency Ltd
Telephone: 0845 201 1630
Website: www.smileys-childcare.co.uk
Summary of Operation: Smileys childcare agency has been an established childcare provider since 1988. The agency specialises in the recruitment of nannies, babysitters etc.
More Information: theukfd.net/71672606

SOCATOTS
Telephone: 0113 244 2005
Website: www.socatots.com
Summary of Operation: Football coaching for kids. SOCATOTS® is the world's first soccer specific physical play programme for children from six months to school age.
More Information: theukfd.net/76188496

Sound Steps Music School
Telephone: 020 8668 4825
Website: www.soundstepsmusic.co.uk
Summary of Operation: Teaching primary school children to play keyboards.
More Information: theukfd.net/54684748

Splat Cooking
Telephone: 0870 766 8290
Website: www.splatcooking.net
Summary of Operation: Splat Cooking is a leading children's cookery school established by Beverley Glock, food writer, celebrity cook, The Times' Children's Food Expert and Ocado's Children's Cookery Queen.
More Information: theukfd.net/67757825

Sports Plus Scheme Ltd
Telephone: 0845 643 1998
Website: www.sportsplusscheme.co.uk
Summary of Operation: Sports Plus have been working in schools since the year 2000. We specialise in delivering high quality sports coaching.
More Information: theukfd.net/05777183

SportsCoach
Telephone: 01932 256 264
Website: www.sportscoach.co.uk
Summary of Operation: Multi-sports for children at weekends and holiday workshops.
More Information: theukfd.net/82112017

Stageability
Telephone: 01376 567 677
Website: www.stageability.co.uk
Summary of Operation: After school classes.
More Information: theukfd.net/05481817

Stagecoach Theatre Arts PLC
Telephone: 01932 254 333
Website: www.stagecoach.co.uk
Summary of Operation: Part-time theatre schools for children aged four to 18.
More Information: theukfd.net/22334167

TalkFirst Baby Signing Ltd
Telephone: 01706 872 816
Website: www.talkfirst.net
Summary of Operation: Providers of quality, educational and enjoyable baby signing classes.
More Information: theukfd.net/33777408

Talking Tots Ltd
Telephone: 01253 735 355
Website: www.talkingtots.info
Summary of Operation: Fun, interactive pre-school classes that help children to communicate with confidence.
More Information: theukfd.net/74838461

The Academy of Contemporary Music
Telephone: 01483 501 231
Website: www.acm.ac.uk
Summary of Operation: ACM operates a music industry relevant training facility, delivering courses in guitar, bass guitar, drums, vocals, music production and music business. Diploma to BA (Hons) Degree offerings attract students aged 16 years upwards who are serious about a career in the music industry.
More Information: theukfd.net/20777470

The Alternative Board - TAB
Telephone: 0800 118 5058
Website: www.thealternativeboard.co.uk
Summary of Operation: Peer advisory boards coaching and consulting. We are accredited by the British Franchise Association (bfa) and part of the Proud to Franchise movement.
More Information: theukfd.net/41764886

The Creation Station
Telephone: 0845 050 8743
Website: www.thecreationstation.co.uk
Summary of Operation: Children's fun arts and crafts activities.
More Information: theukfd.net/70655111

The Rock Project
Telephone: 01745 815 200
Website: www.therockproject.com
Summary of Operation: The Rock Project was started in 2005 by Stuart and Lowri Wynne, who felt that the "old-school" style of teaching music was just not hitting the right note with today's children.
More Information: theukfd.net/46871049

Theatretrain
Telephone: 01992 577 977
Website: www.theatretrain.co.uk
Summary of Operation: Professional training in the performing arts for young people aged six to 18.
More Information: theukfd.net/21319986

Franchise Listings

Timto Ltd
Telephone: 07814 435 380
Website: www.timto.co.uk
Summary of Operation: Timto is a unique and revolutionary children's birthday present wish list service.
More Information: theukfd.net/06672275

Tinies UK Ltd
Telephone: 020 7384 0322
Website: www.tinies.com
Summary of Operation: The UK's leading supplier of nursery nurses and nannies.
More Information: theukfd.net/40642041

Tinytees Golf Ltd
Telephone: 01273 834 028
Website: www.tinyteesgolf.co.uk
Summary of Operation: We offer a fun indoor golf activity programme for young children of ages three and upwards.
More Information: theukfd.net/66160147

Ugly Bug World Ltd
Telephone: 0845 241 7195
Website: www.uglybugworld.com
Summary of Operation: Ugly Bug is an experienced company providing quality activities for children and young people.
More Information: theukfd.net/99426635

Water Babies Ltd
Telephone: 01404 548 348
Website: www.waterbabies.co.uk
Summary of Operation: Specialised baby swimming courses with additional underwater photography service.
More Information: theukfd.net/18031503

Whizzkidz
Website: www.whizzkidz.co.uk
Summary of Operation: Computer literacy for children in a fun and stimulating smallgroup environment. Introductory computer courses for adults by small group tuition.
More Information: theukfd.net/15511455

Xtra Curricula Maths
Telephone: 01492 876 919
Website: www.maths4all.com
Summary of Operation: After school maths tuition for students aged between six and 16.
More Information: theukfd.net/00154411

YogaBugs
Telephone: 0121 7777 792
Website: www.yogabugs.com
Summary of Operation: Creative and fun childrens yoga classes.
More Information: theukfd.net/61202278

SERVICES | Specialised
Pet and Animal Services

10 Little Pigs Ltd
Telephone: 0777 4344 857
Website: www.10littlepigs.com
Summary of Operation: An all inclusive price covers inception to final opening of your new pig farm in Thailand. You become part of the 10 Little Pigs network, where you are provided with top range piglets and a guaranteed selling price after your piglets reach 110kg.
More Information: theukfd.net/63347741

Animals at Home
Telephone: 07970 063 364
Website: www.animalsathome.co.uk
Summary of Operation: Pet taxi, ambulance and pet care services.
More Information: theukfd.net/85050187

Aqua Rentals
Telephone: 07973 625 978
Website: www.aquarentals.co.uk
Summary of Operation: Aquarium supply rental equipment.
More Information: theukfd.net/20352224

Bark Busters UK
Telephone: 0808 100 4071
Website: www.barkbusters.co.uk
Summary of Operation: Home dog training specialising in therapy for behavioural problems with dogs.
More Information: theukfd.net/20037804

Barking Mad Ltd
Telephone: 01524 276 476
Website: www.barkingmad.uk.com
Summary of Operation: Home from home pet care.
More Information: theukfd.net/68713244

Creature Comforts
Telephone: 01352 719 415
Website: www.petsittinguk.co.uk
Summary of Operation: Petsitting services.
More Information: theukfd.net/06337915

Dashin Hounds
Telephone: 028 9048 5186
Website: www.dashinhoundsfranchise.com
Summary of Operation: Dashin Hounds is a unique pet grooming salon and grooming school.
More Information: theukfd.net/10386777

Dial-A-Dog Wash Ltd
Website: www.dialadogwash.com
Summary of Operation: Mobile dog grooming business. We call to customers' homes in ourconverted van to groom their pets.
More Information: theukfd.net/15317616

GB Pet Sitters
Telephone: 0845 094 6425
Website: www.gbpetsitters.co.uk
Summary of Operation: Dog walking pet sitting franchise.
More Information: theukfd.net/21059404

Groomers 4 Pets
Telephone: 01902 843 666
Website: www.groomers4pets.co.uk
Summary of Operation: Groomers 4 Pets offers franchise opportunities in either studio-based or mobile pet grooming.
More Information: theukfd.net/08785747

Home Loving Cats Ltd
Telephone: 07866 717 581
Website: www.homelovingcats.com
Summary of Operation: We offer a superb service for cat owners who seek cat sitting or pet sitting services as an alternative to the substantial stress of a cattery.
More Information: theukfd.net/27798529

MetroDogs
Telephone: 08448 75 75 75
Website: www.metrodogs.co.uk
Summary of Operation: Dog wash franchise and dog grooming by MetroDogs is the first self serve coin operated dog washing facility that is sweeping around the world.
More Information: theukfd.net/60222852

Mobile Dog Wash & Grooming Service
Telephone: 01443 806 151
Website: www.themobiledogwash.co.uk
Summary of Operation: A highly professional mobile dog washing and grooming service.
More Information: theukfd.net/50378308

Oscar Pet Foods Ltd
Telephone: 01772 647 909
Website: www.oscars.co.uk
Summary of Operation: Mobile pet food and accessories business delivering unique product in exclusive territory; taking great care in selecting excellent ancillary product range such as toys and treats for cats and dogs.
More Information: theukfd.net/55455163

Pals4Pets
Telephone: 020 8201 1606
Website: www.pals4petsuk.com
Summary of Operation: Managing and organising professional pet-care services.
More Information: theukfd.net/13555888

Paw Pals (UK) Ltd
Telephone: 01722 501 729
Website: www.paw-pals.co.uk
Summary of Operation: Pet sitting and dog walking.
More Information: theukfd.net/07306590

Pestforce
Telephone: 01205 750 068
Website: www.pest-force.co.uk
Summary of Operation: Pest control. Whether it's your house, garden, farm, football pitch, golf course, bowls lawn, cricket pitch, or even a private runway that's being affected, your pest problems are in safe hands with us.
More Information: theukfd.net/49659962

Pet Carers
Telephone: 01242 573 460
Website: www.petcarers.co.uk
Summary of Operation: Pet Carer – professional pet sitters for dog walking and dog boarding etc.
More Information: theukfd.net/72888527

Petpals (UK) Ltd
Telephone: 01264 326 362
Website: www.petpals.com
Summary of Operation: Professional pet sitting and dog walking company.
More Information: theukfd.net/60853867

Pets on the Move

Telephone: 01563 892 262
Website: www.petsonthemove.co.uk
Summary of Operation: Pet relocation service. Pets on the Move go to great lengths to ensure your pets relocation is stress free. We arrange customs clearance, booking your pet onto a dedicated carrier and more.
More Information: theukfd.net/70769257

The Bunnery

Telephone: 01527 873 467
Website: www.thebunnery.co.uk
Summary of Operation: Rabbit boarding fran.
More Information: theukfd.net/58036243

Trophy Pet Foods Ltd

Telephone: 01367 243 434
Website: www.trophypetfoods.co.uk
Summary of Operation: A mobile pet food business delivering Trophy pet foods, treats and accessories to pet owners in your home area.
More Information: theukfd.net/50616330

Veterinary Thermal Imaging Ltd

Telephone: 0844 544 3314
Website: www.vtifranchise.com
Summary of Operation: Veterinary Thermal Imaging is the first, and remains the only UK company specialising in thermography or thermal imaging across all animal species.
More Information: theukfd.net/56723668

Wagging Tails

Telephone: 01725 518 714
Website: www.waggingtailsuk.co.uk
Summary of Operation: Wagging Tails offers a stress free alternative to kennels or imposing on friends and family when owners go away. We match owner's dogs to one of our highly experienced carers who open their homes to just one family's dogs for a holiday. We are looking for dog owning franchise owners to operate their local area.
More Information: theukfd.net/34385086

Waggy Tails UK Ltd

Telephone: 01273 808 843
Website: www.waggytailsltd.co.uk
Summary of Operation: One-2-one dog training.
More Information: theukfd.net/43156643

SERVICES | Specialised
Other Specialised Services

bfa Associate Member
PC PAL

Franchise Support Centre, 139 Seven Star Road, Solihull, B91 2BN

Telephone: 0121 369 5000
Fax: 0845 467 2724
Email: joinus@pcpal.co.uk
Website: www.pcpal.co.uk/franchise

Summary of Operation: PC PAL is UK's leading on-site computer repair service for users of computers at home and in small businesses. We help people who are looking to run their own computer support business with the backing of PC PAL's strong branding, marketing and training support. No previous IT experience is needed.

Cost of Franchise: £19,999 + VAT
Franchise Owner Contact: Jat Mann
Year Company Established: 2004
Year of First Franchise Owner: 2008
Number of Company Outlets: 1
Number of Franchised Outlets: 7

More Information: theukfd.net/46715441

1/2 Price Ink Cartridges

Website: www.12ink.com
Summary of Operation: Re-manufacture and supply ink cartridges up to 60% savings with locations nationwide.
More Information: theukfd.net/52644844

1StopTele.com

Telephone: 07976 309 711
Website: www.annecto.com
Summary of Operation: A niche telecoms franchise company.
More Information: theukfd.net/37265024

About My Area

Telephone: 0870 062 2212
Website: www.opportunity.aboutmyarea.co.uk
Summary of Operation: The local interactive website.
More Information: theukfd.net/60084545

Suit the City
made to measure suits & separates

Suit the City

Summary of Operation: Suit the City provides high quality made to measure suits and separates for men and women. We use Savile Row fabrics combined with the latest pattern cutting and manufacturing technology to supply clients with the best in made to measure.

Ideal Franchise Owner Profile: You do not need to be a qualified tailor as all training will be provided. This is the ideal business for well-connected professionals who want to run their own business and maintain a high standard of living, whilst offering the flexibility of being your own boss. You are highly motivated, organised and excited by the prospect of growing a successful business for yourself, be it part or full time.

Cost of Franchise: £19,950 + VAT (London), £9,950 + VAT (other territories)
Franchise Owner Contact: Carol Rawson
Year Company Established: 2007
Number of Company Outlets: 1
Number of Franchised Outlets: 1
Number of Franchise Owners Planned: 50
Management Service Fees: £300 per month (London), £195 per month (other territories)
Breakdown of Package: You will receive all your sample suits, a full set of fabric samples, accessories, marketing materials, training manuals and stationery to get you started.

Projected Turnover:
1st Year: £75,000   **2nd Year:** £125,000
3rd Year: £150,000
Projected Profit:
1st Year: £35,000   **2nd Year:** £60,000
3rd Year: £70,000
Financial Assistance Available: Lloyds TSB

Training Provided: You will learn how to measure your clients and have expert help from the manufacturing team. You will be fully trained on fabrics including visits to suppliers. Our partners in colour and image consulting will give you expert advice and support.
Training Location: Initial training will be split between our office in Buckinghamshire, our manufacturing team in North London and our fabric suppliers in various locations in the UK.
Support Services: We will provide you with regular training, marketing support, PR including personalised newsletters, advertisements in the press, special offers and ideas to generate extra business as appropriate.
Areas of Priority Development: UK

More information: theukfd.net/63003411

Suit the City
Denham Farm, Wheeler End,
Buckinghamshire, HP14 3NQ

t: 01494 880 790
t: 020 7060 3535
e: enquiries@suitthecity.com
w: www.suitthecity.com

Franchise Listings

Cash Brokers
Telephone: 01476 574 722
Website: www.cashbrokers.co.uk
Summary of Operation: Pawnbrokers.
More Information: theukfd.net/22316024

Cash Express UK Limited
Telephone: 020 8566 0876
Website: www.cashexpressuk.co.uk
Summary of Operation: Offering an exciting business opportunity operating from premier high street locations providing financial and retail services – buy, sell pre-owned goods, cheque cashing, Western Union, auto log book loans and Bureau de Change.
More Information: theukfd.net/67058735

Cash For Cheques Ltd
Telephone: 020 8573 2400
Website: www.cashforcheques.co.uk
Summary of Operation: Cheque cashing service enabling customers to change their pay cheques, Inland Revenue rebate, insurance payouts etc. without the need of a bank account. Plus money transfer and foreign money exchange.
More Information: theukfd.net/83483210

Clothes Aid Collections Ltd
Telephone: 0870 6074 600
Website: www.clothesaid.co.uk
Summary of Operation: Collection of charity bags from homes.
More Information: theukfd.net/31565815

Coinspinner
Telephone: 0845 055 9651
Website: www.coinspinner.co.uk
Summary of Operation: At Coinspinner, we pride ourselves on offering value, quality and a professional and efficient service in a changing market place and we team this with our guiding principle of always putting people first.
More Information: theukfd.net/55647719

Community View
Telephone: 01792 790 688
Website: www.communityview.tv
Summary of Operation: Community View offers it's franchise owners the opportunity to manage a network of HD flat screen TV's strategically placed in local businesses, e.g. hair salons.
More Information: theukfd.net/15953289

Costcutter Supermarkets Group Ltd
Telephone: 01904 488 663
Website: www.costcutter.com
Summary of Operation: Retail symbol group supplying convenience stores with a full range of groceries, beers, wines, spirits, cigarettes and tobacco at competitive prices.
More Information: theukfd.net/40504140

Creative Concept Marketing
Telephone: 0845 8058 240
Website: www.creativeconceptmarketing.co.uk
Summary of Operation: Creative Concept Marketing is a revolutionary new franchise that offers a rewarding and flexible opportunity to enthusiastic and ambitious people.
More Information: theukfd.net/89436166

Curved Air Marketing Solutions
Telephone: 0161 233 7077
Website: www.curvedairmarketingsolutions.co.uk
Summary of Operation: High-tech, innovative SMS text and IVR (Interactive Voice Response) mobile marketing and business communication solution that reduces business cost and increases marketshare.
More Information: theukfd.net/71145013

Destination Alliances
Telephone: 0845 222 0105
Website: www.destinationalliances.co.uk
Summary of Operation: Destination Alliances facilitates cooperation and joint marketing between tourism businesses (hotels, restaurants and leisure activities), helping them to work together to promote their local area.
More Information: theukfd.net/54590527

Easyfood Ltd
Telephone: 0844 477 34 56
Website: www.easyfood.co.uk
Summary of Operation: Web based ordering system for fast food retailers. Opportunities available for both local franchise owners and area development directors.
More Information: theukfd.net/55509005

Easy-ID Ltd
Telephone: 0800 1123 258
Website: www.easy-idfranchise.co.uk
Summary of Operation: Photobooth franchise for retail applications and event booths for party hire.
More Information: theukfd.net/88239309

Ebusiness UK

Telephone: 01254 279 998
Website: www.ebusinessuk.biz
Summary of Operation: Established in 1998 providing web design and development, e-commerce solutions, search engine marketing and website content management systems.
More Information: theukfd.net/27126777

Eco Buggies

Telephone: 01323 873 555
Website: www.sonicgolf.co.uk
Summary of Operation: Supply of golf buggies to golf professionals on an income sharing basis.
More Information: theukfd.net/80370643

Ecoliving Ltd

Telephone: 0845 301 3120
Website: www.ecolivinguk.com
Summary of Operation: Ecoliving is a specialist provider of micro-renewable energy solutions, distributing innovative and sustainable heating, cooling and ventilation systems.
More Information: theukfd.net/38301564

Ekko

Telephone: 01292 270 592
Website: www.ekkoglass.com
Summary of Operation: Inovative recycling solutions.
More Information: theukfd.net/30650756

Electratest Ltd

Website: www.electratest.com
Summary of Operation: Inspection and testing of electrical appliances and machinery.
More Information: theukfd.net/16020352

EmbroidMe

Telephone: 02476 659 933
Website: www.embroidme.co.uk
Summary of Operation: Full service embroidery, garment printing and promotional products.
More Information: theukfd.net/76453775

Envos

Telephone: 0845 094 9240
Website: www.envos.co.uk
Summary of Operation: Specialises in providing independent environmental management to commercial properties and public buildings, with a full range of energy certification services.
More Information: theukfd.net/46147150

EVAPURE Products Ltd

Telephone: 0845 508 1123
Website: www.evapureplc.com
Summary of Operation: The EVAPURE system is a new, water generating machine which takes moisture out of thin air and turns it into pure drinking water.
More Information: theukfd.net/70608420

Fathom IT

Telephone: 0161 962 9595
Website: www.fathomit.co.uk
Summary of Operation: Providing computer and laptop sales and laptop repairs.
More Information: theukfd.net/45926824

Fireguard Services

Telephone: 01582 469 0000
Website: www.fireguardservices.com
Summary of Operation: Supply, install, commission and service the complete range of fire protection equipment, including extinguishers, fire alarms and emergency lighting.
More Information: theukfd.net/30577765

Focus on You

Telephone: 01202 475 035
Website: www.focus-on-you.net
Summary of Operation: Focus On You supply designer spectacles via informal group meetings and online.
More Information: theukfd.net/41243872

Fone Solutions Ltd

Telephone: 01380 870 517
Website: www.fsfg.co.uk
Summary of Operation: Mobile phone unlocking, repairs and accessories.
More Information: theukfd.net/44694150

Formula One Driver

Telephone: 0871 663 4751
Website: www.formulaonedriver.co.uk
Summary of Operation: Formula one car track days etc.
More Information: theukfd.net/89671140

Future-People Recruitment Ltd

Telephone: 08451 300 390
Website: www.future-people.co.uk
Summary of Operation: Future-people is a source for information about recruitment agencies.
More Information: theukfd.net/46425317

Franchise Listings

Scratch Repair Network
Telephone: 01823 667 986
Website: www.scratchrepairnetwork.co.uk
Summary of Operation: Scratch Repair Network provides a unique glass polishing service which can restore damaged glass and plexiglas at a fraction of the replacement cost.
More Information: theukfd.net/41072924

Shebang Distribution Ltd
Telephone: 01327 304 225
Website: www.shebanguk.net
Summary of Operation: Shebang is a dynamic market leader within the supply and distribution sector of mobile phones, providing a one stop solution for all mobile phone categories for the present and the future.
More Information: theukfd.net/2994366

Shoes Galore Ltd
Telephone: 01202 331 694
Website: www.shoes-galore.co.uk
Summary of Operation: Shoes Galore is a national shoe event company based in the UK. Shoe parties can be organised for home or corporate groups.
More Information: theukfd.net/25125107

Shopper Anonymous
Telephone: 01424 858 230
Website: www.shopperanonymous.co.uk
Summary of Operation: Shopper Anonymous specialises in improving customer service standards by using innovative mystery shopping programs. We specialise in mystery shopping franchise groups in order to feedback to franchisors on the service standards amongst their members.
More Information: theukfd.net/51100140

Signature in Silk Ltd
Telephone: 01543 417 885
Website: www.signatureinsilktrade.co.uk
Summary of Operation: Luxury wedding stationery beautiful favour boxes manufactured in the UK and Italy.
More Information: theukfd.net/08888615

SKYshades (UK) Ltd
Telephone: 01480 498 297
Website: www.skyshades.co.uk
Summary of Operation: A tensile membrane manufacturer and installer.
More Information: theukfd.net/39938590

Solmate Solar
Telephone: 01793 608 709
Website: www.solmatesolar.com
Summary of Operation: Specialist solar energy company that distributes and installs the world's leading solar energy systems.
More Information: theukfd.net/54716517

Southwest Greens
Telephone: 0845 230 4794
Website: www.southwestgreens.co.uk
Summary of Operation: Southwest Greens UK is one of the worldwide family of independent distributors of Southwest Putting Greens.
More Information: theukfd.net/70775720

Sphere Mania
Telephone: 08448 003 045
Website: www.spheremania.com
Summary of Operation: Adventure sport.
More Information: theukfd.net/56169325

Spiral Cellars Ltd
Telephone: 0845 241 2768
Website: www.spiralcellars.com
Summary of Operation: Supply, delivery and installation of prefabricated concrete wine cellars, designed to be installed within a client's home.
More Information: theukfd.net/95834393

Spit 'n' Polish Shoeshine Company Ltd
Telephone: 020 8334 8924
Website: www.shoeshine.net
Summary of Operation: The UK's first network of shoeshine booths.
More Information: theukfd.net/06514809

SportCheck
Telephone: 0845 388 1312
Website: www.sportcheck.co.uk
Summary of Operation: Enhances the way in which a club or school administrator, coach, teacher or manager can get a message to their members or students and participants quickly and cost effectively.
More Information: theukfd.net/68887011

Stained Glass Overlay (UK) (SGO)
Telephone: 01603 485 454
Website: www.sgouk.com
Summary of Operation: Decorative stained glass supplier.
More Information: theukfd.net/36623844

Starbrite Chemicals Ltd
Telephone: 01293 434 250
Website: www.starbrite.co.uk
Summary of Operation: Suppliers and manufacturers of cleaning chemicals and sundry lines. Van sales opportunity in solid repeat business sector.
More Information: theukfd.net/63460141

Successful Security Ltd
Telephone: 028 9269 8090
Website: www.successfulsecurity.com
Summary of Operation: Till fraud total monitoring solution, whereby each till transaction is superimposed onto the video.
More Information: theukfd.net/33000846

Taylor Skelton Walters (TSW) PLC
Telephone: 01491 577 432
Website: www.profitinland.co.uk
Summary of Operation: Land development specialist.
More Information: theukfd.net/47880104

Telechief
Telephone: 01832 270 905
Website: www.telechief.com
Summary of Operation: Telechief provide a personal and precise telemarketing service, which delights our customers time and again.
More Information: theukfd.net/52952905

The Beautiful Bling Co Ltd
Telephone: 01535 676 363
Website: www.beautifulbling.co.uk
Summary of Operation: Bringing together a wide range of jewellery selected from all over the world from family run jewellery suppliers.
More Information: theukfd.net/46210655

The Diverse Finance Co.
Telephone: 0845 225 2917
Website: www.diversefinance.co.uk
Summary of Operation: Loans.
More Information: theukfd.net/13306782

The Great British Balloon Company
Website: www.thegreatbritishballoon.co.uk
Summary of Operation: Will provide decoration for any special event.
More Information: theukfd.net/43655466

The Hairforce
Telephone: 07720 838 271
Website: www.thehairforce.co.uk
Summary of Operation: Head lice removal service.
More Information: theukfd.net/53999764

The Mortgage Shop
Telephone: 353 1890 882 984
Website: www.themortgageshop.net
Summary of Operation: The Mortgage Shop's rationale is to help home buyers arrange mortgage finance in the most simple and straightforward way possible explaining the complicated procedure of house purchase in the simplest of terms.
More Information: theukfd.net/15436554

The PC Support Group Ltd
Telephone: 0845 223 3116
Website: www.pcsupportgroup.com
Summary of Operation: The PC Support Group provide corporate quality IT support to small businesses and home users at a value for money price, delivered in a local and personal way.
More Information: theukfd.net/42555828

The Video Inventory Agency
Telephone: 0845 230 5197
Website: www.videoinventoryagency.co.uk
Summary of Operation: Video inventories to protect landlords and their assets.
More Information: Turn to page 51 or visit theukfd.net/65651290

The Wacky Cake Heaven
Telephone: 07799 453 621
Website: www.thewackycakeheaven.co.uk
Summary of Operation: Empowering women (or men) with ideas and networking together.
More Information: theukfd.net/19118955

The Wedding Planner School
Telephone: 0131 208 4177
Website: www.theweddingplannerschool.uk.com
Summary of Operation: Wedding planning school.
More Information: theukfd.net/21722114

The Will Writing Company
Website: www.willwriting.co.uk
Summary of Operation: Will writing and estate planning services.
More Information: theukfd.net/67265815

The Winning Ticket
Telephone: 0845 017 2454
Website: www.thewinningticket.co.uk
Summary of Operation: Professional fund raising management franchise.
More Information: theukfd.net/31682919

Top Corner Events
Telephone: 020 7700 1888
Website: www.topcorner.co.uk
Summary of Operation: Sport leagues and events.
More Information: theukfd.net/76787362

TopMatch International
Telephone: 0844 678 0136
Website: www.topmatch-international.com
Summary of Operation: Personal matchmaking specialists.
More Information: theukfd.net/56824741

Total Soft Water
Telephone: 01582 461 313
Website: www.totalsoftwater.com
Summary of Operation: Water softeners and drinking water filter supplier.
More Information: theukfd.net/71375360

Town Talk Ltd
Telephone: 0845 686 5855
Website: www.towntalk.org.uk
Summary of Operation: Franchise owners have the chance to join an established national network of town centre websites.
More Information: theukfd.net/77042728

UK Taekwondo
Telephone: 07770 622 776
Website: www.uk-taekwondo.com
Summary of Operation: Taekwon-Do martial arts.
More Information: theukfd.net/09374066

UK Towns on the Web
Telephone: 0845 388 4040
Website: www.uktownsontheweb.com
Summary of Operation: Information portal sites about your local town.
More Information: theukfd.net/43802192

UKXFactor/KwikMatch Ltd
Telephone: 0870 871 7777
Website: www.ukxfactor.com
Summary of Operation: Speed dating.
More Information: theukfd.net/66378320

Vergas
Telephone: 01425 463 203
Website: www.vergas.co.uk
Summary of Operation: Offering the water industry a comprehensive manufacturing, installation and commissioning service.
More Information: theukfd.net/44733064

Webmasters Design Ltd
Telephone: 0844 736 2740
Website: www.webmastersdesigns.com
Summary of Operation: Web design.
More Information: theukfd.net/57578937

Weve-a-Gift
Telephone: 01259 722 180
Website: www.weve-a-gift.com
Summary of Operation: Weve-a-Gift manufacture high quality, unique woven gifts.
More Information: theukfd.net/25104610

When The Music Stops
Telephone: 0845 230 3199
Website: www.whenthemusicstops.com
Summary of Operation: Dating franchise.
More Information: theukfd.net/87851811

Willwriting Systems (UK)
Summary of Operation: Will writing and related services.
More Information: theukfd.net/15645253

Winzer Wurth Industrial Ltd
Telephone: 01483 412 811
Summary of Operation: Würth is proud to be an active partner to the automotive repair and refinishing trade.
More Information: theukfd.net/3023764

XS Items.com
Telephone: 0845 200 8370
Website: www.xsitems.com
Summary of Operation: E-bay trading business.
More Information: theukfd.net/73180440

Yourhomepagein
Telephone: 01202 651 320
Summary of Operation: The only interactive community website designed to help you get the very best from where you live, in a one stop package.
More Information: theukfd.net/05175644

The Irish Franchise Directory

Franchising in Ireland has experienced expansion in recent years with growth predicted for the near future. It has been described as one of the essential new enterprise sectors contributing to general wealth creation with almost 200 franchises in operation (as of 2011). The growth of the franchise industry presents an excellent opportunity for people wanting to start their own business in Ireland as there still is massive scope for new and different franchise systems to enter the Irish market as well as Irish brands expanding through franchising. The outlook for franchising in Ireland looks very positive.

The Irish Franchise Directory

Automotive

Car Medic (Ireland)
Telephone: +353 42 935 4300
Website: www.carmedic.ie
Summary of Operation: Car Medic have built a fantastic reputation for providing high quality SMART repairs to minor paintwork scratches, bumper scuffs, alloy wheels and dents to car body work - eliminating the inconvenience and potential expense of using a body shop.

Munster Tool Co
Telephone: +353 21 432 2300
Website: www.munstertoolco.ie
Summary of Operation: Established in 1980, Munster Tool Co supplies top quality automotive tools and garage equipment to the automotive, agricultural, plant hire and HGV and allied industries.

Business 2 Business

ActionCOACH (Ireland)
Telephone: +353 1 832 0213
Website: www.paulfagan.actioncoach.com
Summary of Operation: Business coaching.

Antal International Network (Ireland)
Telephone: +353 1 231 4675
Website: www.antal.com
Summary of Operation: Antal can assist in defining what type of company suits you, what culture you would excel in, where your skills add value.

BCM Cost Management Service
Telephone: +353 61 400 580
Website: www.ukbcm.com

Bua Training
Telephone: +353 1 635 0066
Website: www.buatraining.com
Summary of Operation: Bua delivers the training courses that will get your office working efficiently.

Cash Converters (Ireland)
Website: www.cashconverters.ie
Summary of Operation: One of the number one retailer of pre-owned and graded goods and financial services provider, has transformed the concept of buying and selling second hand goods.

Club Print Media Ltd
Telephone: +353 66 713 6470
Website: www.clubprint.ie
Summary of Operation: We work together with Sports Clubs throughout Ireland, providing advertising services which generate much needed revenue for clubs.

Conexus International
Telephone: +353 1 438 6402
Website: www.conexus-international.com

Content Collector Ireland
Telephone: +353 86 172 2224
Website: www.contentcollector.ie
Summary of Operation: Content Collector provides businesses with a complete solution. We gather professional photographs, floorplans, BERs (Building Energy Ratings), 360° virtual tours and general information for publishing to the web and for print, quickly and cost effectively.

Dooley Group
Telephone: +353 1 201 0300
Website: www.dooleytv.ie
Summary of Operation: Auctioneers.

Fast.net
Telephone: +353 27 51624
Website: www.myfast.ie
Summary of Operation: The most effective way to promote your business.

Focal Point Coaching (Ireland)
Telephone: +353 42 932 8030
Website: www.declanloy.ie
Summary of Operation: Business and executive coaching.

Icon Business Solutions
Telephone: +353 65 684 5862
Website: www.iconbusinesssolutions.co.uk
Summary of Operation: The objective of the Icon Business Advisor is to help you, the business owner, move your focus and time, away from working in the business, to working on your business' development. Not only will this enable you to achieve sustainable growth, but it will also allow you more freedom to enjoy the lifestyle you have only dreamed about.

Kendlebell (Ireland)
Telephone: +353 1 813 4552
Website: www.kbell.ie
Summary of Operation: Provider of personalised outsource solutions for the SME sector in Ireland. We offer solutions to companies that wish to focus on their core business. If they are out of the office, engaged on another call or simply do not wish to be disturbed, we will supply a trained Kendlebell Personal Assistant to answer for them.
More Information:
franchiseireland.com/25278314

Leadership Management Ireland
Telephone: +353 1 278 8313
Website: www.lmi.ie
Summary of Operation: In order to achieve a competitive advantage, businesses must have an edge. People provide the sustainable edge. By investing in people and developing leaders throughout the organisation you can compete locally and internationally.

Musgrave Group
Telephone: +353 21 480 3000
Website: www.musgrave.co.uk
Summary of Operation: Our approach is to co-create brands with our retail partners, and equip them with the sales, marketing, IT, finance and logistical expertise that come with the most advanced retail model.

Ology Ireland
Telephone: +353 91 472 125
Website: www.ologybusiness.com
Summary of Operation: A guide to professional business services.

Synergy Stocktaking
Telephone: +353 1 473 8128
Website: www.synergystocktaking.ie
Summary of Operation: Stocktaking services, increasing profitability for pubs, hotels, restaurants and nightclubs everyday.

TaxAssist Accountants (Ireland)
Telephone: +353 1 818 6835
Website: www.taxassist.ie
Summary of Operation: TaxAssist Accountants are the largest network of accountants who focus their accountancy skills specifically on small businesses and taxpayers needing a tax return in Ireland.

The Investment Club Network (TICN)
Telephone: +353 44 75737
Website: www.ticn.com
Summary of Operation: Our desire is to inspire you to become financially independent.

Cleaning

Callawash
Telephone: +353 1850 202 111
Website: www.callawash.com
Summary of Operation: Mobile vehicle valeting.

Caremark (IE)
Telephone: +353 1 295 1747
Website: www.caremark.ie
Summary of Operation: We provide care for anyone who wishes to remain in their own home regardless of their disability, illness or situation.

Chemdry (Ireland)
Telephone: +353 1 830 3940
Website: www.chemdry.ie
Summary of Operation: Carpet cleaning.

Cork Hygiene Ltd
Telephone: +353 21 434 1411
Website: www.corkhygiene.ie
Summary of Operation:

Drisafe Carpet & Upholstery Cleaning
Telephone: +353 1 450 1604
Website: www.drisafe.com
Summary of Operation: Carpet and upholstery cleaning. Ceiling, grout and tile cleaning.

Eco Car Wash
Telephone: +353 1 707 1012
Website: www.ecocarwash.ie
Summary of Operation: Ireland's eco friendly valeting and mobile trolley system. Providing professional valeting, external hand wash/mini-valet service and franchise opportunities.

Ecowash Mobile Europe Ltd
Telephone: +353 41 980 6022
Summary of Operation: Waterless car wash and polish service that comes to you.

GR ProClean (Ireland) Ltd
Telephone: +353 61 210 758
Website: www.grpro-clean.ie
Summary of Operation: Cleaning.

Franchise Listings

Jan-Pro of Dublin
Telephone: +353 1 296 3101
Website: www.jan-pro.com/dublin
Summary of Operation: Commercial cleaning.

Pristine.ie
Telephone: +353 1890 252 309
Website: www.pristine.ie
Summary of Operation: Pristine.ie is a leading premium residential cleaning company in Ireland. Our aim is to provide you the customer with a total homecare cleaning service tailored to meet your own particular needs.

PuriFry
Telephone: 0845 463 2312
Website: www.purifry.co.uk
Summary of Operation: PuriFry provide their core Fryer Management Service to cost and environmentally conscious Caterers, providing them with cost reductions, improvements in cleanliness and health & safety through cooking oil filtration and fryer cleaning. The service also extends to waste oil removal, knife sharpening and decarbonising tank rental.
More Information:
franchiseireland.com/68398085

Rainbow International Ireland
Telephone: +353 21 477 8783
Website: www.rainbowintl.com
Summary of Operation: Rainbow International® provides 'best practices' with integrity and the highest of standards in restoration and cleaning services.

RecoPro
Telephone: +353 1 247 8880
Website: www.recopro.ie
Summary of Operation: Recopro provides decontamination, cleaning and restoration services for residential and commercial properties. We've been in the business for 10 years, helping people recover from property damage, returning families to their homes and getting businesses running again.

Restoration Team Ltd
Telephone: +353 1890 930 906
Website: www.rteam.ie
Summary of Operation: Cleaning and restoration service.

Sonic Golf (Ireland)
Telephone: +353 1 834 7653
Summary of Operation: Ultrasonic golf cleaning business.

The Mattress Doctor Ireland
Telephone: +353 61 307 098
Website: www.mattressdoctor.net
Summary of Operation: Mattress cleaning service.

Whiffaway Hygiene
Telephone: +353 71 915 0789
Summary of Operation: Hygiene and cleaning services.

Delivery & Distribution

Fastway Couriers (Ireland)
Telephone: +353 1 807 4763
Website: www.fastway.ie
Summary of Operation: Courier service. Let Fastway show you how to save money on your courier costs.

Mail Boxes Etc
Telephone: +353 1 491 2447
Website: www.mbe.co.uk
Summary of Operation: Whether you're looking for worldwide parcel delivery, courier or postal services, print and copy, mailbox rental or a virtual office package, you can trust the experts at Mail Boxes Etc.

Penny Black
Telephone: +353 1 662 9655
Website: www.highex.ie
Summary of Operation: Distribution company specialised exclusively in the fashion industry.

PostNet
Telephone: +353 1 497 9301
Website: www.postnet.ie
Summary of Operation: In our one-stop shops we provide a range of products and services which include; national and international postal and courier services, internet access, packaging, office supplies and business services.

Water Filters Direct
Telephone: +353 1890 345 837
Website: www.irish-water-filters.com
Summary of Operation: Water filters.

Food

Abrakebabra
Telephone: +353 1 496 7162
Website: www.abrakebabra.com
Summary of Operation: Abrakebabra is an Irish based fast food franchise.

Apache Pizza
Telephone: +353 1 883 4555
Website: http://apache.ie
Summary of Operation: We are committed to developing and expanding Apache Pizza in order to become the biggest and the best pizza retail and delivery operator in Ireland.

BB's Coffee and Muffins (Ireland)
Telephone: +353 61 319 181
Website: www.bbscoffeeandmuffins.com
Summary of Operation: Muffins are the main focus with, fresh, rich coffee to complement their popular muffin.

Berry Fresh
Telephone: 02892 613 001
Website: www.berryfresh.co.uk
Summary of Operation: Is a leading national distributor of assorted fresh berries.

Bistro Bianconi
Telephone: +353 1 406 0400
Website: www.bistrobianconi.ie
Summary of Operation: Inspired by the elegant charm of a classic Italian 'Ristorante's & Pizzeria's' with a contemporary buzz and stylish interiors, Bistro Bianconi brings you the true taste and enjoyment of Italy.

Bojangles
Telephone: +353 1 496 0047
Summary of Operation: A quick service restaurant chain based on a distinctive, flavourful chicken served with fresh buttermilk biscuits.

Burger King (Ireland)
Telephone: +353 1 662 8230
Website: www.burgerking.co.uk
Summary of Operation: Flame grilled, fully certified Aberdeen Angus Beef burger restaurants.

Burritos 'N Blues
Telephone: +353 1 498 1805
Website: www.burritosandblues.com

Butlers Chocolates Cafe
Telephone: +353 1 671 0599
Website: www.butlers.ie
Summary of Operation: Everything to do with chocolate.

Carry Out
Telephone: +353 22 30 100
Website: www.carryout.ie
Summary of Operation: Carry Out, one of Ireland's leading specialist off licence franchises, first opened its door in 2003 and since then has grown to over 50 stores located nationwide, with ambitious plans by its new parent company, The Barry Group, to double that number in the next three years.

Charisnack (Ireland)
Telephone: 0845 123 1132
Website: www.charisnack.ie
Summary of Operation: Delivering a superb selection of healthier snacks and smoothies directly into the workplace.

Chick King Ltd
Telephone: +353 45 449 202
Website: www.chickking.ie
Summary of Operation: Chick King is an Irish based fast food franchise, which is rapidly expanding to many locations in Ireland. Chick King use premier chicken products that are produced with our own in house chicken coating.
More Information:
franchiseireland.com/77173016

Eddie Rockets
Telephone: +353 1 679 5484
Website: www.eddierockets.ie
Summary of Operation: Eddie Rockets is about all things retro, fusing classic American fare with exciting new menu additions, all brought to you in a feel good 1950s diner.

Esquires Coffee Houses (Ireland)
Telephone: +353 91 700 055
Website: www.esquirescoffee.com
Summary of Operation: A chain speciality coffee houses with locally owned and operated management. For our customers we offer a friendly atmosphere to meet and relax and to enjoy premium beverages and quality food.
More Information:
franchiseireland.com/18876642

Franchise Listings

Extreme Pizza Ireland
Telephone: +353 86 386 2253
Website: www.extremepizza.com
Summary of Operation: At Extreme Pizza, we're always experimenting with new ways to test the palette, to push the pizza experience to a higher level.

Fitzers
Telephone: +353 1 677 1155
Website: www.fitzers.ie
Summary of Operation: Fitzers is a Dublin institution. What sets us apart is the superb cuisine and eclectic blend of ingredients which embues each restaurant with the character and atmosphere that has become the Fitzers hallmark.

Four Star Pizza
Telephone: +353 1 293 6494
Website: www.fourstarpizza.ie
Summary of Operation: Four Star Pizza specialise in the home delivery and carry-out service of our special recipe pizza. Each pizza is made to order from the finest ingredients and is delivered to the customer's door within 30 minutes. Carry-out pizzas are ready in 10 minutes.

Gloria Jean's Coffees (Ireland) Ltd
Telephone: + 353 87 252 1423
Website: www.gloriajeanscoffees.ie
Summary of Operation: Gloria Jeans Coffees is one of the fastest growing and successful retail coffee franchise operations in the world.
More Information:
franchiseireland.com/31875321

Godfather's Pizza
Telephone: +353 1 664 0010
Website: www.godfatherspizza.ie
Summary of Operation: We specialise in the Pizza Home delivery and take away business in the fastmoving world. It is the quality of our product and the quality of ourservice that separates us from our competitors.

Gourmet Burger (Ireland)
Telephone: +353 1 497 7821
Website: www.gourmetburgercompany.ie
Summary of Operation: We have adopted a farm to fork philosophy and believe that all the food you consume in our restaurants should be fully traceable.

Hard Rock Cafe
Telephone: +353 1 671 7777
Website: www.hardrock.com
Summary of Operation: Our Cafe has a very relaxed and friendly feel to the place and we have the most up to date and cutting edge music and videos, we advise all visitors to kick-back and enjoy what we are so proud to offer.

Juice Zone (Europe HQ)
Telephone: +353 87 255 7509
Website: www.juicezone.com
Summary of Operation: Healthy fair, serving fresh and nutritious food and drinks that help people feel better.

La Croissanterie
Telephone: +353 1 478 1245
Summary of Operation: La Croissanterie, one of the initiators of French-style quick-service food, serves you all day, offering products to meet every need.

Luigi Malone's International Franchising Ltd
Website: www.luigimalones.com
Summary of Operation: A perfect place for all dining requirements.

McDonald's Restaurants (IE)
Telephone: +353 1 208 0020
Website: www.mcdonalds.ie
Summary of Operation: McDonald's is one of only a handful of brands that commands instant recognition throughout the world. With over 32,000 restaurants in over 100 countries, serving over 50 million people everyday, McDonald's is by far the world's largest food service company.

Mocha Beans
Telephone: +353 91 763 886
Website: www.mochabeans.com
Summary of Operation: The freshest and best tasting coffee with a range of delicious, healthy fresh foods. Most of our baking is also done in-house, so our desserts are straight out of the oven.

Munchies
Telephone: +353 1 613 7707
Website: www.munchies.ie
Summary of Operation: Scrumptious and filling sandwiches with quality organic fair-trade coffee.

Nosh & Coffee
Telephone: +353 1 805 0999
Website: www.noshandcoffee.ie
Summary of Operation: Quality coffees, good food, relaxing atmosphere and stylish surroundings are all attributes that defines a Nosh & Coffee outlet.

O'Briens Ireland
Telephone: +353 1 472 1406
Website: www.obriensonline.com
Summary of Operation: Our famous made-to-order hot or cold sandwiches - Shambos, Tripledecker®, Wrappos® and Toosties® - literally built to each customer's taste. The extensive selection includes gourmet coffees, patisseries, deli dishes, salads, snacks and a wide range of soft drinks, including freshly made smoothies and juices from the instore juice bar offerings.

On the Grapevine
Telephone: +353 1 235 3054
Website: www.onthegrapevine.ie
Summary of Operation: Wine shop.

Papa John's Ireland
Telephone: +353 91 774 100
Website: www.papajohns.ie
Summary of Operation: Papa John's Pizza is one of the leading pizza companies in the world.

Puccinos (Ireland)
Telephone: +353 86 838 3936
Website: www.puccinos.com
Summary of Operation: Fresh coffee and sandwiches.

Quiznos Sub (Ireland)
Telephone: +353 1 814 0600
Website: www.kylemore.ie
Summary of Operation: Contemporary and traditional restaurant offering. A speciality and healthy option menu, with new innovative food delivery options and the use of the very latest in technology.

Stretch-n-Grow Ireland Ltd
Telephone: +353 1 832 2653
Website: www.stretch-n-grow.ie
Summary of Operation: Stretch-n-Grow classes can provide children with the activity, instruction and encouragement required to develop to their full potential.

Subway Development Ireland
Telephone: 0800 085 5058
Website: www.subway.ie
Summary of Operation: Fast food sandwich outlets. The Subway chain offers an exceptional franchise opportunity which provides franchise owners with the tools and knowledge to run their own successful business.

Supermac's Family Restaurant
Telephone: +353 91 753 511
Website: www.supermacs.ie
Summary of Operation: Supermac's is Ireland's largest and fastest-growing indigenous fast food group.

The Counter (Ireland)
Telephone: +353 76 602 6900
Website: www.thecounter.ie
Summary of Operation: Premium burger restaurant.

The Wine Buff
Telephone: +353 61 313 378
Website: www.thewinebuff.com
Summary of Operation: The Wine Buff is Ireland's biggest independent specialised wine retailer, we are passionate about wine and always on hand to give advice.

West Coast Coffee
Telephone: +353 1 478 9932
Website: www.westcoastcoffee.ie
Summary of Operation: West Coast Coffee operates American style espresso bars in the Dublin area. Our company is 100% Irish and was established in 1998. We were one of the first Irish firms to identify and operate in this particular market niche.

Yo Sushi
Telephone: +353 87 257 3868
Website: www.yosushi.com
Summary of Operation: YO! Sushi brought the concept of a Japanese 'kaiten' sushi bar that delivered food to customers via a conveyor belt travelling 8cm per second to the masses.

Zumo Natural Juice and Smoothie Bar
Telephone: +353 1 878 8641
Website: www.zumosmoothiebar.com
Summary of Operation: Kiosk based offer of fresh made juice and smoothies.

Franchise Listings

Health & Beauty

Bailine.com
Telephone: +353 83 425 1202
Website: www.bailine.com
Summary of Operation: Bailine is an organisation operating a successful system for improving female beauty, health and well-being.

Beauty Store
Telephone: +353 61 396 988

Bootcamp Ireland Military Style Fitness Training Ltd
Telephone: +353 1 234 3797
Website: www.bootcampirelandfranchise.com
Summary of Operation: Bootcamp Ireland has been putting men and women of all fitness levels through their paces,using military style fitness techniques and real military instructors since 2004.

Boston Brand Bars
Telephone: +353 1 894 7944
Website: www.bostonbrandbars.com
Summary of Operation: Boston Salons are conveniently located in shopping centres across Ireland.

Contours Express (Ireland)
Telephone: +353 85 111 4449
Website: www.contoursexpress.ie
Summary of Operation: Ladies fitness and weight loss studio.

Energie Fitness Ireland
Telephone: +353 86 606 2025
Website: www.energie.ie
Summary of Operation: At énergie we share a passion for fitness and wellbeing. Our clubs are owned and operated by passionate and committed entrepreneurs.

Figure8
Telephone: +353 61 439 100
Website: www.figure8.ie
Summary of Operation: Figure8 is a group of women's health clubs that deliver advanced programs for women's fitness and weight loss. Figure8 provides a friendly environment, and uses a combination of the most advanced training techniques, pilates and yoga, together with metabolism balancing expertise.

Fitness Together
Telephone: +353 1 496 5829
Website: www.fitnesstogether.ie
Summary of Operation: The leader in personal training.

Home Instead Senior Care (Ireland)
Telephone: +353 1 206 8056
Website: www.homeinstead.ie
Summary of Operation: To you, it's about finding trustworthy care for your ageing loved one. To us, it's about providing the highest-quality home care services to fit you and your family's needs.

Life Pharmacy
Telephone: +353 1 404 1700
Website: www.lifepharmacy.ie
Summary of Operation: Life Pharmacy is an exciting new pharmacy concept that helps trusted local pharmacists to offer you premium health care products and services as well as advice for living well.

Motivation Weight Management Clinics
Telephone: +353 1 293 8020
Website: www.motivation.ie
Summary of Operation: We have been helping people to lose weight in Ireland for over 15 years.

My Gym Ireland
Telephone: +353 61 423 030
Summary of Operation: Fitness.

MY GYM Ireland / MY GYM Limerick
Telephone: +353 61 423 030
Website: www.mygymlimerick.com
Summary of Operation: Fitness.

Paul Goldin Clinic
Telephone: +353 1 280 2797
Website: www.paulgoldin.com
Summary of Operation: The Paul Goldin Clinic is recognised as one of the finest hypnotherapy and psychotherapy clinics in Europe.

Sharkey's Cuts for Kids (Ireland & UK)
Telephone: +353 86 380 4790
Website: www.sharkeyscutsforkids.com
Summary of Operation: At Sharkey's Cuts for Kids, we know that kids and parents want something different with their haircut experience.

The Little House of Avalon

Telephone: 0909 68302
Website: www.littlehouseofavalon.com
Summary of Operation: The most beautiful holistic, peaceful place to recharge your batteries naturally.

Tone at Home

Telephone: +353 1 895 6743
Website: www.vibroplates.ie
Summary of Operation: Fitness and weight loss.

Ultimate Woman

Telephone: +353 87 225 0594
Summary of Operation: Fitness for women.

Universal Hair & Scalp Clinics Ltd

Telephone: +353 1 679 3618
Website: www.universalclinics.com
Summary of Operation: Universal Clinic provides hair and scalp treatments and products to combat hair loss, thinning hair and related problems, such as dandruff, dry skin flakes, itching and dry or oily scalp as well as alopecia and psoriasis in both men and women.

Leisure & Travel

Hotel Express Ireland Ltd

Telephone: +353 1 213 0729
Website: www.hotelexpress.ie
Summary of Operation: Hotels.

Print, Signs & Design

Cartridge Green

Telephone: +353 1 210 3868
Website: www.cartridgegreen.ie
Summary of Operation: Cartridge Green is Ireland's fastest growing printer cartridge franchise. Our services are offered to both home and business users in a unique way that makes their printing more efficient, cheaper and greener.
More Information:
franchiseireland.com/75733266

Re:Charge Cartridges

Telephone: +353 1 405 9919
Website: www.rechargecartridges.com
Summary of Operation: We are the largest refiller and remanufacture of both inkjet and laser cartridges in Ireland.

Snap Printing

Telephone: +353 1 413 5080
Website: www.snapprinting.ie
Summary of Operation: Snap is now Ireland's leading design, print and business promotion company.

Property Care

Acme Blinds (Ireland)

Telephone: +353 21 428 0400
Website: www.acmeblinds.ie
Summary of Operation: Our range of products is second to none, from internal blinds to external awnings and canopies through to security products.

Allied Carpets

Telephone: +353 1 456 6662
Summary of Operation: Allied Carpets has established itself as one of the leading companies in the supply of carpets to the home or office.

Color Glo

Telephone: +353 1 839 2403
Website: www.colorglo.ie
Summary of Operation: One of the leading repair and restoration specialists.

Mr Handyman UK & IE

Telephone: +353 87 255 3047
Website: www.mrhandyman.com/ie
Summary of Operation: Handyman and home service.

Perma-Glaze

Telephone: +353 86 822 5202
Website: www.permaglaze.com
Summary of Operation: Perma-Glaze is a worldwide leader in the reglazing and resurfacing of numerous surfaces and fixtures.

Roche Bobois

Telephone: +353 1 653 1650
Website: www.roche-bobois.com
Summary of Operation: Furniture.

Senator Windows

Telephone: +353 53 915 5300
Website: www.senatorwindows.ie
Summary of Operation: They sell their fully certified products through a network of independent agents.

Surface Doctor (Ireland)

Telephone: +353 1 294 0261
Summary of Operation: Resurfacing anything from baths and tiles to kitchen units and appliances, onsite. Our services are equally suited to domestic and commercial premises.

The Ultimate Floor Sanding Company

Telephone: +353 1 825 1371
Website: www.theultimatefloorsandingfranchise.co.uk
Summary of Operation: Floor sanding.

Tilesavers

Telephone: +353 1 855 2606
Website: www.btw.ie
Summary of Operation: BTW (formerly Tilesavers) is Ireland's leading retailer of bathrooms, tiles and woodfloors. It is the country's largest Irish-owned retailer of bathrooms, tiles, floor coverings and related products.

Wessex Conservatories Ltd

Telephone: +353 21 496 2220
Website: www.wessex-windows.co.uk
Summary of Operation: Wessex Window Systems supplies, manufactures and installs doors, windows and conservatories for homes and commercial premises.

Real Estate

David Reid Ireland

Telephone: +353 1890 252 613
Summary of Operation: Property Sales

Re/Max Ireland

Telephone: +353 1 629 5060
Website: www.remax-ireland.com
Summary of Operation: Estate agents.

Retail

ADM Londis PLC

Telephone: +353 45 837 900
Website: www.londis.ie
Summary of Operation: Your local independently owned Londis store offers convenience, quality and value all at the heart of your community. 100% Irish owned, we pride ourselves on our emphasis on friendly customer service, quality produce and excellent value.

Gala Retail Services Ltd

Telephone: + 353 45 910 066
Website: www.gala.ie
Summary of Operation: Gala stands out as a contemporary convenience group with a twist. High standards, coupled with its focus on servicing the local community, make Gala stores some of the best in the country.

Premier Premaman

Telephone: +353 1 612 0880
Website: www.premaman.com
Summary of Operation: At Prémaman, you will find everything that the mother-to-be, the baby and the child (up to 10 years) may need: clothes, accessories, and nursery items. All together in a single sales outlet!

SPAR (Ireland) Ltd

Telephone: +353 1 409 0300
Website: www.spar.ie
Summary of Operation: SPAR is one of Ireland's largest retail food store chains with over 470 high quality, conveniently located outlets covering three differing SPAR retail formats.

Tally Weijl (Ireland)

Telephone: +35 36 143 9200
Website: www.tally-weijl.ie
Summary of Operation: Tally Wiejl's fashion offers the latest trends – for every woman, for every situation and for every budget. An international fashion label based in Basel, Switzerland, the company is represented worldwide in 30 countries with over 680 stores globally and employs over 2,500 people.

The Bizmart Group

Website: www.bizmart.com
Summary of Operation: The business store.

Specialised – Animals & Pets

Aussie Pet Mobile (Ireland & UK)

Telephone: +353 1 832 0058
Website: www.aussiepetmobile.ie
Summary of Operation: Aussie Pet Mobile provides dog grooming for all dogs and cats. We offer a 15 Step mobile dog grooming treatment for all breeds of dogs and cats.

Husse (Ireland)
Telephone: +353 45 881 551
Website: www.husse.ie
Summary of Operation: Husse sells and markets a wide range of premium quality dog and cat food, cat litter and various accessories throughout the whole world. We deliver the products with Husse vans directly to your door with no extra charge.

Mobile Dog Wash (Ireland)
Telephone: +353 21 434 5812
Website: www.mobiledogwash.ie
Summary of Operation: A highly professional mobile dog washing and grooming service.

Truly Nolen Ireland
Telephone: +44 28 9263 8162
Website: www.trulynolen.com
Summary of Operation: Pests are vectors of disease and a danger to your family's health. They may also cause physical damage to your home's infrastructure.

Specialised - Children & Education

FitKids (Ireland)
Telephone: +353 81 830 0350
Website: www.fitkids.ie
Summary of Operation: FitKids are fun gymnastic fitness, classes, camps and parties for kids from one to 12 yrs. FitKids is a great foundation for any sport and is equally suitable for boys and girls as it develops the fundamentals of fitness: flexibility, agility, balance, co-ordination, strength and endurance.

Formula Fun
Telephone: +353 87 232 3161
Website: www.fomulafun.ie
Summary of Operation: A Formula Fun event is a fabulous idea for any children's party, giving them an experience they will always remember. Indoor or outdoor, this fun and safe experience is ideal for a stylish cool and different children's party.

FutureKids (Ireland)
Telephone: +353 1 215 7220
Website: www.futurekids.ie
Summary of Operation: Futurekids is a global leader in helping schools use technology to transform education.

Helen O'Grady Drama Academy
Telephone: 048 9146 4337
Website: www.helenogrady.co.uk
Summary of Operation: After school drama classes for children. Aims to provide a self-development through drama programme for children.

Kids Party Club
Telephone: +353 1890 252 382
Website: www.kidspartyclub.ie
Summary of Operation: We developed the model for the Kids Party Club.

Kumon Educational Ireland
Telephone: +353 1 640 1812
Website: www.kumon.ie
Summary of Operation: Maths and English after school study centres for children.

Little Kickers Ireland
Telephone: +353 1 212 2826
Website: www.littlekickers.ie
Summary of Operation: At Little Kickers the focus is very much on fun - a national network of informal yet professionally run training classes where enthusiastic boys and girls are given a helping hand to stand on their own two feet.

Toby World
Telephone: +353 66 719 2469
Website: www.tobyworld.ie
Summary of Operation: Largest play centre open 10 to 6 daily.

Vincent Shoe Store
Telephone: +353 87 932 2069
Website: www.vincentshoestore.com
Summary of Operation: Vincent Shoe Store is a company specialising in shoes for children up to 10 years old.

Specialised - Other

4Home Superstores
Telephone: +353 21 437 2308

Ambience Venue Styling
Telephone: +353 1 845 5211
Website: www.ambiencevenuestyling.com
Summary of Operation: If you are looking for a full venue styling service or simply wedding chair covers to hire you've come to the right place.

Apple Green
Telephone: +353 1 512 4800
Website: www.applegreen.ie
Summary of Operation: Motorway service station and retail outlets.

Ark Recycling Ltd
Telephone: +353 81 836 5828
Website: www.arkrecycling.com
Summary of Operation: Ark Recycling is a small company, independent, owner operated, ethical and dedicated to research and development of better ways to take care of ourselves and the environment. ARK Recycling has the latest future proof technology to mine existing landfils without any emmisions or pollution, to produce clean, useful and saleable products, and restore the land to it's former environmentally friendly state.

Cartridge World Ireland
Telephone: +353 91 764 044
Website: www.cartridgeworld.ie
Summary of Operation: Ink cartridge refils.

CeX Ireland
Telephone: +353 1 466 0525
Summary of Operation: Retailer of second-hand electronic and digital entertainment products.

Computer Troubleshooters Ireland
Telephone: +353 91 867 888
Website: www.comptroub.ie
Summary of Operation: Computer Troubleshooters is the largest international network of franchise owners providing onsite computer services to small businesses.

Concerto Ireland
Telephone: +353 1890 876 611
Website: www.concertonetworks.ie
Summary of Operation: Computer repair and more with your on-demand technology team.

Cubic Telecom
Telephone: +353 1 448 1261
Website: www.cubictelecom.com
Summary of Operation: Cubic Telecom lets your customers roam anywhere in the world - for a fraction of the normal costs. Our mobile technology platform also lets you tailor an infinite number of services for your customers.

Eason
Telephone: +353 1 858 3800
Website: www.easons.com
Summary of Operation: Main supplier in Ireland of books, newspapers and magazines.

Eircom
Telephone: +353 1 803 0700
Website: www.eircom.net
Summary of Operation: Broadband provider.

Fast-Fix Jewellery Repairs
Telephone: +353 1 612 1465
Website: www.fast-fix.ie
Summary of Operation: Fast-Fix offers a while-you-shop service that fits jewellery and watch repair services around your busy lifestyle.

Foot Solutions (UK and IE)
Telephone: +353 21 427 2711
Website: www.footsolutions.com
Summary of Operation: At Foot Solutions, we use the most advanced technology combined with a full understanding of biomechanics of feet and gait, along with the highest quality footwear on the planet to fit your unique feet. Through our customised solutions, we will improve your comfort and body alignment and help you achieve better health through your feet.

Great Gas
Telephone: +353 22 23 989
Website: www.greatgas.ie
Summary of Operation: Irish-owned fuel supplier.

Howards Storage World (Ireland)
Telephone: +353 1 294 8003
Website: www.hsw.ie
Summary of Operation: Howards Storage World® has literally thousands of products to help you in your quest for storage. Add in a little helpful advice from the friendly staff in store and you'll be well on your way to living clutter free.

I Quit Smoking International Ltd
Telephone: +353 51 877 071
Website: www.iqsintl.com
Summary of Operation: I Quit Smoking is an international franchise network offering a proven, quick and pain-free method to help people quit smoking.

Momentum for Growth
Telephone: +353 45 446 548

National Energy Assessors
Telephone: +353 1890 793 793
Website: www.nea.ie

Reisswolf S. Ireland
Telephone: +44 28 3082 11 40
Website: www.reisswolf.net
Summary of Operation: Dealing with the destruction of documents for companies.

Signs Express (Ireland)
Telephone: +353 1 839 5096
Website: www.signsexpress.ie

Sky Business Centre
Telephone: +353 1 885 1700
Website: www.skybusinesscentres.co.uk

Spring Soft Systems
Telephone: +353 57 933 2171
Website: www.springsoft.ie
Summary of Operation: Water treatment.

Statoil Ireland Ltd
Telephone: +353 1 636 8277
Website: www.statoil.com
Summary of Operation: Statoil is an international energy company with over 35 years experience on the Norwegian continental shelf, today with operations worldwide.

Telefonica O2 Ireland
Telephone: +353 1 609 5000
Website: www.o2.ie
Summary of Operation: We are one of the leading communication providers in Ireland.

The Franchise Group Ireland
Telephone: +353 1 612 1459
Website: www.the-franchise-group.ie

The Inkdrop Frachise Co. (Ireland)
Telephone: +353 1 823 7536
Website: www.inkdrop.ie

The Water Doctor Ltd
Summary of Operation: Established more than a decade ago, Water Doctor is the market leader in the water treatment and specialty chemical market.

The Zip Yard Franchising Ireland Ltd
Telephone: +353 1890 333 444
Website: www.thezipyard.ie
Summary of Operation: Irelands premier clothing alterations, dress restyling, tailoring and repairs franchise.
More Information:
franchiseireland.com/26718423

W.S.I. (Ireland)
Telephone: +353 51 330 579
Website: www.webdesign-ireland.net
Summary of Operation: Global internet solutions provider.

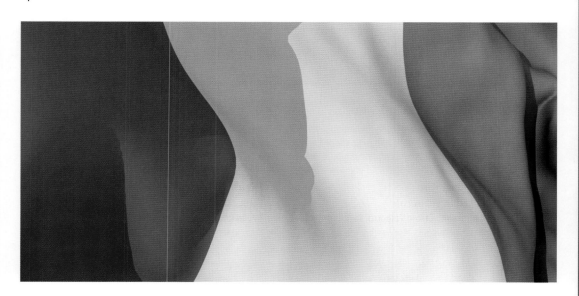

Ireland Franchise Directory

Your new source of franchise opportunities available in Ireland

Franchising offers a great way to become your own boss and own a business. You can retain an association with a head office organisation that can provide training, support and national presence that solo start-ups have to cope without.

Ireland Franchise Directory is continuously updated allowing you to get in touch with Irish franchises quickly and easily. Just find the franchise you are interested in, fill in the short registration form and your information request will be sent to the franchisor. On the site you can view detailed information or browse statistical information on brands currently franchising in Ireland.

You have the ability to search for franchise opportunities by business category, place of operation and investment requirements with the free online information request service, making it possible for you to find the ideal franchise.

Visit Ireland's most comprehensive online franchise resource at:
www.IrelandFranchiseDirectory.com

FREE **Reader** Response Service

For further information on any brands featured in The UK Franchise Directory, please complete ALL sections.

TICK: ☐ I would like more information from the following selected brands. I understand that my details, including email address, must be passed on to the selected brands ONLY.

Featured Franchise Brands.................TICK HERE

Brand	Page	Tick
Agency Express (JC)	216	☐
All Trades Network (TU)	191	☐
Assured Security Shredding (MP)	44-45,139	☐
Auntie Anne's (NW)	99	☐
Bairstow Eves (MP)	226	☐
BCR Associates (GP)	140	☐
Betterclean Services (GP)	36-37	☐
Blue Ribbon Care (MP)	30-31,175	☐
Business for Breakfast (BB)	139	☐
Card Connection (MP)	234	☐
Caremark (GP)	175	☐
Cargocall Franchising (GP)	238	☐
Cash & Cheque Express (JC)	118	☐
Cash Converters (JC)	114	☐
Century 21 (BB)	61	☐
CerTax Accounting (KY)	140	☐
CeX (NW)	115	☐
Chemex International (KY)	235	☐
CityLocal (KY)	141	☐
Computer Troubleshooters (BB)	55	☐
ComputerXplorers (KY)	242	☐
Cost Centre Services (JC)	136	☐
Dream Doors (GP)	119	☐
Dublcheck (TU)	164	☐
EnviroVent (BB)	192	☐
etyres (RL)	128	☐
FDS (RS)	137	☐
FiltaFry Plus (KY)	164	☐
Fita-Seal (KY)	140	☐
Global Cruising (RL)	208	☐
Granite Transformations (MP)	190	☐
GreenThumb (KY)	188-189	☐
House-Hut (GP)	228	☐
India Jane (RL)	118	☐
Leaps & Bounds (KY)	243	☐
LIPA 4:19 (TU)	243	☐
London House (GP)	141	☐
Mac Tools Europe (KY)	236	☐
Martin & Co (BB)	228	☐
Marvin's Menswear (RS)	116	☐
McDonald's (JC)	4-5,99	☐
Merry Maids (KY)	165	☐
Minster Services Group (KY)	160-161	☐
MOLLY MAID (GP)	166	☐
NBC Bird and Pest Solutions (JC)	191	☐
Northwood (GP)	229	☐
Office Canopy Group (MP)	141	☐
Ovenclean (KY)	162-163	☐
OvenU (BB)	166	☐
PC PAL (KY)	254	☐
Perfect Pizza (JC)	98	☐
Pizza Hut (JC)	2,23,100	☐
Platinum Property Partners (RL)	227	☐
Primesigns (MP)	218	☐
Recognition Express (KY)	219	☐
Riverford Organic Vegetables (BB)	27	☐
Safeclean (GP)	166	☐
ServiceMaster (KY)	165	☐
Snack-in-the-Box (GP)	238	☐
Stockcheck (BB)	141	☐
Suit the City (JC)	255	☐
Susan Hepburn Clinics (RL)	174	☐
Tatty Bumpkin (MP)	243	☐
The Camping and Caravanning Club (KY)	210	☐
The Video Inventory (BB)	51	☐
The Wedding Guide(JC)	220	☐
The Zip Yard (KY)	117	☐
Tongue Tied (MP)	138	☐
TruGreen (KY)	192	☐
Two Men And A Truck (KY)	237	☐
Well Polished (TU)	166	☐
Wilkins Chimney Sweep (BB)	192	☐

Reader Response

alphaTALK (RC) ....84-85, 95 ☐	FranExec (NW)...................................92 ☐
Anglia Finance (RC) ....46-47, 91 ☐	FranManuals (RC).............................92 ☐
Brand Protect (RC) ....82-83, 93 ☐	FranPower (MA) ....94 ☐
European Franchising Online (DI)..............214 ☐	Insight 2010 Report (RC) ....16-17 ☐
FDS Anglia & London (NW/PH) ....86 ☐	ip21 (RC)...................................78-79, 93 ☐
FDS South East (MP)................................87 ☐	Ireland Franchise Directory (MS)..............280 ☐
FDS Midlands (KY) ....89 ☐	Jargon Buster.....................................50 ☐
FDS North (TU) ....88 ☐	Lloyds TSB (RC) ....41-43, 91 ☐
FDS Southern (GP)..................................90 ☐	Subscriptions...................................322 ☐
FDS FranMatch (RL) ....71, 93 ☐	Tech4T (RC) ....80-81, 95 ☐
Franchise Development Services (RC)..........62 ☐	The Franchise Magazine (FM) ....332 ☐
Franchise International Online (DI) ....214 ☐	The Franchise Magazine App (FM)...............61 ☐
Franchise Success TV (RC) ....94 ☐	The Franchise Magazine Online (DI)..........287 ☐
FranDesign (LD) ....94 ☐	The UK Franchise Directory Online (MS)....323 ☐

If you don't have a specific brand in mind and would like further information on a particular type of franchise or place of operation, please complete this section. Again, we'll pass your details on to companies relevant to your choices. Please tick this box ☐ to confirm that you are happy for us to do so.

SECTORS TICK

Accountancy ☐	Electrical ☐	Personal ☐	**TYPE OF FRANCHISE**
Agriculture ☐	Entertainment ☐	Pest Control ☐	Single Unit ☐
Automotive ☐	Environmental ☐	Pets ☐	Area Developer ☐
Beauty ☐	Estate Agents/Lettings ☐	Photography ☐	Master Franchise ☐
Beverages ☐	Fashion ☐	Print & Design ☐	Resales ☐
Business 2 Business ☐	Financial ☐	Recruitment ☐	Management ☐
Care ☐	Food ☐	Repair & Maintenance ☐	
Chemical ☐	Footwear ☐	Retail ☐	**LOCATION**
Children ☐	Franchise ☐	Safety ☐	High street retail ☐
Cleaning ☐	Garden ☐	Sales ☐	Kiosk based ☐
Communications ☐	Health ☐	Security ☐	Office based ☐
Computers ☐	Hire ☐	Services ☐	Restaurant based ☐
Consultancy ☐	Horticulture ☐	Signs ☐	Secondary retail ☐
Customisation ☐	Indoor Property ☐	Sports ☐	Vehicle based ☐
Delivery ☐	Legal ☐	Storage ☐	Work from home ☐
Distribution ☐	Luxury ☐	Supplies ☐	Dedicated premises based ☐
Education/Training ☐	Manufacture ☐	Travel ☐	
	Outdoor Property ☐	Used Goods ☐	

COMPLETE: MY DETAILS
The UK Franchise Directory 24th Edition

NAME: ....

ADDRESS: ....

....

COMPANY: ....

EMAIL (THIS MUST BE COMPLETED): ....

TELEPHONE: ....

AREAS OF GEOGRAPHICAL INTEREST: ....

MY AVAILABLE CAPITAL (THIS MUST BE COMPLETED): £ ....

FREE **Reader** Response Service

For further information on any brands featured in The UK Franchise Directory, please complete ALL sections.

TICK: ☐ I would like more information from the following selected brands. I understand that my details, including email address, must be passed on to the selected brands ONLY.

Featured Franchise Brands.................TICK HERE

Agency Express (JC)	216 ☐	London House (GP)	141 ☐
All Trades Network (TU)	191 ☐	Mac Tools Europe (KY)	236 ☐
Assured Security Shredding (MP) 44-45,139 ☐	Martin & Co (BB)	228 ☐
Auntie Anne's (NW)	99 ☐	Marvin's Menswear (RS)	116 ☐
Bairstow Eves (MP)	226 ☐	McDonald's (JC)	4-5,99 ☐
BCR Associates (GP)	140 ☐	Merry Maids (KY)	165 ☐
Betterclean Services (GP)	36-37 ☐	Minster Services Group (KY)	160-161 ☐
Blue Ribbon Care (MP)	30-31,175 ☐	MOLLY MAID (GP)	166 ☐
Business for Breakfast (BB)	139 ☐	NBC Bird and Pest Solutions (JC)	191 ☐
Card Connection (MP)	234 ☐	Northwood (GP)	229 ☐
Caremark (GP)	175 ☐	Office Canopy Group (MP)	141 ☐
Cargocall Franchising (GP)	238 ☐	Ovenclean (KY)	162-163 ☐
Cash & Cheque Express (JC)	118 ☐	OvenU (BB)	166 ☐
Cash Converters (JC)	114 ☐	PC PAL (KY)	254 ☐
Century 21 (BB)	61 ☐	Perfect Pizza (JC)	98 ☐
CerTax Accounting (KY)	140 ☐	Pizza Hut (JC)	2,23,100 ☐
CeX (NW)	115 ☐	Platinum Property Partners (RL)	227 ☐
Chemex International (KY)	235 ☐	Primesigns (MP)	218 ☐
CityLocal (KY)	141 ☐	Recognition Express (KY)	219 ☐
Computer Troubleshooters (BB)	55 ☐	Riverford Organic Vegetables (BB)	27 ☐
ComputerXplorers (KY)	242 ☐	Safeclean (GP)	166 ☐
Cost Centre Services (JC)	136 ☐	ServiceMaster (KY)	165 ☐
Dream Doors (GP)	119 ☐	Snack-in-the-Box (GP)	238 ☐
Dublcheck (TU)	164 ☐	Stockcheck (BB)	141 ☐
EnviroVent (BB)	192 ☐	Suit the City (JC)	255 ☐
etyres (RL)	128 ☐	Susan Hepburn Clinics (RL)	174 ☐
FDS (RS)	137 ☐	Tatty Bumpkin (MP)	243 ☐
FiltaFry Plus (KY)	164 ☐	The Camping and Caravanning Club (KY)	210 ☐
Fita-Seal (KY)	140 ☐	The Video Inventory (BB)	51 ☐
Global Cruising (RL)	208 ☐	The Wedding Guide(JC)	220 ☐
Granite Transformations (MP)	190 ☐	The Zip Yard (KY)	117 ☐
GreenThumb (KY)	188-189 ☐	Tongue Tied (MP)	138 ☐
House-Hut (GP)	228 ☐	TruGreen (KY)	192 ☐
India Jane (RL)	118 ☐	Two Men And A Truck (KY)	237 ☐
Leaps & Bounds (KY)	243 ☐	Well Polished (TU)	166 ☐
LIPA 4:19 (TU)	243 ☐	Wilkins Chimney Sweep (BB)	192 ☐

Reader Response

If you don't have a specific brand in mind and would like further information on a particular type of franchise or place of operation, please complete this section. Again, we'll pass your details on to companies relevant to your choices. Please tick this box ☐ to confirm that you are happy for us to do so.

SECTORS	TICK						TYPE OF FRANCHISE	
Accountancy	☐	Electrical	☐	Personal	☐		Single Unit	☐
Agriculture	☐	Entertainment	☐	Pest Control	☐		Area Developer	☐
Automotive	☐	Environmental	☐	Pets	☐		Master Franchise	☐
Beauty	☐	Estate Agents/Lettings	☐	Photography	☐		Resales	☐
Beverages	☐	Fashion	☐	Print & Design	☐		Management	☐
Business 2 Business	☐	Financial	☐	Recruitment	☐			
Care	☐	Food	☐	Repair & Maintenance	☐		LOCATION	
Chemical	☐	Footwear	☐	Retail	☐		High street retail	☐
Children	☐	Franchise	☐	Safety	☐		Kiosk based	☐
Cleaning	☐	Garden	☐	Sales	☐		Office based	☐
Communications	☐	Health	☐	Security	☐		Restaurant based	☐
Computers	☐	Hire	☐	Services	☐		Secondary retail	☐
Consultancy	☐	Horticulture	☐	Signs	☐		Vehicle based	☐
Customisation	☐	Indoor Property	☐	Sports	☐		Work from home	☐
Delivery	☐	Legal	☐	Storage	☐		Dedicated premises based	☐
Distribution	☐	Luxury	☐	Supplies	☐			
Education/Training	☐	Manufacture	☐	Travel	☐			
		Outdoor Property	☐	Used Goods	☐			

COMPLETE: MY DETAILS   The UK Franchise Directory 24th Edition

NAME: ....

ADDRESS: ....

....

COMPANY: ....

EMAIL (THIS MUST BE COMPLETED): ....

TELEPHONE: ....

AREAS OF GEOGRAPHICAL INTEREST: ....

MY AVAILABLE CAPITAL (THIS MUST BE COMPLETED): £ ....

TICK: ☐ I would like to receive *The UK Franchise Directory* online newsletter each month.

Return this form by fax to:
+44 (0) 1603 630 174
By post to: *The UK Franchise Directory*, Franchise House, 56 Surrey Street, Norwich, NR1 3FD

Or complete online at:
theukfd.net/interact/login.php

FREE **Reader** Response Service

For further information on any brands featured in The UK Franchise Directory, please complete ALL sections.

TICK: ☐ I would like more information from the following selected brands. I understand that my details, including email address, must be passed on to the selected brands ONLY.

Featured Franchise Brands...............TICK HERE

Brand	Page	
Agency Express (JC)	216	☐
All Trades Network (TU)	191	☐
Assured Security Shredding (MP)	44-45,139	☐
Auntie Anne's (NW)	99	☐
Bairstow Eves (MP)	226	☐
BCR Associates (GP)	140	☐
Betterclean Services (GP)	36-37	☐
Blue Ribbon Care (MP)	30-31,175	☐
Business for Breakfast (BB)	139	☐
Card Connection (MP)	234	☐
Caremark (GP)	175	☐
Cargocall Franchising (GP)	238	☐
Cash & Cheque Express (JC)	118	☐
Cash Converters (JC)	114	☐
Century 21 (BB)	61	☐
CerTax Accounting (KY)	140	☐
CeX (NW)	115	☐
Chemex International (KY)	235	☐
CityLocal (KY)	141	☐
Computer Troubleshooters (BB)	55	☐
ComputerXplorers (KY)	242	☐
Cost Centre Services (JC)	136	☐
Dream Doors (GP)	119	☐
Dublcheck (TU)	164	☐
EnviroVent (BB)	192	☐
etyres (RL)	128	☐
FDS (RS)	137	☐
FiltaFry Plus (KY)	164	☐
Fita-Seal (KY)	140	☐
Global Cruising (RL)	208	☐
Granite Transformations (MP)	190	☐
GreenThumb (KY)	188-189	☐
House-Hut (GP)	228	☐
India Jane (RL)	118	☐
Leaps & Bounds (KY)	243	☐
LIPA 4:19 (TU)	243	☐
London House (GP)	141	☐
Mac Tools Europe (KY)	236	☐
Martin & Co (BB)	228	☐
Marvin's Menswear (RS)	116	☐
McDonald's (JC)	4-5,99	☐
Merry Maids (KY)	165	☐
Minster Services Group (KY)	160-161	☐
MOLLY MAID (GP)	166	☐
NBC Bird and Pest Solutions (JC)	191	☐
Northwood (GP)	229	☐
Office Canopy Group (MP)	141	☐
Ovenclean (KY)	162-163	☐
OvenU (BB)	166	☐
PC PAL (KY)	254	☐
Perfect Pizza (JC)	98	☐
Pizza Hut (JC)	2,23,100	☐
Platinum Property Partners (RL)	227	☐
Primesigns (MP)	218	☐
Recognition Express (KY)	219	☐
Riverford Organic Vegetables (BB)	27	☐
Safeclean (GP)	166	☐
ServiceMaster (KY)	165	☐
Snack-in-the-Box (GP)	238	☐
Stockcheck (BB)	141	☐
Suit the City (JC)	255	☐
Susan Hepburn Clinics (RL)	174	☐
Tatty Bumpkin (MP)	243	☐
The Camping and Caravanning Club (KY)	210	☐
The Video Inventory (BB)	51	☐
The Wedding Guide(JC)	220	☐
The Zip Yard (KY)	117	☐
Tongue Tied (MP)	138	☐
TruGreen (KY)	192	☐
Two Men And A Truck (KY)	237	☐
Well Polished (TU)	166	☐
Wilkins Chimney Sweep (BB)	192	☐

Reader Response

Services To The Franchise Sector............TICK HERE

alphaTALK (RC) ....84-85, 95 ☐	FranExec (NW).......................................92 ☐
Anglia Finance (RC) ....46-47, 91 ☐	FranManuals (RC).................................92 ☐
Brand Protect (RC) ....82-83, 93 ☐	FranPower (MA) ....94 ☐
European Franchising Online (DI)..............214 ☐	Insight 2010 Report (RC) ....16-17 ☐
FDS Anglia & London (NW/PH) ....86 ☐	ip21 (RC)..78-79, 93 ☐
FDS South East (MP)...........................87 ☐	Ireland Franchise Directory (MS)............280 ☐
FDS Midlands (KY) ....89 ☐	Jargon Buster...................................50 ☐
FDS North (TU) ....88 ☐	Lloyds TSB (RC) ....41-43, 91 ☐
FDS Southern (GP)................................90 ☐	Subscriptions...................................322 ☐
FDS FranMatch (RL) ....71, 93 ☐	Tech4T (RC) ....80-81, 95 ☐
Franchise Development Services (RC)..........62 ☐	The Franchise Magazine (FM) ....332 ☐
Franchise International Online (DI) ....214 ☐	The Franchise Magazine App (FM)..............61 ☐
Franchise Success TV (RC) ....94 ☐	The Franchise Magazine Online (DI)..........287 ☐
FranDesign (LD)...................................94 ☐	The UK Franchise Directory Online (MS)....323 ☐

If you don't have a specific brand in mind and would like further information on a particular type of franchise or place of operation, please complete this section. Again, we'll pass your details on to companies relevant to your choices. Please tick this box ☐ to confirm that you are happy for us to do so.

SECTORS	TICK						TYPE OF FRANCHISE	
Accountancy	☐	Electrical	☐	Personal	☐		Single Unit	☐
Agriculture	☐	Entertainment	☐	Pest Control	☐		Area Developer	☐
Automotive	☐	Environmental	☐	Pets	☐		Master Franchise	☐
Beauty	☐	Estate Agents/Lettings	☐	Photography	☐		Resales	☐
Beverages	☐	Fashion	☐	Print & Design	☐		Management	☐
Business 2 Business	☐	Financial	☐	Recruitment	☐			
Care	☐	Food	☐	Repair & Maintenance	☐		LOCATION	
Chemical	☐	Footwear	☐	Retail	☐		High street retail	☐
Children	☐	Franchise	☐	Safety	☐		Kiosk based	☐
Cleaning	☐	Garden	☐	Sales	☐		Office based	☐
Communications	☐	Health	☐	Security	☐		Restaurant based	☐
Computers	☐	Hire	☐	Services	☐		Secondary retail	☐
Consultancy	☐	Horticulture	☐	Signs	☐		Vehicle based	☐
Customisation	☐	Indoor Property	☐	Sports	☐		Work from home	☐
Delivery	☐	Legal	☐	Storage	☐		Dedicated premises based	☐
Distribution	☐	Luxury	☐	Supplies	☐			
Education/Training	☐	Manufacture	☐	Travel	☐			
		Outdoor Property	☐	Used Goods	☐			

COMPLETE: MY DETAILS   The UK Franchise Directory 24th Edition

NAME: ....

ADDRESS: ....

....

COMPANY: ....

EMAIL (THIS MUST BE COMPLETED): ....

TELEPHONE: ....

AREAS OF GEOGRAPHICAL INTEREST: ....

MY AVAILABLE CAPITAL (THIS MUST BE COMPLETED): £ ....

TICK: ☐ I would like to receive *The UK Franchise Directory* online newsletter each month.

Return this form by fax to:
+44 (0) 1603 630 174
By post to: *The UK Franchise Directory*, Franchise House, 56 Surrey Street, Norwich, NR1 3FD

Or complete online at:
theukfd.net/interact/login.php

The Franchise Magazine

Your complete online source for franchise opportunities

The Franchise Magazine reproduced online and FREE TO VIEW

Order your copy of *The Franchise Magazine* or subscribe to 8 editions for only **£19.50**

See the latest tweets from the Editor of *The Franchise Magazine*. Join the conversation: **Twitter:@TheFranchiseMag**

FOLLOW ME!

Real life franchise owner stories, get a taste of the franchising life!

Read all the latest featured franchise profiles from a range of brands.

Keep up to date with *The Franchise Magazine* Blog... **talking about the latest news, new franchise brands, tips on choosing the right franchise for you and more!**

Keep up to date with the next **Franchise Events and Exhibitions.**

The best advice on How to **Successfully** Franchise your Business.

Once you have found a UK franchise that interests you, simply complete the request form to receive further information from that company.

Call **01603 620301**
Email **enquiries@fdsltd.com**
Visit The Franchise Magazine
Online at **www.TheFM.net**

Food & Beverages

Retail

Index Categorical

Automotive

Business 2 Business

Cleaning & Maintenance

Health & Beauty

Indoor/Outdoor Property Care

Leisure & Travel

Print, Signs & Design

Real Estate & Lettings

Sales, Delivery & Distribution

Specialised | Children & Education

Index Categorical

Specialised | Pet & Animal Services

Specialised | Other Specialised Services

Irish Franchise Directory

Index Alphabetical

Index Alphabetical

Index Alphabetical

Publication Showcase

The UK Franchise Directory has been published by FDS for over 24 years and now lists over 1,500 franchisors. In every edition there are over 50 pages of advice and guidance on owning a franchise and how to franchise your business written by FDS and other experts in the field of franchising. *The UK Franchise Directory* is a must read for anybody considering franchising and is one of the most trusted resources for serious prospective franchise owners in the UK. The aim of this publication is to educate prospective franchise owners on the wide range of opportunities available to help them find the right franchise to suit their skills, financial capability and future aspirations.

www.TheUKFranchiseDirectory.net

Since its launch in 1985, *The Franchise Magazine* has become one of Britain's most successful publications for franchise owner recruitment. The consistent quality and high standard of professional editorial makes it one of today's most sought after publications of new and established franchise opportunities. *The Franchise Magazine* is dedicated to promoting ethical and professional franchising and is readily available at franchise and business start-up exhibitions. Every issue is distributed nationwide through leading newsagents, supermarkets, redundancy counselling centres, professional advisors and British Franchise Association events. *The Franchise Magazine* is designed specifically to help educate, motivate and recruit franchise owners, alongside well-researched supporting editorial, legislation updates, advisory features and valuable information on a variety of topics relating to the franchise industry.

www.TheFranchiseMagazine.net

Representing quality, emerging and established franchise brands from around the world that are actively expanding their franchise networks within Ireland, *Irish Franchise Magazine* is published twice a year and is also available online at www.IrishFranchiseMagazine.net. *Irish Franchise Magazine* is a highly valuable tool for franchisors aiming to penetrate this growth market. Each edition is distributed via newsstands, enterprise and development agencies, resettlement centres, banks, and at franchise exhibitions. Within every edition, there are company profiles, franchise owner case studies, news, exhibition previews and advice and guidance aimed at educating and informing both franchise owners and franchisors.

www.IrishFranchiseMagazine.net

Scottish Franchise Magazine is published once a year and distributed throughout Scotland at hotels, accountants, enterprise organisations and newsagents nationwide. *Scottish Franchise Magazine* is totally dedicated to reporting on franchise news and Genuine Business Format Franchise opportunities throughout Scotland. Every edition provides a proven method of helping franchisors to recruit new franchise owners on a regular basis.

www.ScottishFranchiseMagazine.net

Website Showcase

TheFranchiseMagazine.net is the online counterpart to one of the UK's best selling franchise publications, *The Franchise Magazine*. Following its re-launch, TheFranchiseMagazine.net is easy to navigate, as visitors are able to browse every printed edition of the magazine by franchise category or by advertiser. The website also contains information about many franchise opportunities in the UK, the best advice and guidance for franchise owners and franchisors, as well as real life franchise owner stories. With the latest franchise news uploaded daily, TheFranchiseMagazine.net is a valuable resource for anyone looking to invest in a franchise.

The
Franchise
M a g a z i n e

www.TheFranchiseMagazine.net

The online version of *The UK Franchise Directory* is continuously updated and allows you to get in touch with franchises quickly and easily – just find the franchise you are interested in, fill in the short registration form and your information request will be sent to the franchisor. On the site you can view detailed information or browse statistical information about brands currently franchising in the UK. You have the ability to search for opportunities by business category, place of operation and investment requirements with the free online information request service, making it possible for you to find the ideal franchise.

The United Kingdom
FRANCHISE
Directory

www.TheUKFranchiseDirectory.net

European Franchising online (EuropeanFranchising.net) offers listings of European and International franchise profiles. Originally a print publication, *European Franchising* now profiles famous and emerging international franchise opportunities seeking investors to expand in European markets via national or regional Master franchising. *European Franchising* is easy to navigate, as visitors are able to browse franchise opportunities by business category or by advertiser. The website contains information on genuine European franchise opportunities, latest franchise news, guidance for franchise owners and franchisors as well as the European Franchise Showcase.

€UROPEAN
FRANCHISING

www.EuropeanFranchising.net

Like *European Franchising*, *Franchise International* online (Franchise-International.net) was formerly a print publication and is now available as a website providing information on the latest international franchise opportunities. *Franchise International* is updated daily and now has improved navigation, as visitors are able to browse through international franchise opportunities by category or advertiser. The website contains latest franchise news, advice and guidance for franchise owners and franchisors, as well as the International Franchise Showcase. *Franchise International* is a valuable source of information for people looking to invest in a franchise.

FRANCHISE
INTERNATIONAL

www.Franchise-International.net

IrelandFranchiseDirectory.com showcases leading business opportunities available in Ireland, allowing you to easily request information from them. On the site you can view detailed information and franchise opportunities can be searched by category or investment level. The website is continuously updated and allows you to get in touch with these franchises quickly and easily. A free information request service makes it possible for you to find the right franchise.

Ireland
Franchise
Directory

www.IrelandFranchiseDirectory.com

SUBSCRIBE to a WORLD of Franchising

*ON THE COVER PRICE OF A SUBSCRIPTION TO THE FRANCHISE MAGAZINE. APPLIES TO UK RESIDENTS ONLY.

SUBSCRIBE FROM ONLY £19.50! FREE UK P&P

FRANCHISE SUBSCRIPTIONS – UKFD 24TH EDITION

☐ YES PLEASE. I would like to order a subscription to *The Franchise Magazine* for 8 editions

☐ YES PLEASE. I would like to order a copy of the 24th edition of *The UK Franchise Directory*

CONTACT DETAILS

Name:

Company Name: (if applicable)

Address:

Postcode:

Tel: Email:

Cardholder's Address: (if different from above)

Postcode:

PAYMENT DETAILS

☐ Cheque made payable to FDS Ltd   ☐ Credit Card (all debit/credit cards accepted)

8 EDITIONS:
For the amount of:
☐ £19.50 United Kingdom
☐ £45 Europe
☐ £76 Rest of the World

1 DIRECTORY:
For the amount of:
☐ £25 United Kingdom
☐ £40 Europe
☐ £50 Rest of the World

8 EDITIONS PLUS 1 DIRECTORY: For the special price of:
☐ £39.50 United Kingdom
☐ £64.50 Europe
☐ £94.50 Rest of the World

PAYMENT DETAILS

Credit Card Number:

☐☐☐☐ ☐☐☐☐ ☐☐☐☐ ☐☐☐☐

Start Date: /   Expiry Date: /

Issue Number: Security Number: found on the signature strip

Signature:

I would like to receive further information on these or similar titles by email YES ☐ NO ☐

Please POST this order form to: Franchise Development Services Ltd, Franchise House, 56 Surrey Street, Norwich, NR1 3FD, ENGLAND